KENTUCKY SPRING

Sister James Maria Spillane, S.C.N.

ABBEY PRESS, ST. MEINRAD, INDIANA

NIHIL OBSTAT:

JOHN A. BARKER
Censor Deputatus

IMPRIMATUR:

✠ THOMAS J. MCDONOUGH
Archbishop of Louisville
April 10, 1968

CHAPTER ONE

1812-1813

Snow drifted slowly down from the leaden sky. It settled softly on the already whitened ground as two riders, emerging from a densely wooded path, stopped abruptly at the edge of a clearing. The girl, riding side-saddle, tossed the reins loosely over the horse's neck and then sat motionless.

"Well, here we are, Kit," her tall, bronzed companion drawled, his voice deliberately casual.

There was no sound from the girl.

Turning sideways in his saddle, Tom Elder looked for the half smile that his pet name usually brought to her lips, but apparently Catherine Spalding had not heard him. She was gazing fixedly across a clearing that bristled with stumps at a rough log cabin, its harshness softened now by the snow. Her dark eyes did not waver. She seemed to be alone in this wilderness, alone with a vision. Suddenly Tom felt left out, a complete stranger in this world which clearly belonged to his favorite niece.

Intently he studied the illuminated face framed by curly wisps of chestnut hair which escaped from the red woolen scarf tied firmly under the soft but purposeful chin. He noted the oval cheeks flushed delicate pink by the cold, the deep blue eyes set off by the dark curved line of brow, a straight nose slightly tilted at the tip, and a generous mouth with always a hint of laughter in the dimples at each corner. Until now Tom hadn't realized that his niece was so lovely, even beautiful, and she was going to . . . .

His roan moved restlessly and nuzzled her bay. Still his niece sat motionless. Was it possible, he mused, that this handsome girl of nineteen was the same little maid who had come with her widowed mother and baby sister from Maryland not so many years ago? Tragedy had followed her. He saw her again, an orphan of six, her hair the color of new rope, curling to her shoulders, her eyes bright with unshed tears, one chubby hand clutching a wooden doll, the other clasping the pudgy fingers of her little sister Ann.

"Mummie's gone to heaven," she had gravely informed him, "and Ann and I are going there too someday."

"Of course you are," he had declared just as gravely. For one long moment she had looked up at him and then had slid her tiny hand trustingly into his big one.

As the days went by, he had marveled at the way she faced her new life. But why should he have been so surprised? Catherine was of heroic blood. Some of her ancestors had felt the avarice of the degenerate Henry VIII; others, the taxes of his son Edward; and still others, the rope at Tyburn under "Good Queen Bess." They were Lincolnshire Spaldings who centuries before had given their castle with its small Gothic chapel to the Benedictines. Under these holy men this property had become the renowned abbey of Spalding, one of the few spared by Henry, only to fall into the clutches of his son Edward.

Around this famous abbey had grown up the market town of Spalding on the river Welland, about ninety-three miles from London. It was from this town that Thomas Spalding, worn out by persecution and impoverished by heavy yearly fines for refusing to worship in the Anglican Church, set out for Maryland in 1657. There he prospered so well that at the time of his death he owned a large plantation and several small farms.

From such an illustrious line had come that little girl with her charming ways and her fearless, yet gentle eyes. Ever since she had come into his family Tom Elder had done his best by her. In both lean and fat years he had striven to give her the best education his means allowed. As she grew, she had twined herself around his heart, and had it not been for Father David .... He shrugged and honestly faced the fact that if Father David had not lighted the flame of Divine Love in her young heart, another might have fired it with a less worthy love. And what earthly flame could have made her half so radiant? He sighed.

Instantly Catherine turned, her eyes anxious. "You must be tired, Uncle Tom," she apologized. "I shouldn't have kept you waiting like this. Let's go on."

"Not yet, Kit. I have something to say to you before we get to the cabin. You know how I am around strange women," he grumbled, dismounting.

As she slid from her saddle to the white ground, he caught her in his arms and kissed her soundly on the cheek. For a moment she clung to him and then smiling tremulously, drew back, tears glistening in her eyes.

"Remember, Kit," he said, taking her hand gently, "my door is always open to you. If you find this life too much," he motioned toward the desolate cabin, "don't hesitate to come back."

Catherine's head lifted a little. "I'll remember, Uncle Tom," she promised quietly, "although I'm sure I'll never need to. I've wanted—oh, so long—to do something for God, and now's my chance, right here in my own Kentucky."

"Your Kentucky!" he teased. "Don't forget you were born in St. Charles County, Maryland."

"Yes, I know, on December 23 in the year 1793," she retorted quickly. "But Maryland doesn't need me and Kentucky does."

He put his hand on her shoulder and looked soberly into her eager face. "As I've tried to tell you so often, Kit, there's no sense to it. What can you and two other women do for Kentucky by living in a miserable log cabin like that?" He made a disparaging gesture toward the building. "Don't be foolish! Kentucky's still a man's country. You women—"

"Uncle Tom, why can't you see?" she interrupted,

her eyes pleading for understanding. "Kentucky's had her winter. You men helped her through that. Now it's her spring—Kentucky spring—and the time has come for women in her fields. It's up to us to teach Kentucky's children the love and service of God. That's why Mary Rhodes and the others went to Loretto to become nuns under the direction of Father Nerinckx."

"Yes, and don't forget her sister Ann died there last month."

"But she was never strong anyway and had lung fever before—"

He cut her short. "Convent life's too hard in Kentucky. That's all. Both Father Nerinckx and Father David should realize that."

"Uncle Tom, she died a spouse of Christ," Catherine said softly. "That was worth everything."

Tom felt his heart melting, but he went on stubbornly. "Well, if it's nuns you girls want to be, you could go to Baltimore. There are convents there in buildings. Not deserted log cabins. A convent in Kentucky is just a dream of these French priests. They forget that they're in a new world, not in France. They forget too that we're at war. A war that we're losing," he finished grimly.

"Uncle Tom, how can you say that?" Catherine whirled around to face him, her eyes flashing.

"Well, it's the truth," he drawled with a slow smile. "We haven't made progress in Canada, have we, in spite of all the men Kentucky's sent to the front?"

"But we've defeated the British on the seas," she countered. "Remember the *Guerriere*'s colors were struck to our *Old Ironsides*."

"True," Tom laughed, "England may be Queen of the Seas, forcing our men onto her ships, but Captain Bainbridge showed her who's king." His face sobered. "But things on land aren't going well at all. Clay and his 'War Hawks' may have brought disaster upon us."

They stood silent, the snow falling noiselessly around them.

Catherine's face was troubled. "But, Uncle Tom, surely you wouldn't want us to take the treatment the English have been giving us since the Revolution. If we did," she straightened her shoulders unconsciously, "they wouldn't have any respect for us. Clay knows that. So he urged President Madison to declare war."

"You're right, Kit," her uncle nodded slowly, "but what'll happen if we get the worst of it?"

"Uncle Tom, you're impossible!" she said scornfully, softening her words with a playful shake of her head. "Of course we won't. Surely we're no worse off now than when you and Father fought in the Revolution, are we?"

Thoughtfully Tom flicked the snow with his whip. "To tell you the truth, Kit, your father and I were both too young then to realize the danger of a little country's standing up a big one. Youth's like that, you know. Never knows when it's in danger nor when it's licked. We were just lucky that time."

"Lucky! You mean God was on our side," she corrected.

"I knew you wouldn't let that go by," he parried. "But now," he patted his horse's head absent-mindedly, "just for the sake of agreeing, suppose we *do* win. You'll still be in this log cabin. What help will *that* be to our country?"

"Plenty! We'll be teaching its future citizens to love their country and their God."

He looked at her pleadingly. "Now, Kit, be reasonable. Where will you *get* pupils in this place? And if they do come, where will you put them?"

Delighted, he saw Catherine's jaw set. Now they had reached that part of the argument he loved. His niece was blessed with a logical mind, he had always told his wife, and for that reason he enjoyed arousing her. But he was disappointed this time, for they were interrupted. As she turned to answer him, she saw two women at the cabin door.

Instantly her expression changed to one of excitement. "Look, Uncle Tom, they must have seen us!"

5

Grudgingly he held the stirrup while she mounted, and then he sprang into his own. "They might have waited," he muttered.

"But they *have* waited for nearly two months, you know," she laughed as she slapped the reins playfully against her horse's head. "Teresa Carrico and Elizabeth Wells have been here at St. Thomas's since December, and it's now the twenty-first of January in the year of Our Lord eighteen hundred and thirteen. Naturally they're eager for my arrival because Father David promised them a rule of life as soon as the third postulant came."

They had almost reached the door of the cabin and both were silent. Dismounting, they threw the reins over an old stump, each carefully avoiding the other's eyes.

Soon Catherine, snow and all, was caught in the warm embrace of Teresa Carrico.

Elizabeth Wells stood a bit stiffly in the doorway. "Bring the child in, Teresa," she counseled. "Do you want to freeze her and us too?"

Tom Elder followed rather reluctantly, closing the door after him and mentally making note of the fact that the cold within seemed to differ little from the cold without. He would remember this and bring some warm quilts when he came again. His daughter Clementina, now Mrs. Clarke, at whose home Catherine had spent much time the past two years, had sent some baggage ahead. But of course she had not seen the abject poverty of this place.

While his niece was removing her long cloak and untying her heavy scarf, Tom glanced about. Everything was in deep shadow, the grey light barely penetrating the glazed paper which covered the small square window. The only breath of cheer came from the fireplace, where a half-consumed log crackled and hissed.

Soon his eyes became accustomed to the greyness. Then in the center of the room he could make out two three-legged stools on either side of a rough table made from half a log with the split side up. In one corner was a long bench in front of what appeared to be a loom. In another corner a crude ladder was secured to the logs. Sleeping quarters above, he thought. Must be very small.

His gaze returned to the puncheon floor, and to his consternation he saw a growing puddle near his feet. In his excitement he had forgotten to remove his buskins and the snow had melted. Time to go, he decided. Womenfolk and puddles never agree even when the women are trying to be patient nuns.

"Well, Kit. I—I—mean—Catherine," he corrected hastily as he noticed Elizabeth's lifted eyebrow and construed the nickname to be the innocent cause. "I must be moving on. Have to get back as far as Abells before dark, you know, and this snow may turn into a blizzard 'fore long."

His left hand closed over the latch; his right grasped the strong cold fingers of the girl he loved as a daughter. His eyes sought hers and held them. "Don't forget," he whispered. "My door is always open. The latch is always up. And I'm not convinced that it's Kentucky spring—yet!"

He was rewarded with a sudden flash from the deep-set eyes. The lifting of the head and the stern setting of the jaw which accompanied it assured him that tears didn't have a chance. He was satisfied. Catherine was a soldier all the way through. No hardship would dismay her.

Before Elizabeth could open the door, he was out and freeing his horse. There was a chorus of farewells as he mounted hastily. Seated, he turned. The three women were grouped in the doorway. Teresa had her arm around Catherine, her cheery round face bright with genuine warmth and motherliness, her sturdy figure eloquent of hard work and great strength. No aristocrat, Teresa, but a true Kentucky pioneer woman, strong and courageous. He had liked her at once, and he was glad for Catherine's sake that she was there.

By contrast, Elizabeth Wells, who stood behind the two, was almost stately. But there was something wooden about her. Although there was a smile on her lips, her eyes were not warm, and Tom had long ago learned to question a smile that did not affect the eyes. She was, he knew, the sister of General Wells and of Captain Wells, both officers of the invading forces in Canada. Perhaps worry about their safety explained her coldness. Well, she would warm up to Catherine—everyone did.

By now he had reached the edge of the clearing. Turning, he looked back at the cabin. The door was shut; no one was in sight. He wheeled abruptly and headed into the woods, the bay trotting riderless behind him.

Meanwhile, in the cabin Catherine was sitting on a stool by the fire talking to Elizabeth, but her eyes followed Teresa, who had already lit a tallow candle and had placed it on the crude table in the middle of the room. Now she was near the hearth busy stirring something in a frying pan.

Catching Catherine's eye, she smiled. "You must be hungry after your long ride. I'm ashamed that I didn't offer your uncle some refreshment, but he was off so quickly I didn't have time. Move over there," she motioned to the table, "and we'll have a bite to eat."

Catherine picked up her stool and set it near the table. "Don't worry about Uncle Tom, Teresa. He wouldn't have stayed to eat anyway." Then recalling his words in the clearing, she added, "He's very shy around strange women."

Teresa smiled understandingly and went back to the hearth.

Suddenly, unaccountably, Catherine found the room which at first had seemed forbiddingly drear, warm with a charity and joy which recalled the day of her First Communion. Well, she thought, there *is* a resemblance. Then Our Lord gave Himself to me; today I'm giving myself to Him. In a daze she drank the sage tea and nibbled on the dry cornbread. The voices of the others seemed to come from a great distance. Desperately she longed to be alone to relish this extraordinary feeling of joy. Then all at once she realized that community life would always be like this. She would seldom be alone.

She struggled to break the spell. "Do you think," she began hesitatingly, "that—." A loud knock interrupted her.

Startled, all three jumped up and stood facing the door. Teresa was the first to regain control. She moved deliberately to the window, peered out, and then hastened to the door and opened it. In walked Father David, who could easily be mistaken for a portly snowman. In an instant he had his coat and boots off and was handing them to Teresa.

Then he spied Catherine and his eyes lighted up. Without a word he went directly to her. She and her companions knelt while he made the Sign of the Cross over them, his hands lingering longest over the bent head of the newcomer. Something seemed to tell him that her life and his would from that moment be linked in a spiritual bond.

As he helped her up, Catherine's eager eyes photographed for her mind this priest who had already meant so much to her and who was destined to mean much more —the corpulent figure, the curly grey hair reaching nearly to the broad shoulders, the straight nose, and the finely chiseled lips. Deep lines of care were the only visible traces of his arduous missionary life.

"I've been on a sick call," he informed them, "and I stopped in, hoping that Catherine would be here."

"Yes, Father, she came about an hour ago," volunteered Elizabeth, drawing up another stool. "We were just giving her something to eat. Would you care for some cornbread and sage tea?"

"Indeed I would," he declared, seating himself cautiously, for past experience had taught him the frailty of the convent furniture. "It's getting colder by the minute, and I've been riding for more than four hours."

Satisfied that the stool would hold him, he turned to Catherine. "You're most welcome," he said kindly.

Then he addressed them all in a more solemn tone. "In honor of this occasion—the coming of the third aspirant

—we shall name this dwelling Nazareth. And may the Holy Family, who lived at the first Nazareth, be your model, now and always!" He paused a moment. "Now that you are three, we shall have a superior, the oldest. That's you, Elizabeth. And here," he said, drawing out a piece of paper and handing it to her, "is your rule of life for the present. I've been trying to get Mother Seton of Emmitsburg to send us at least one of her Sisters to train you, but so far I have been unsuccessful. Therefore," he added good-humoredly, "I suppose I must undertake that pleasant duty myself, thoroughly incompetent though I am."

He cleared his throat. "You'll notice on that paper two hours devoted to study." Elizabeth nodded. "As you know, you are destined for teaching, but you'll also notice that there is a set time for mental and vocal prayer and for recreation and work. Nothing—absolutely nothing—can be accomplished without prayer, but with it—everything!"

"And what about our habit?" inquired Teresa, looking up from the heavy stocking she was knitting.

Father David's deep laugh surprised himself, for he rarely laughed. "Still women, I see! Well, until your number is larger, I believe you should wear a simple dress—no frills! But there will be a habit someday, never fear."

He rose stiffly. "It's late, and I must leave. Besides, Catherine here should be getting some sleep. But let's say the rosary together before I go."

They knelt, and the poor room—which must have been much like the one at Nazareth in Galilee—was filled with the praises of her who once swept and cleaned for the little Son of God and for Saint Joseph, his foster father. After the last invocation Father David rose slowly, and giving the girls a general blessing, went out into the night.

Catherine stifled a yawn. The long ride, the prayers, and the peace she felt in her inmost being had made her

10

drowsy. She was relieved when Elizabeth announced, "Time for bed."

Teresa was busy banking the fire, but she turned to warn, "Be careful, Catherine, when you get to the loft not to stand up or you'll bump your head. It's so low we have to kneel or sit to dress and undress."

"I'll remember," Catherine promised laughingly as she climbed the makeshift ladder.

Elizabeth was already at the top, holding a flickering candle. In the light of its feeble rays she pointed to a straw pallet on the floor. There were no beds. When each was in her place, Elizabeth blew out the candle. Darkness enveloped them.

Later, as Catherine lay on the straw listening to the soft breathing of her two companions, she knew without doubt that this was the beginning of an adventure which would end only with eternity. She tried her best to recapture the joy she had experienced her first hour at Nazareth, but it had given way to a deep peace and a sense of being at home.

"Thank you, God," she murmured sleepily.

And then for some reason she thought of her sister Ann, but only momentarily, for not even that thought could keep her heavy eyes open.

CHAPTER TWO

1813

"Teresa, I've finished," Catherine called softly.

"You mean that stretch of warp is done already?" Teresa exclaimed, turning from the fireplace where she was pushing a log into place. "Well, you certainly have learned the first step quickly." She put down the tongs and hastened to the loom.

Catherine's face flushed with pleasure. "I'd better learn quickly," she said, giving Teresa her place. "If we want to make cloth for the seminarians and for ourselves, not to mention selling some, I'll have to move even faster than this."

"You will as you go along," Teresa assured her, deftly pulling the finished homespun around the cloth beam and straightening another stretch of the warp. "There you are! That's about the easiest part of the weaving. Now all you have to do is start over."

"I knew there was some catch to it!" Catherine chuckled as she jerked the string which sent the shuttle flying.

"Don't go too fast, Catherine," cautioned Elizabeth, "or I won't be able to keep ahead of you with the spinning. You *do* have to have thread, you know."

"Yes, indeed," laughed Catherine happily.

It was the day after her arrival. That morning the three aspirants had agreed that Elizabeth would spin, Catherine weave, and Teresa take care of the cooking, sewing, and other household tasks. Since Catherine did not know how to weave—her sister Ann had always done that—it fell to Teresa's lot to show her. By the middle of the afternoon she had become quite adept. As the

12

pedaling of the treadle and the jerking of the shuttle strings became mechanical, her mind was free to review the past few hours spent at her new home.

She smiled as as she thought of the loft where she had spent the night. If sleeping soundly on a straw pallet laid on a cold floor was any indication of a true vocation, then she really had one. Only once did she awaken, and that was when the wind, shifting to the northeast, beat the snow furiously against the rough logs near her head. Even then she had stayed awake only long enough to whisper a prayer for Uncle Tom's safety and had promptly fallen asleep again.

It must have been about four o'clock when she felt a gentle shake and opened her eyes to see Teresa bending over her. For a moment she was startled. Where was she? Then she remembered. Nazareth! Only Teresa's restraining hand kept her from jumping up and bumping her head against the rafters so perilously close. Mutely she nodded her thanks, sat up carefully, and reached for her shoes. Her hand encountered a soft cold substance and instinctively jerked back. With difficulty she repressed a scream. For a moment she sat there tense. Then suddenly she relaxed as she realized that the soft cold substance was only the snow which had drifted in between the logs during the night. How fortunate she had not screamed! Elizabeth and Teresa would certainly have laughed at her or—worse—would have thought her too tender for this hard life. That would be unbearable. Next time, she promised herself grimly, she would be more careful where she put her shoes for the night. Luckily it was so cold in the loft that the snow had not melted. Emptying it out quickly, she set her teeth to keep them from chattering and thrust her feet bravely into the icy shoes.

When she came down the ladder a little later, Teresa was using a home-fashioned bellows to fan the fire. Elizabeth motioned for her to come closer. Then all three knelt facing the blazing logs to say their morning prayers.

13

By the time they had finished, their faces were rosy, their backs thoroughly chilled.

After dressing warmly, they set out for the chapel, a room in the seminary building a half mile distant. The snow came up to the tops of their shoes, and they proceeded Indian style, Elizabeth in the lead. It was bitter cold. The driving snow, no longer soft, cut their faces and fell so thick that they had to hold hands to keep together. They struggled through the small drifts and skirted the big ones.

At last they stumbled upon the steps of the seminary and entered the narrow door in a gust of wind. It was cold in the dark vestibule but the calm was most welcome. After a moment's pause they groped their way through a narrow hall into a large room which, Catherine later learned, served as a refectory and study hall for the seminarians during the week and became a chapel for the neighboring Catholics on Sundays. Crossing this room, Elizabeth opened another door. Even before Catherine's eyes had become accustomed to the darkness, she saw the familiar glow of the vigil light. As she began to see more clearly, she could make out the forms of seven young men, Father David's seminarians, kneeling close to the altar.

After a little while, one of them went out, returned in cassock and surplice, and lit the two candles near the tabernacle. Their feeble glow was sufficient to scatter the darkness of the crowded room and reveal evidence of the seminarians' brave attempt to beautify their chapel. Catherine's eyes misted compassionately. The rough wall above the altar was covered with a curtain of printed cloth, in the center of which was an oil painting of Christ, His arms outstretched. Besides this there were two pictures representing the carrying of the cross and the crucifixion and two smaller oils in gilt frames.

Lovingly her eyes rested on the white-veiled tabernacle and approved the exquisitely embroidered cloth hanging gracefully over the sides of the wooden altar; then her gaze traveled slowly, reverently, up to the bronze crucifix beside which stood images of the Blessed Mother and Saint John. Something about this sorrowful group fascinated her. She turned reluctantly away to finish her inspection. On the lace-draped ledges of the altar were six silvered candlesticks holding yellow wax candles. A dull red cotton cloth, worn in several places, covered the altar steps.

Catherine's inspection was cut short by the entrance of Father David. The Holy Sacrifice commenced. As his strong, reverent voice began in Latin the psalm, "I shall go unto the altar of God," and the seminarians responded, "To God who giveth joy to my youth," her heart beat so joyfully that she wondered if her companions, kneeling close to her, could hear it. With St. Peter she thought, "Lord, it is good to be here." And her heart sang. Every morning would be like this! Every morning there would be the Holy Sacrifice! Every morning Christ would come again to His own! What did the hardships matter? Cold grows warm in the presence of grace; poverty becomes wealth; sadness, joy. Now she understood the words of the great apostle, "Who will separate us from the love of Christ? Will affliction, or distress, or persecution, or hunger, or nakedness, or peril, or the sword?" No, none of these things could separate her from Christ, the Christ of Nazareth. He was here in the wilderness and here she would make her abode. No hardship could drive her away.

The faint tinkle of the warning bell stilled her heart as she waited breathless for that tremendous moment when He becomes present on the altar ... *My Lord and my God!* The little bell rang again. *Lord, I am not worthy.* How she longed to receive Him! But no one stepped forward. She, like the others, had to ask Him to come in spirit, since weekly Communion was all that was permitted at that time. Time slipped away.

Aroused by a touch on her shoulder, she realized suddenly that Mass was over. Rising, she followed her two companions out into a world transformed. The storm had ceased; the wind was still. Before her stretched a

15

fairyland where hundreds of trees lifted their jeweled branches toward the rising sun.

How quickly, thought Catherine, God can clothe drabness with beauty! And her heart lifted when she contemplated the thought that what He does so wonderfully in nature, He does more wonderfully yet in grace. The ugliness of poverty and the pain of sacrifice would blossom into loveliness when borne for Him.

So engrossed was she with this thought that she failed to see the stump half hidden by a drift and, much to her companions' amusement, she landed in a heap in the soft snow. Teresa helped her up.

"Asleep again?" she whispered.

"No, still," acknowledged Catherine ruefully.

Back at the cabin they had breakfast—if it deserved that name—prepared in the one cooking utensil they owned, a frying pan which Father David had given them and which Teresa used for everything. First, she baked the cornbread in it. After she removed that, she used it to mix the middling, a sort of gravy made of flour and milk seasoned with bits of bacon, and put it back on the fire until the mixture was brown. Then she poured that out, scrubbed the pan, and used it to boil the sage tea, their only drink. Since there were no plates, the middling was served on the cornbread which they ate with their fingers because there were no forks, only a spoon and two knives. But even this shortage had its good points, for the less there was to use, the less there was to wash!

After this first meal there was a consultation, and Elizabeth assigned the work. The morning flew by. Dinner was an echo of breakfast, and work began again. The day was almost over, the first full day at Nazareth, and....

Teresa's voice broke the reverie. "Catherine, will you help me to get some water? Father David should be here soon, and it'll be too dark after he leaves. It gets dark so early now," she added as she reached for her heavy cloak.

Catherine responded with alacrity. She was not used

to sitting so long, and besides, she was eager to be out in the snow, to drink in its beauty. She took the wooden bucket and they started out.

"Don't be too long," Elizabeth called after them. "It's still very cold."

"We'll hurry," Teresa said, fastening her scarf around her neck. "Besides, we won't have to go to the spring today. The snow'll do just as well—although of course we'll have to get more of it."

Catherine glanced up at the trees above her, a little disappointed. The ice had melted from their branches and they no longer sparkled. But down below, the snow was still white and beautiful. She pushed her bucket deep into the nearest feathery drift and drew it out almost full. Then she began to fill it to the brim by cupping her hands, scooping up great quantities of snow, and emptying it into the bucket. Suddenly she chuckled. Her hands reached for another handful and pressed it into a firm ball. She looked around for her companion. The unsuspecting Teresa was a perfect target. Taking careful aim, Catherine was just about to throw when she heard a muffled step behind her. Whirling around, she saw Father David. She dropped the snowball, her face scarlet.

He appeared not to notice. "It's time for instructions," he called out and then went into the cabin without waiting.

Holding her skirt high, Catherine joined Teresa and told her in a laughing undertone about the snowball.

"Serves you right!" Teresa declared with mock indignation. "Imagine trying to snowball me! Shame on you!"

Without warning she reached down swiftly, seized a handful of snow, and rubbed Catherine's face with it. Then while her victim, stunned by the suddenness of the attack and blinded by the snow, reeled dizzily, she ran to the cabin and disappeared. Finally recovering, Catherine wiped her face and brushed the snow from her skirt.

When she entered the cabin, Teresa, looking innocent and proper, was seated on one of the stools. Elizabeth,

17

holding a burning taper, was lighting the lamp, a shallow metal vessel shaped like a pie pan with a ring handle on one side and a wide mouth on the other. The wick, a piece of woolen cloth soaked in pork grease, lay in the pan with one end projecting a little over the rim.

Father David waited until Catherine brought up her stool.

"Well, how do you like our life here at Nazareth?" he inquired, watching her closely.

"I love it, Father!" she answered quickly.

His glance rested on her approvingly. "You'll find some of it hard," he warned, "but it's wonderful how God gives the strength to do our work for Him. Why, before coming here, I feared I couldn't stand the hardship of riding a horse because of the weakness of my back, but actually I find that I am better than ever. I'm in charge of three congregations—St. Joseph's, St. Michael's, and St. John's. And I'm almost always on the road, but the riding never bothers me at all."

He reached for a book and opened it. But Catherine was not ready for lessons yet. There were too many other things she wanted to know.

"About how many miles must you travel to your missions, Father?" she queried, her eyes shining.

"Well, it differs," he explained, closing the book. "Sometimes it's twenty and at other times thirty miles between, depending on what road I take. Even forty miles fatigues me only a little now. And even then a good night's sleep soon refreshes me," he concluded.

The lamp sputtered and threatened to go out. Teresa watched it anxiously until it brightened again.

"Does Bishop Flaget ever go with you?" Catherine asked.

At the Bishop's name Father David's eyes sparkled. "Oh yes, often! Not long ago he went with me to bless a chapel which eleven families had just built in the middle of four hundred acres of land, thirty-five miles through the woods from St. Stephen's where we stayed at the time. For more than twenty miles of the trip we

18

had rain. We were drenched and stayed that way until bedtime when we dried out the best we could. Of course," he confessed, "I was afraid the consequences would be disastrous, but no evil resulted. That's the way the good God takes care of us when we do His work generously."

Teresa stole a sly look at Catherine. "You see, Catherine, a little snow won't hurt you," she remarked mischievously.

"No! unless it's in the shape of a ball," added the priest, glancing at Catherine, who promptly blushed, remembering what he had seen.

Inwardly planning to snowball Teresa the next day, Catherine quickly changed the subject. "Do your seminarians sing the Mass, Father?"

Her choice of subject was excellent, for Father David enjoyed talking about music. "No, but I hope they will soon, for if there is one thing I miss on these missions, it's singing. Sometimes I make up for it in the woods as I travel along, singing Vespers and Compline or one of the Little Hours. Then I think of our choir at St. Mary's, Baltimore." His voice grew wistful. "And sometimes too of our Brother Babade, who often sang his Office in his room in the middle of the night. Even if I haven't anyone to form a choir with me," he observed cheerfully, "at least I have the echoes which always answer loud and long."

Elizabeth, who had not been taking an active part in the conversation, looked up from her sewing. "Aren't there any singers around here?" she questioned.

"Oh yes, we have many, both men and women," he acknowledged quickly. "They call themselves trebles, counters, and basses, and they've learned to sing, if you can call it that, from the singing masters in these regions. When I hear them," he continued with a smile, "I am reminded of what Boileau said of the singing of his companions in his *Satyre du Repas,* 'They contract their throats, open their mouths halfway and their noses all the way.'" His three listeners burst into laughter.

"Worse than that," he went on when they were quiet,

"is the way they mark time. They blast out each beat of a long note. This remarkable feat they call 'swelling' but I call it 'thumping.'" And Father David demonstrated this vocal achievement by banging vigorously on the log table until the lamp sputtered.

"I've tried, but it's labor lost. *Naturam expellas furca, tamen recurret.*" Seeing their puzzled faces, he translated, "That means, 'You may drive out nature with a pitch fork, but it will always return.' I certainly hope you can help the children to carry a tune. In that way they'll soon sing the way I want them to. But," he added moving the sputtering lamp carefully, "we are spending too much time just talking."

He picked up the well-worn grammar and opened it. "I'd better get on with your lessons in grammar and mathematics, or I'll be late for my seven o'clock Latin classes with the seminarians."

CHAPTER THREE

1813

Green, green, and more green—everywhere one looked that early morning in June, 1813. Ecstatic with delight, bluebirds, cardinals, jays, and robins flitted here and there, brightening first one branch and then another with the red and blue of their glittering wings. The air was cool and delicately perfumed with honeysuckle and wild roses. Above, in the blue fields of the sky; white clouds skipped and frolicked.

On the ground near an old stump a robin hopped, cocking his shining head first to one side then the other, suddenly thrusting his beak into the sod to pull out a long, protesting worm. Not far away a woodchuck, convinced that spring had made room for summer, was carefully clearing away the fallen leaves which choked his burrow, and a grey squirrel scampered up a stately elm, his tail a perfect question mark.

But the green fields around St. Thomas's were not to be left to the birds and animals all day, for across the meadow came a rather nondescript group of girls, chatting and laughing. Three were dressed in coarse homespun; the other three in a little better material, but scarcely in fashion. By far the oddest feature of the little procession, however, was the fact that all six were carrying their shoes.

As the group approached a rail fence around a pasture, an inquisitive bluejay took a good look and then flew into a nearby tree shrieking, "Thief, thief!"

But the girls paid not the slightest attention. Catherine, Teresa, and Elizabeth, familiarly known as Betsy, were walking along speaking quietly, but Polly Beaven, Harriet Gardiner, and Mary Gwynn all seemed to be talking at once. They cared little that no one listened. The flow of words delighted their ears and relaxed their tongues, for hadn't they been absolutely silent for seven whole days during Father David's retreat? And hadn't they just "come out" that very morning? They found much to discuss after so long a silence, particularly since in a few minutes they were going to elect one of their group as Mother!

On Easter Monday, 1813, Polly, Harriet, and Mary had joined the new community. Since the original cabin was entirely too small for six, Father David had found them a larger one not far away. They used one of the rooms on the first floor of this cabin as a kitchen and refectory; the other as a community room. Above, in the half-story attic, the six of them slept. They still had no beds, but they enjoyed the luxury of being able to stand erect with inches to spare. This building also had its disadvantages. The former occupants had left the dwelling in such ruinous condition that at mealtime the Sisters often sat on the floor around the fireplace, their feet dangling from the projecting ends of the puncheon floor and the sleepers which had been burned off around the hearth.

The jay, from his secure perch in the tree, watched the girls curiously. At last they reached the fence.

"Isn't there a gate somewhere?" moaned Harriet, smoothing her long full skirt and looking ruefully at the obstacle before her.

"Don't worry. It's easy to get over. I'll show you," comforted Teresa, a veteran at this sort of thing. Suiting action to words, she gathered her skirt in one hand, grasped a post with the other, and with a quick motion was safe on the other side. Betsy and Catherine were soon over, and Mary and Polly followed suit.

"Well, I guess if you can do it, I can," Harriet said in a small voice totally lacking in conviction. But somehow her full skirt eluded her, and a blackberry bush added to the confusion by catching a bit of the hem. Part way over, she was caught, unable to go one way or the other. At the sight all laughed heartily, but sobered by her genuine distress, they controlled themselves sufficiently to assist her—Teresa clambering back over the fence to release the offending hem and Mary helping her down.

When they had all reached the end of the field, Betsy called a halt.

"I think we'd better put on our shoes now," she directed, seating herself on a stump. "Father David realizes that we must save them because it'll be a long time before we can afford new ones, but I'm sure he wouldn't think it dignified to appear barefoot before the parishioners."

"Just think," Polly exclaimed, busily unraveling a knot in her shoe string. "When we take these off again, we'll have elected a Mother. I wonder who she'll be."

"I don't wonder," Teresa put in quickly. "I know."

"Who?" they chorused, every face turned toward her.

"Why, Catherine, of course!"

There were four "Yeses" in instant agreement. Only Elizabeth and Catherine were silent. The moment was an awkward one for both of them. Elizabeth had been superior since January, and Catherine sensed her hurt now that she was practically being told that the others preferred Catherine, who was so much younger.

To ease the situation, Catherine turned toward Teresa. "That's what you think, my dear," she said lightly, "but time will tell. We'd better hurry or we'll be late for Mass."

The girls continued to talk, but their voices were subdued. Some of the sunshine had gone out of the day. A cloud of uneasiness marred the perfect harmony which had united them at the beginning of the walk to chapel.

One by one they filed into the dim interior. Catherine remembered that other momentous day when, in a flurry of snow, she had been blown in at the same door. The little room was the same except that now fresh flowers bloomed in the cedar vases. After the seminarian had lighted the candles, Catherine could see that these were field poppies, chosen, no doubt, because of their hue, for the Mass was in honor of the Holy Spirit.

Assisted by Father David and Father Chabrat, Bishop Flaget in his episcopal robes officiated. When the *Domine Non Sum Dignus* sounded, the six girls approached the altar.

Mass ended. The *Veni Creator* was intoned, but still the little group knelt motionless in the dim chapel. Each one in her heart was begging the Spirit of Wisdom to guide her in the selection of a leader for this little band. So much depended upon the result!

* * * * *

At last Father Chabrat reappeared. Less than a year before he had been ordained at the Dominican church of St. Rose, the first of Father David's little group of seminarians to become a priest. He beckoned to Elizabeth, who followed him into the room. Bishop Flaget and Father David sat near a log table on which lay several pieces of paper and a quill pen. Elizabeth went immediately to the Bishop, knelt and kissed his ring, and remained on her knees for his blessing; Father David also gave his blessing. Then she rose slowly and, seating herself nervously at the table, wrote on the paper her choice for a Mother, an Assistant, and a Procuratrix. Quickly she returned to her place in the chapel. Then Teresa entered the room and followed the same procedure. Catherine, Mary, Harriet, and Polly came in turn, wrote their choices, and returned to their places. For what seemed an hour they continued to kneel while the votes were tallied. Finally Father Chabrat appeared in the doorway and beckoned to them. With poorly concealed excitement, the girls followed him and stood facing the Bishop. He held the fateful paper in his hand.

"We have counted your votes," he announced gravely, indicating the paper he held before them, "and as a result of your own choice, the following are selected: Catherine Spalding, Mother; Harriet Gardiner, Assistant; and Betsy Wells, Procuratrix."

All eyes turned toward Catherine. Her face was drained of color. Her mind was whirling with the thought of the tremendous responsibility which was hers. A girl of nineteen to lead this little group to holiness by the practice of the spiritual and corporal works of mercy! To be their Mother—to sacrifice for her Sisters at all times, to comfort them in affliction, to rejoice with them in success, to correct them when they went astray, to direct them on the way to God! Yet, Catherine consoled herself, although young and inexperienced, she was not alone in this task. God was with her, and He, in His wisdom, would direct her. The color slowly returned to her cheeks and tears flooded her soft eyes. Her companions had chosen her to be their Mother. With God's grace she would not fail them.

Slowly she knelt before Bishop Flaget, who again imparted his blessing and assisted her to rise. She then went to Father David, who was still seated. As she knelt before him, she glanced up into his kindly face, and her heart lifted at the smile of approval and encouragement he gave her. Then he was pleased. God be praised!

"And now," she heard Bishop Flaget's voice as if at a great distance, "you must come and acknowledge your Mother."

Father David motioned her to a bench. One by one her Sisters came and knelt before her in token of obedience. Later she recalled little of Bishop Flaget's speech congratulating the group on being God's choice among so many in his vast diocese. He urged them to fidelity through trials and hardships and assured them that union and charity would secure for them the unfailing companionship of Jesus.

Father David also addressed the group, telling them that they should rejoice that their dwelling was called Nazareth. "This beautiful name," he concluded, "should unceasingly remind you, my spiritual daughters, of the Holy Family's home, where Jesus grew in wisdom and grace before God and man. There the Son of God, seeking to be unknown, gave us the example of perfect purity of life, of the obedience, humility, and poverty that ought to be the riches of our religious house— *Caritas Christi Urget Nos.*"

These final words burned themselves into Catherine's mind and warmed her heart. "Let that, dear Lord, be my motto—our motto," she murmured softly. "The Love of Christ urges us."

* * * * *

Two months passed, dropping as lightly into eternity as a faded leaf drops to the ground. Father David sat at his log table writing to Father Bruté, who had taught with him at St. Mary's Seminary in Baltimore and who had succeeded him as spiritual director to Mother Seton at Emmitsburg. He told him in detail about the recent election and then continued:

I am watching Catherine's remarkable gifts of mind and body beautifully unfold.... The firmness and kindness with which she rules and the respect of the Sisters for her authority assure me a solid foundation is being laid....

Mother is humble, courageous, kind, loving; her whole heart and soul are in the work she came to accomplish. She seems to be a born leader.

The tone of her voice is soft and gentle, but deep and earnest. Her words are few and concise, with an enunciation so distinct that they are sure to be remembered. Her manner, intelligence, and beautiful modesty are an attraction to all who meet her.

With such a leader, the Sisters will do much good by teaching, but for that work the establishment of a school is necessary. All the labor of preparing these bright girls for their future work devolves upon me.

This last sentence forcibly reminded him that he had work to do. Carefully wiping his quill, he placed it in the holder and gathered up his books. As he strode across the sunny fields to Nazareth, he thought about the help that he had hoped to get from Mother Seton.

"The least she might have done is to send Sister Kitty," he grumbled to himself as he entered the little cabin.

"Father?" questioned Mother Catherine as she opened the door for him.

"Oh, I was just talking to myself," Father David explained. "I'm still trying to get a Sister from Emmitsburg to come here to train you. First of all, I'm really not fitted for the task. Besides, I'm too busy with the seminarians and missions to give you sufficient time. Oh well," he sighed, dropping his books on the table and drawing up a stool, "you'll just have to put up with me, I suppose."

"Indeed, we'll be glad to!" put in Harriet quickly. "But of course it would be easier if you had help. You've too much to do already."

"Oh, I wasn't thinking of that." Father David shook his head. "What I really want is a good novitiate training for you. And that I'm not prepared to give. If I had a rule, perhaps—"

"But we do have a rule, don't we, Father?"

"Yes, but it's really just what I can remember from the one St. Vincent de Paul wrote for his Daughters of Charity in France. Bishop Flaget brought a copy to Mother Seton when he came to America in 1810. She gave it to Archbishop Carroll, who had the Sulpicians make certain necessary changes to cover the activities of her American Sisters. In France, you know, St. Vincent's Sisters taught only the poor. In this country the Sisters must teach the well-to-do for two reasons. First, there are practically no schools for the wealthy; secondly, there is no money for sustaining free schools. By having wealthy girls in their school, the Sisters can afford to admit the poor and educate them for nothing."

"Were you at Emmitsburg, Father, when those rules were adopted?" asked the usually silent Polly.

"No, I left three months before, but I know from Father Bruté that they are well suited to America. That's why I'm so interested in getting them—*and* a Sister from Emmitsburg for you."

Mother Catherine's strong, deft fingers, industriously plying a needle through a new piece of homespun, stopped in midair. "Do you have any particular Sister in mind, Father?" she asked.

"Indeed, I have! Sister Rose White. She's perfectly suited for the work, but" he added ruefully, "I know they won't let me have her because she's the logical one to succeed Mother Seton. If Sister Kitty had health and energy, she'd be well qualified. Even Sister Fanny would do. She'd be a fine one to instruct you in teaching. But why talk about it? I know I won't get anyone!" He was the picture of despair. Suddenly his face brightened. "The Will of God be done! We'll manage somehow."

"Of course we will, Father," consoled Sister Teresa. "We Kentuckians have always been able to manage—even Indians."

Father David smiled, but his face clouded again as he noticed the abstracted gaze of Sister Betsy Wells. She appeared totally uninterested in the discussion which meant so much to the rest. Lately she had changed. And this was not the first time he had noticed it. Shortly after the election, she appeared to grow indifferent. Was it because a younger person had been chosen Mother? He wasn't positive, of course, but whatever the cause, she had changed completely. Never too cheerful, she was now moody and aloof. In fact, in the letter to Father Bruté, which even now was lying unfinished on his log table, he had written:

Our nunnery is making progress. I am very well pleased with my little Mother, who is nineteen, and with her Assistant, who is seventeen. They have prudence and discretion beyond their age and experience. All six Philotheas are persevering; only one gives me any trouble. She is a changed person, a spirit out of gear, singular...I am afraid I shall be obliged to send her away...

"Yes, I'm afraid I shall," he said aloud.

"Shall what, Father?" the Sisters asked simultaneously, looking at him curiously.

"Shall have to begin my grammar lesson," he parried, glad that he had escaped so easily. He glanced at Betsy. She was still looking off into space.

CHAPTER FOUR

1814

Mother Catherine straightened up and pushed her sunbonnet back from her face. It was a perfect August day, the sky cloudless and the air cool. All around her the fruits of the spring planting were evident: in the distance, the tall corn standing guard over the adjoining stubble field where the wheat and the oats had been harvested; to her left, the delicate fern of the carrots and the tall lance-like blades of the onions; to her right, the vines of the cucumbers and the cantaloupe and the broad milky-green leaves of the fat cabbages; at her feet, the sturdy bean plants, their leaves shading the slender sheaves from the sun.

She bent down again, her hands pushing aside the rich green, her fingers breaking off the tender pods. There would be no shortage of food this winter, she thought. Suddenly her fatigue left her, dropping off as easily as the spider she had frightened slipped from the vine to the ground. At least *this* year she wouldn't hear the disturbing news that there was only one cupful of cornmeal left and not even a grain of salt to season it with. She could still see the misery in Teresa's brown eyes when she had reported this shortage. Things had looked bleak that day, but even then she had managed to whisper to Teresa, "God will provide," and had added with a wry smile, "oh ye of little faith!" The brown eyes had met hers steadily, and gradually the misery in them had disappeared.

Left alone she had sunk to her knees and prayed as she had never prayed before, for never had the words "Give us this day our daily bread" meant so much to her. Yes, she had prayed with all her strength, not for herself but for her Sisters; not for luxuries but for the necessities of life; and she had risen from her knees calm and confident that God had heard her prayer.

And of course He had. That very afternoon Bishop Flaget had come to visit. Familiar with poverty himself, he had recognized their need. When leaving, he pressed a five-dollar bill into her hand, telling her that if the Sisters could refund it they might do so; otherwise she could consider it a gift. How her spirits had risen then! Five dollars! She had rushed into the kitchen to show it to Sister Teresa, who swung her around in joy.

It was shortly after this that three postulants had applied for admission. When she asked Father David about them, he reminded her of the poverty of the little community and of the imprudence of adding three mouths to feed. But remembering the five dollars which had come at just the propitious moment, she had smilingly asked, "Should we close the way to heaven to these souls for fear of becoming bankrupt?" Even Father David had no argument for that, and a week later three happy postulants presented themselves at Nazareth.

A year! It didn't seem possible that a year had passed since the Sisters had elected her Mother and that at last they were about to embark upon their work of teaching. She stood. Shading her eyes, she turned to where the new building was going up. The seminarians, who had already finished a log cabin the same size as the one in which the Sisters were living, were working on a passageway to join the two. Robert Abell, James Derrigaud, John Moretti, and Walter Coomes were hard at work as long sawyers. Peter Shaffer and Jack Simms were making shingles. Several other willing workers were "botching" the cabin walls, while still others were filling the space between the logs with split wood. The seminarians would be finished soon, and then they were going to cover the entire structure with clapboards to give the cabins the appearance of a frame house.

As she stood watching the scene, her memory whisked her back to a day when Uncle Tom, swinging her up into the saddle before him, had asked her if she wanted to go to a "log raising." When she had looked puzzled, he explained that a poor family nearby needed a new cabin and that several of their neighbors had decided to build one for them. She had been in her glory that June morning, riding through the cool, fragrant woods, her small hands tight on the reins. All too soon they had come to a clearing. Stacked nearby were four piles of logs of different sizes, two for the long sides of the cabin and two for the short ones. Then she knew they had reached their destination and she had slipped to the ground.

Since she had never seen a cabin go up before, she settled herself comfortably under a gigantic pin oak and watched the proceedings with lively interest. No time was wasted. At once a dozen men gathered around Uncle Tom and elected him and three others "corner men." The four thus chosen immediately set about their business of notching and fitting the logs which several others handed to them. Meanwhile, in the shade of a locust, another group began splitting logs about eighteen inches in diameter and hewing them with broad axes to make puncheons.

By the time the cabin was a few rounds high, these men had finished the floor boards; they climbed over the uncompleted log sides to lay the sleepers first, then the puncheon floor. Meanwhile Uncle Tom and his helpers placed the final rounds of logs and began the roof, cutting the end logs shorter until a single one formed the support for the ridge. Then they covered them with split logs. At one side of the cabin a tall young man in a coonskin cap busied himself sawing an opening about three feet wide, while another fashioned a door of upright pieces of timber about three inches thick. In the rear two brothers were making a wide opening for the log chimney, leaving enough room for the back which would be of stone.

Everyone worked steadily, stopping only for a short time for dinner. By late afternoon the cabin was finished. The weary men sat around under the trees and smoked and talked about the crops. Catherine had been happy just to sit and listen.

During the conversation one of the workers chanced to remark that the poor family had little or no furniture. Glancing at each other knowingly, the men, without a word, got up and set to work again with a will. In no time there was a simple table made from a split slab, supported by four round legs set in auger holes, some three-legged stools, and a rude bed of wide boards supported by two poles. A few pegs around the walls for clothes, a shelf of clapboards, and the furnishings were complete.

Mother Catherine remembered how poor and mean the finished dwelling had looked to her then in comparison with Uncle Tom's frame house with the curl maple and wild cherry furniture, which he had brought on a raft down the Ohio from Maryland. But now, after the dilapidated cabins that she had lived in. . . . She smiled, remembering the crude furniture, the burned sleepers, and the loft of their first cabin.

Suddenly she realized that she had been standing idle, and bending down she worked steadily. When her apron was full, she gathered the ends in one hand and her skirt in the other and started for the cabin, walking briskly.

Near the front door was a rough bench in the shade of a sugar maple. She wearily sat down and prepared to string the beans. The hum of the spinning wheel drew her eyes to the interior. There Agnes, the latest postulant, was working industriously, now and then stopping to wipe her face.

"Come out here, my dear," Mother Catherine called. "It's cooler outside than in today. In fact, you may even find a breeze, and you can help me string these beans."

Agnes obeyed promptly. "It *is* much cooler out here," she murmured gratefully as she settled herself on the bench and transferred a handful of beans from Mother's coarse apron to her own.

Mother Catherine glanced sideways at the flushed face. "It won't be long before the building is finished," she said, "and then we'll be able to take up teaching."

"Father David will be happy when *that* day comes," Agnes said, dropping a handful of broken beans into her lap. "And Sister Ellen will be a wonderful teacher, I'm sure." Her face lighted up. "The other day in class she had us spellbound while she read *The Ancient Mariner*. When she finished, she told us all about William Wordsworth and Samuel Coleridge. They're living in the Lake District of England and are experimenting with a new type of poetry. To show us how different it is, she read some of their poetry and then some of Milton's and Pope's. You know how much expression Sister uses when she reads. Well—" she stopped suddenly. "Oh, there she is now!"

Mother's eyes shifted from the postulant to the broad back of a Sister who was carrying a bucket of water toward the new cabin. As soon as the seminarians who were working on the building saw the Sister, they dropped their tools. Quickly filling their gourds, they tilted them and drank thirstily, splashing the rest of the water on their hot faces.

The two on the bench watched in silence for a moment. Sister Ellen, catching sight of them, waved. They waved back. The thread of conversation was broken, but Agnes did not mind. Right now Sister Ellen O'Connell was far more interesting than the poets.

"How did Sister Ellen happen to come to Nazareth anyway, Mother? Maryland is so far away."

"She learned about us through Father David," Mother Catherine replied thoughtfully. "You see, she met Father when he was living in Baltimore, and he became her spiritual director. When he came to Kentucky, she continued to write to him. Her father, Michael O'Connell, was a professor of literature and an interpreter. He died shortly after our community was established and Ellen wanted to join us immediately. But Father David advised her to prepare for greater usefulness by acquiring a little experience. For a while she taught in Baltimore."

They lapsed into a silence punctuated by the rhythmical snap, snap of the beans. "It must have been a long, hard journey from Baltimore here," Agnes commented, reaching over for another handful.

"Indeed it was! Sister Ellen regaled us for days with her experiences. Most of them were funny. You know how easily she can change a serious topic into a humorous one."

"She certainly can," agreed the postulant. "Especially when someone is homesick." She flushed at having betrayed her own secret.

Mother Catherine regarded her kindly. "We all go through that some time, dear. If we didn't, our sacrifice wouldn't be worth anything, but," she continued with a sympathetic pat on the shoulder, "it's soon over."

Since Agnes found this a dangerous topic, she hastily changed the subject. "How long did it take Sister Ellen to get here?"

"About thirteen days. It was the middle of April when she arrived. You see, she had to go by coach to Pittsburgh first and then by flatboat the rest of the way. Since she brought many of her father's books, she had quite a bit of baggage and that made her traveling slower."

Agnes chuckled. "She wouldn't be without her books, would she? But they're a great help to us," she added soberly. "You know, though, I would have been frightened to death at night on the Ohio. The daytime might be rather pretty, but the night—ugh."

"So you'd be frightened on the black Ohio at night, would you?" They both started and turned around. Sister Ellen laughed. "I didn't mean to scare you. It's just too bad you weren't along on that trip so I could have told you some of my ghost stories—the ghoul of a moon,

35

the lap, lap of the inky waters on the side of the boat, the hooting of an owl—"

"That's enough, Sister Ellen," Mother Catherine smiled. "You make me shiver." She moved over on the bench. "The school's coming along, isn't it?"

Sister Ellen seated herself beside them. "It certainly is, Mother. When the seminarians finish the outside with clapboard, we'll have just as fine a building as I left in Baltimore."

She put down her empty bucket and reached for some beans. "You know, Mother, I'm worried about Mr. Wesley. He didn't come out of his cabin to get a drink as usual. Mr. Morgan said he was sick last night."

Mother Catherine's quick eyes glanced down the row of four log cabins beside the gravel path. Before the arrival of the Sisters, these buildings had been occupied by slaves; now they housed several elderly men whom the Sisters had rescued from utter destitution. In return these men helped with the gardening and weaving as much as they could. Mr. Wesley, whom Sister Ellen had just mentioned, was regarded as a saint.

Rising hastily, Mother gave her stringbeans to Agnes and started down the path. "Come on, Sister Ellen," she called over her shoulder. "We'll see if Mr. Wesley is in the weaving cabin."

Sister Ellen followed to the small cabin which housed the old loom that Mother Catherine herself had used when she first came to Nazareth. At the door Mother paused a moment, then lifted the latch. Sister Ellen heard her gasp and quickly joined her inside. Mr. Wesley was slumped over the loom, his hands still resting on the beam. It wasn't necessary to go nearer to see that he was dead.

Mother Catherine's face was sad as she helped Sister Ellen lay the thin body on the floor. "May God rest his soul," she murmured as she closed the glazed eyes. "I'm sure he went straight to heaven and will be Nazareth's first advocate before the throne of God. See if you can find Father David, Sister Ellen. I'll stay here."

* * * * *

A week after Mr. Wesley's funeral the new school was ready. Joined to the old building, it gave the Sisters five rooms in all. They were especially proud of the covered front porch and the small reception hall. Before long they had the large room on the ground floor outfitted with long benches for prospective students and the room above converted into a dormitory for the Sisters. But what about the old dormitory? Speculation among the Sisters ran high as to its use. They had seen Mother Catherine and Sister Teresa going up and down the narrow stairs sometimes carrying mysterious bundles. Yet no one had been allowed to investigate.

Finally Sister Ellen could stand it no longer. So one night at recreation she brought up the subject. "Tell us what you're going to use the old dormitory for, Mother," she begged. "We're dying of curiosity."

Looking up from her sewing, Mother Catherine found every eye on her. "Don't do that just now, I beseech you, Sister Ellen," she teased. "None of us has the time for a funeral. Besides, we need you to teach."

"Well, I'm afraid if I don't find out what you two are up to, I'll really die," Sister Ellen pleaded, her eyes sparkling with excitement.

Mother Catherine folded the material she was working on. "Frankly," she said, "I'm glad you asked, for we were going to take you upstairs soon anyway. However, if it will prevent a few deaths, we'll do it right now, won't we, Sister Teresa?"

In a twinkling all the sewing disappeared, and Mother Catherine, taking the candle, preceded them up the narrow steps. Sister Teresa followed her. Then came Sister Ellen and the others. At the top Sister Ellen strained her eyes to see into the little room lighted only by the rays of the flickering candle. At first, thinking that her eyes were deceiving her, she just stood there on the top step and stared. It took protestations from below to propel her into the room and restore her voice.

37

"An altar!" she gasped. "Oh, Mother, how wonderful!"

By this time Mother was surrounded by the others, all asking questions at the same time. "If you'd only wait a minute," she protested, putting her hands to her ears, "I'll tell you everything." Indicating Sister Teresa, she said, "We've been planning this a long time. In fact, ever since the seminarians started on the new building. You know, when they built their new chapel, they made a larger and finer altar. For various reasons, however," she smiled knowingly at Sister Teresa, "Sister and I have always preferred this one, although it is not nearly so beautiful as the new one." The candle flickered, and she shielded the flame with her left hand.

"Well, in short, we asked Father David for the old one, and he gladly gave it to us. The seminarians had quite a time figuring how to get it up here. One day when all of you were out gathering firewood, they decided to take it apart and carry it up piecemeal. That was the solution, and here it is."

Holding the candle high, she moved closer to the altar so that they might examine it. When the babble of conversation had died down, Sister Ellen said reverently, "It will almost seem as if we had Our Lord with us."

"He *is* going to be here," Sister Teresa burst out, no longer able to keep the secret. "Father David's going to bring the Blessed Sacrament tomorrow morning from the church." Tears flooded her eyes. "Yes, Our Lord is really coming to live with us at last."

For a moment there was a stunned silence as the Sisters strove to grasp this tremendous truth. Then the spell was broken by joyous exclamations. There was little sleep that night for any of them.

Early the next morning the Sisters hurried across the dew-drenched fields to escort their sacramental Lord and Master to their home. Father David wrapped the humeral veil around the ciborium, intoned the *Pange Lingua*, and started across the meadow. The Sisters and the seminarians took up the hymn.

James Derrigaud and Peter Shaffer, swinging thurifers, led the way; the rest followed. There were no tiny girls strewing rose petals in this idyllic procession, but the wild flowers looked up and seemed to smile as their Lord went by, and the birds sang more sweetly than usual to greet Him in this triumphal procession of the Blessed Sacrament—perhaps the first in the state of Kentucky.

On reaching the chapel, Father David celebrated Mass. In honor of the occasion all were permitted to receive Holy Communion. Later Mother Catherine, her eyes soft, whispered to Sister Teresa, "No trials, no difficulties can ever seem hard again, since Our Lord Himself has come to live with us."

As if that were not enough to mark a gala day, another great event took place that same afternoon. About four o'clock Sister Harriet came in breathless to inform Mother Catherine that Mr. O'Brien, a neighboring farmer, was in the reception hall to see the Sisters about teaching his little girl.

"Find Sister Ellen," Mother Catherine directed. Then removing her work apron she went into the stiff little parlor. In one chair sat Mr. O'Brien obviously very uncomfortable; in the other, his nine-year-old daughter Cecilia, looking a fit subject for execution. Mother Catherine tried to relieve Mr. O' Brien by giving the customary assurances tendered to school-bereaved parents from time immemorial. Under this treatment, he relaxed a little, but not Cecilia. In vain Mother Catherine smiled at the solemn child sitting so primly on the high stool in her starched pinafore, her long pigtails pulled over her shoulders, and her feet, encased in buttoned shoes dangling a foot above the floor. Cecilia merely continued to stare stonily.

"If you can take her, ma'am, I'll see that she gets here every day," Mr. O'Brien promised. "My wife and I want Cecilia to have the best education we can give her, and when Father David told us you were ready to open a school, we came right away."

With that, Sister Ellen appeared. "Here," Mother said, taking the reluctant child by the hand and leading her to Sister Ellen, "here is your teacher."

Cecilia glanced up timidly into the cheery face and fell an instant victim to its charms. The small brown hand slipped willingly into the large one, and the two of them were off to see the schoolroom.

Solemnly Sister Ellen led the little girl to her desk. Taking out a large book, she wrote in it. "You're the first to have your name written in this book, Cecilia. Want to see it?"

The child nodded and looked curiously at the hieroglyphics which Sister Ellen told her read: Cecilia O'Brien, daughter of Harold O'Brien of Nelson County, entered Nazareth Academy, August 18, 1814.

Shyly she looked up into the kind eyes; then suddenly pushing her pigtails behind her vigorously, she squared her small shoulders and spoke for the first time. "When I grow up, I'm going to be a teacher, like you."

Years later, when Cecilia was Sister Cecily, Sister Ellen loved to remind her of this moment.

CHAPTER FIVE

1814-1816

The war which had been raging far from the convent cabin in the wilderness was ended. But Mother Catherine and her little band did not know it, and every time the Sisters knelt to pray—which was often—they remembered the danger threatening their beloved country and pleaded for her triumph and for the safety of her soldiers. To the east, Washington, the capital of their growing republic, lay in ruins; but the soul of the nation, like the phoenix of old, had risen unharmed, manifesting itself in the stirring anthem, "The Star Spangled Banner."

True, disaster had struck hard and fast. But the Americans, although chastened by carnage and destruction were, as Catherine had predicted, triumphant, not because of any great victories in the conflict but because in Europe the English were engaged in the Napoleonic Wars and were not in position to throw full strength against the United States. As early as March, 1813, Czar Alexander I of Russia, the land whose bitter cold had defeated the great French general, had offered through John Quincy Adams, American minister to Russia, to mediate the Anglo-American war. His purpose of course was to free the English from their American conflict so that they could play a stronger role in the continuing war against Napoleon. But communication was slow, and it was not until early 1814 that Congress confirmed a peace commission consisting of Adams, Gallatin, Bayard, Clay, and Russell to negotiate peace. Finally, on Christmas Eve in 1814 at Ghent, Belgium, a peace treaty with England became a reality.

Yes, the War of 1812 was ended at last. But the British in New Orleans did not know it; neither did Andrew Jackson. On the very day the treaty was signed, Old Hickory was gathering six thousand men, among them two thousand Kentuckians under General Adair, to meet twenty thousand British at New Orleans and to drive them from American soil. It meant nothing to him that he was outumbered. All he asked was the opportunity to strike a blow for his country. The people of New Orleans, terrified by the strength of the English, filled the churches and begged God and His Blessed Mother to help them. The Ursuline Sisters promised a Solemn High Mass each year in honor of Our Lady of Prompt Succor if the Americans won. In just twenty-five minutes the main battle was over, leaving 2,000 British and 71 Americans dead.

Months later the news of the treaty of peace and of Jackson's astounding victory on January 8 reached Kentucky through volunteers slowly drifting home. From them the Sisters also learned of the Americans' triumphant entry into New Orleans to the strains of the *Te Deum* and of General Jackson's visit to the Ursuline Sisters to thank them for their prayers. No longer did America need to hang her head, for she had proved herself stronger than the Mistress of the Seas and had gained new respect among the nations. Mother Catherine was overjoyed.

About this same time the Sisters of Charity of Nazareth likewise achieved a victory. They secured Father David's permission to adopt a habit. With light hearts and much laughter they gathered in their poorly furnished community room on an October afternoon in 1815 to see the results of long hours of planning and sewing. No group of modern society women in Dior's famous salon could have looked with more eager or critical eyes at the model than did the eleven Sisters who crowded around Sister Harriet Gardiner that day. Standing nearby with heads cocked to one side and eyes bright with a creative look were Sister Teresa and Sister Ellen. Everyone had contributed to the planning of the habit by giving suggestions, but these two had made the ideas a reality.

Mother Catherine noted with approval the full black worsted skirt, the neat bodice, the wide sleeves, which extended to the wrists, and the short narrow cuffs worn under the sleeves.

"I like it very much, Sister Ellen," she said, bending down to break off a thread.

"Now let's see the rest," Sister Polly urged, leaning over the table in her excitement.

Triumphantly Teresa produced a black circular cape with a small black collar which fitted snugly around Sister Harriet's neck. "This," she remarked, pinning it in place, "is very easy to make, and this"—she held up a homespun apron—"can readily be replaced by cotton for work." Last of all, on Sister Harriet's hair, which was pulled severely back from the forehead, she placed a black cambric cap made much like the one worn by Mother Seton's Sisters.

"When we get rosary beads, we shall wear them at the side," Mother Catherine said, straightening the cape over Sister Harriet's shoulders.

Again and again Sister Harriet had to walk up and down the community room while the Sisters feasted their eyes on the garb which would, from that moment, mark them as Sisters of Charity of Nazareth, Kentucky.

When all had looked to their hearts' content, Mother Catherine turned toward the Sisters. "Do you think we can get eleven of these habits made before Father David receives the new rule from Emmitsburg? If so, I think he'll allow us to adopt both at the same time."

There was an instant chorus of agreement. "Then," observed Sister Teresa sagely, "we'd better stop the admiring and get to work. There'll be much spinning, dyeing, and weaving to do even before we start the sewing."

But there was no need to urge anyone. The spinning wheel whirred endlessly and the loom groaned from use. By the time Father David had received the rule and had made a few modifications, the habits were ready and were laid carefully on the tables in the community room for his blessing.

On April 7, 1814, each Sister took her habit in her arms, kissed it, and put it on while breathing the prayer:

> I am unworthy, O my Jesus, to be clothed with the livery of Thy spouses, yet give me the grace to wear it faithfully until death, and grant that the sentiments of my heart may be worthy of Thee and of my holy vocation. Amen.

An hour later the Sisters appeared for Mass at St. Thomas's. No regiment was prouder of its uniform than were the Sisters of Charity that day. At home, lessons were a little slow in getting under way as round eyes took in the change of garb and small tongues wagged over the style—or lack of it.

The school was nearly a year old now and had grown until there were thirty-four pupils. The majority of them. following the example of the first boarder, Ann Lancaster of Nelson County, lived at the school, as the distance to their homes was too great to be traveled every day.

Mother Catherine's ever vigilant eyes and busy brain foresaw and provided for needed improvements: new rooms for domestic work and a fine stone spring house, which was also used as a dairy.

Clothed now in the simple habit, the Sisters were so rich in their poverty that they could cherish the multiplied hardships of their lives. And their days were hard! After breaking their fast with a bit of dry corn bread and a cup of rye coffee without sugar and often without milk, they labored for long hours in the fields, the kitchen, the washhouse, and the schoolroom. When after the usual prayers they assembled for dinner, hunger made palatable a piece of cornbread and fat middling with dandelion greens or some other plain vegetable cooked on the fire made with the branches they had gathered in the woods. After this they toiled on until the evening meal, a cup of sage tea and the usual morsel of cornbread. But what of that? Christ had often gone hungry. Their pupils must be served first and they, the humble servants of the poor, must take what was left.

No one was more cognizant of the hardships of the Sisters than was Father David, but he had no resources. All he could do was to encourage them on their hard road. Often, as he stood before them in the crowded chapel under the eaves, his eyes would mist and his voice quaver as he exhorted them to persevere. They were his children who were walking this hard road, and he suffered with them, but neither he nor they must forget that that same arduous road would lead to unending happiness. And then his words would pour out in a torrent: "Toil on, noble souls, toil on. After a wearisome day made light by joy within, you will sit around the homemade candle to knit or sew or spin, enjoying the evening recreation, when all laugh to heartily at the little mishaps of the day, and when too you strengthen one another by words of edification. When the reading and prayers are over, you will go to take rest on your straw pallets, dreaming sweet dreams of future blessing awaiting you above, to rise refreshed in the morning for Mass, meditation, and another day's labors.

"Some will grow faint-hearted and withdraw; but swerve not, faithful souls, for heaven blesses your work. That burning ground your bare feet are treading becomes God's own; ere long, prosperity will smile upon your home. You may have gone to your Father above before the hundredfold promised in this world is given to your community, yet shrink not; the hundredfold you already possess is the peace of your own hearts, and when you have gone hence, pray that those whom Providence shall call to continue the good work you have begun may be animated by the same spirit."

There was, moreover, another thing that Father David could do besides giving words of encouragement, and that was to obtain from Bishop Flaget the permission for the Sisters to make vows. Over three years had passed since the little community had come into being. They had adopted a habit, but the really distinguishing mark of the religious was still lacking. Father David knew how much the Sisters desired vows. Now that they had been sufficiently tried and had not been found wanting, he and Bishop Flaget decided that on the Feast of the Purification of the Blessed Virgin Mary, February 2, 1816, Mother Catherine, Sister Teresa Carrico, Sister Harriet Gardiner, and Sister Mary Beaven (Sister Polly) would be allowed the privilege of pronouncing annual vows of Poverty, Chastity, and Obedience. The example of these fortunate ones would be followed a month later, on March 25, by Sister Nancy Lynch, Sister Mary Gwynn, Sister Ellen O'Connell, and Sister Martha Gough.

There was to be no elaborate ceremony, he told them, no dressing in bridal gown, no ceremonious donning of the habit, simply the solemn consecration of their lives to God. In a single act they would give all to Him. In this, as in all other things, they would imitate the unassuming Christ.

The Chosen, as the first group laughingly called themselves, could hardly wait for the great day. Meanwhile there was much work to make the time pass faster. Four new homespun habits must be made, for every bride fits herself out in a new gown for her beloved. Not only that, but each Sister, whether she was making vows or not, would have to make a new headress as well because a few weeks before, Father David had given the Sisters permission to change the black cap they had worn at first to a white one resembling a small sunbonnet with a double bow on top—white to symbolize the purity of mind and heart that should be characteristic of the Brides of Christ. Since Mother Catherine considered Profession Day an excellent time for all the Sisters to change, each had a cap to make.

Finally everything was in readiness and the great day dawned, cold, crisp, and clear. As she crossed the fields,

Mother Catherine's heart sang. She had asked God for snow on this her espousal day, and now all around her an ermine mantle covered the frozen earth. The Bridegroom had laid out the finest of carpets for His Brides. "If days can be twins," she mused happily, "today is twin to my first day at Nazareth, snow and all."

In a dream she followed the others into the chapel. She saw nothing. In vain she tried to read the prayers of the Mass. It was impossible. Her eyes refused to focus on words that morning; joy filled her heart. At the altar Father David, Bishop Flaget, and Father Chabrat moved with dignity and reverence through the solemn ritual.

At the *Lord, I am not worthy* the four Sisters moved slowly to the communion rail. Father David turned to face them, holding the Sacred Host. Mother Catherine looked up reverently. Then her clear, sweet voice rang through the small chapel, calling on the vast court of heaven to be witness of her espousal:

O Almighty and Eternal God, I, Catherine Spalding, though unworthy of appearing before Thee, yet confiding in Thy infinite goodness and mercy and moved with the desire to serve Thee, in the presence of the ever Blessed Virgin, of St. Joseph our tutelar father, of St. Vincent de Paul our holy patron, and of all the heavenly court, devote my whole being and faculties to Thy service and that of the poor members of Jesus Christ, binding myself by the simple vows of poverty, chastity, and obedience for one year according to the meaning and extent attached to the same vows, humbly beseeching Thy infinite goodness through the Blood of Jesus Christ to receive this, my consecration to Thee, and as Thou hast enabled me to conceive the desire of it, so mayest Thou give me the grace faithfully to accomplish it. Amen.

March had come in like a lion and had gone out like a lamb. The days were warm now, too warm for the season. Mother Catherine sat listlessly at her desk. School was over for the day and she was tired, exhausted. A slow smile curved her lips. "So young and so utterly worn out," she said to the empty room, and then laughed outright. "If I'm this tired at twenty-three, what will I be at seventy? But there's no rest for the wicked," she sermonized herself as she attacked the stack of papers before her. "Work! That's what I wanted! And I got it! How Uncle Tom would tease me now!"

A childish shout attracted her attention. Glancing through the window, she saw a troop of the boarders, marshalled by Sister Ellen, emerging from the woods, their pinafores full of dead branches for the kitchen fire. Evidently Sister had promised a reward to the one who had gathered the most, for they were all crowding around, showing her their booty. Whoever won, Mother Catherine would never know, but the awarding of the prize must have been accompanied by one of Sister Ellen's witty sallies, for they all laughed as they ran off to the kitchen.

After the children had gone, Mother Catherine continued to sit staring out the window. Suddenly she rose, and going to the door, pulled down a branch of a sugar maple which grew nearby. She scanned it intently for a moment. "Buds," she burst out, "buds! Why it's spring again! No wonder I'm so tired. I might have known it was spring fever! Catherine, you'll never change, I'm afraid." Humming a little tune, she seated herself again at the desk and briskly set about correcting Cecilia's arithmetic paper, which was on the top of the pile.

An hour later she had finished every one of the papers and was just about to leave when Sister Harriet came in with a letter. "Mr. O'Brien brought it, Mother, when he came after Cecilia this afternoon," she explained.

Mother's heart skipped a beat as she recognized her sister's handwriting. Ann! she thought; I hope there's nothing wrong. Hurriedly she tore open the envelope and her eyes raced along the lines. Then with a relieved sigh she turned to Sister Harriet, her voice trembling with emotion. "So often," she observed, "things seem to happen in threes! First the habits, then our vows, and now this." She handed the letter to Sister Harriet. "Please read it out loud, Sister. Maybe my eyes are deceiving me."

Sister Harriet's hand shook a little. Was the news good or bad? She began: "Dear Catherine, Father David has given me permission to enter Nazareth next week—"

"Then it *is* true, Sister!" cried Mother Catherine, interrupting her. "That little possum! Keeping such good news from me! I'll take care of her!"

She took the letter from Sister Harriet and read it again. "God is so good," she murmured. "Just think! Ann, my little sister, is coming to stay—forever."

CHAPTER SIX

1816

"My, but this thing's heavy!" Sister Polly muttered setting down the wooden bucket with a thud. Some of the water spilled out and, mixing with the dust, became a blob of brown mercury rolling on the surface of the thirsty soil. She watched, fascinated for a moment, and then her grey eyes scanned the sky. Oh, if it would only rain! But the great blue expanse above her was innocent of even the smallest cloud. She sighed and reached down to pick up the bucket again. Just then she noticed someone —no, there were two people coming across the fields from St. Thomas's. Shading her eyes from the glare of the sun, she looked again and recognized Bishop Flaget and Father David. Seizing the bucket, she hastened to the convent.

By the time the visitors had reached the building, all the Sisters were assembled. True, some were still tying apron strings and adjusting caps, but they were present. It was the first time Bishop Flaget had seen them in their habits, and his eyes spoke approval although he made no comment.

When they were all seated in the plain community room, he began without preamble, "You must pray hard, Sisters, for tomorrow, by the grace of God, we shall lay the cornerstone of the cathedral in Bardstown, and Father David here," he placed his hand on the priests' shoulder, "will preach." The joy in his voice communicated itself to his audience, and their faces glowed with pleasure.

Mother Catherine leaned forward in her chair. "We'll pray hard," she promised. "Our little congregation and the diocese are certainly growing together. Imagine a cathedral! The next thing you know we'll have a coadjutor."

Bishop Flaget and Father David exchanged glances. Did Mother Catherine know, Bishop Flaget asked himself, that he had already asked for Father David? But how could she? No, she had just happened to strike the secret truth. But unless she was diverted, she would soon uncover the rest. Mother Catherine was keen. Bishop Flaget realized that fact very well, and since the negotiations concerning Father David were not making much headway in Rome, he hastened to resume the discussion of the laying of the cornerstone.

"You know," he continued, ignoring the remark about the coadjutor, "nine years ago I conceived the design of my cathedral, but the poverty and the pressing needs of the diocese made it seem rashness to engage in an undertaking so far above my means. This year, however, Father David counseled me that it was time and told me to trust in Divine Providence."

Mother Catherine nodded. How often Father David had advised her to trust in Providence!

"And Divine Providence *did* come to my aid," the Bishop continued, "in the form of a good carpenter, John Rodgers, from Baltimore. He has already perfected the plans and promises to oversee the construction. Money is naturally very important in this venture," he remarked, pulling a paper from his pocket, "and this report tells me that $14,000 has been collected already. Much of it came from France of course, but my episcopal city, Bardstown, has contributed $5,000, a splendid amount for so small a town."

While he was speaking, Father David was opening the large roll which he carried under his arm and was spreading it on the table. He motioned the Sisters to come closer. "Here are the plans and a sketch of the completed cathedral."

There were murmurs of approval and exclamations over the size of the building. Sister Teresa, nearer than the others, noticed in one corner the date—July 16, 1816 —with the notation, "cornerstone," in the Bishop's writing.

Bishop Flaget regarded the Sisters with interest as they clustered around the table like happy children. "I had really intended engaging Maximilian Godfrey to design the building," he explained, addressing himself to Mother Catherine. "He was the architect who made the plans for the chapel at St. Mary's, Baltimore, and who taught design at the college there. I told him about the cathedral, but somehow he never got around to it." He shook his head slowly and sadly. "There are so many things in every life that one never seems to get around to. Time has a way of slipping past us before we can make full use of it."

At this remark Father David looked up from the paper with a quizzical smile. "Twenty-one hundred miles in thirteen months hardly bears out that statement—in your regard, at least," he remarked dryly, carefully rolling up the blueprints. "Cincinnati, Springfield, Dayton, Detroit, Montreal, Quebec, Niagara, Pittsburgh—all visited in quest of souls. That doesn't sound to me like letting time slip past." He turned to face the Sisters. "I tell him," he said, deliberately ignoring the plea in Bishop Flaget's eyes, "that he should stay home and let a priest visit all those places. After all, the people won't receive any more advantage from the visit of a bishop than from a simple priest like Mr. De Andreis or Mr. Richard, and then poor David would not be left alone."

"Poor David," mimicked the Bishop, "seems to manage quite well without me. In fact, I think he does better when I'm away," he remarked with a smile. "But we must move on. I've promised to show these drawings to the seminarians, and it's growing late."

Outside he turned once more to the Sisters grouped in the doorway. "I'm sure you noticed that I've selected the Feast of Our Lady of Mt. Carmel for the ceremony, and I needn't explain why. But pray, pray, that I myself may be the cornerstone and a holy ornament of the cathedral, which will be the first large church in this vast territory and a model for those which will follow."

Some months after the Bishop's visitation, Mother Catherine, engaged in hearing spelling in her classroom opposite the new brick chapel which had been completed a few weeks before, was interrupted by a knock. She sent Cecilia O'Brien to the door. The child dropped a deep curtsy when she saw Father Badin standing on the porch. Cecilia knew this priest well; indeed, he had baptized her and had often said Mass in her home. Only a week before she had heard her father say that Father Badin had gone to St. Louis to visit the new bishop, Louis DuBourg, whom Bishop Carroll had appointed administrator of the newly acquired Louisiana Territory in 1812 and whom Pius VII had made a bishop three years later. Bishop DuBourg, unfamiliar with the problems of such a vast territory, had sent for Father Badin, who had taken care of a great portion of this territory single-handed, prior to 1810. The Bishop felt that he could learn much from Father Badin's experiences.

Patting Cecilia on the head, the priest followed her into the room where the other children stood at rigid attention until he smiled, saying, "Mother Catherine, don't you think it's too lovely today for such fine young ladies to stay inside? How about a short recess?"

Twenty heads turned simultaneously to Mother. Twenty pairs of eyes lit with expectancy.

"You may go," she said. "I'll be at the door when it's time to come in. Don't go too far."

She clapped her hands and the children knelt for Father Badin's blessing; they filed out sedately, each turning at the door to curtsy. Father watched them leave and then observed quietly, "Your school seems to be flourishing."

"It surely is," she agreed gayly. "We'll have to be building again soon if the pupils continue to come in such large numbers as they did this year."

"That's fine. I know Betsy will be happy about that."

A slight furrow appeared between Mother's eyes. Even

though she knew that Betsy Wells was happy as Father Badin's housekeeper, she was sorry that one of the original three had left Nazareth. Besides, she was still convinced that Betsy should be a religious.

"How is she?" she asked with genuine concern.

"Fine, both as to health and as to housekeeping." He smiled. "When I'm home, she takes good care of me, and when I'm away, she looks after everything else." He paused to examine one of the children's books. When he continued, there was a pensive note in his voice. "But I still can't get her to take any compensation, for she holds with St. Paul that 'piety with sufficiency is great gain.' She'll have to accept something though when I return to France."

"France!" Mother was startled. "For good?"

"I'm not sure. That'll depend on what I find when I get there. I'm afraid I'm too much attached to Kentucky to stay for the rest of my life, yet one never knows."

"But we need you here!"

Father Badin shook his head sadly. "Not any more. With Bishop Flaget, Fathers David and Nerinckx and all the new priests who have been or will be ordained here at St. Thomas's, Kentucky will be cared for. I'm no longer necessary as I was when I was the only priest in these regions. Besides, it's for the best. As you know, the Bishop and I have had our differences."

Mother nodded thoughtfully. She, like everyone else, had heard about the difficulty between Bishop Flaget and Father Badin over ecclesiastical property, and she felt that the misunderstanding stemmed from the fact that it was hard for Father Badin to distinguish between what was church property and what was his own.

"Anyway," he continued as she remained silent, "a trip to France will do no harm. I'm sure I can get help for Kentucky from my friends and relatives there. In fact, my brother wrote me recently that in Lyons a wealthy girl named Marie Jaricot has started a society whose function it is to help the missions. Perhaps I can get her interested. At least, I can try."

"Oh, I know you *can* and *will* help us from France," Mother interposed quickly, "but nobody can ever replace you here, for *you* are Kentucky."

Father Badin smiled at her outburst. "I'll remember that when I'm in La Provence," he promised. "But now I'd better be getting on, for I promised Vincent I'd not be gone long."

"But what'll happen to Betsy when you leave?" Mother's voice was worried.

"Oh," he reassured her, "I'll see that she's well taken care of. I couldn't desert my convert, you know. She'll have a good bed and some furniture, besides two ewes and lambs, a sow, and a calf. And she may stay right there on my plantation or, if she wishes, take the thirty-nine acres I bought from Mrs. Langly. In addition, a hundred dollars cash will be paid her at my death as a compensation for her services." He paused thoughtfully. "I don't think she'll bother with any of it, however."

"Why?" Mother was puzzled.

"Because I think that after I leave, she'll join the Dominicans."

Mother's eyes shone. "Oh, I'm so glad! I do think Betsy belongs in a religious order even if not at Nazareth, and I hope she'll be happy at St. Rose's."

"I think she will." Father Badin took a step toward the door, then turned. "As you perhaps know," he said sadly, "once I too dreamed of starting a religious order in Kentucky. Evidently such was not God's will though, for something always went awry. But where I failed, Father David and Father Nerinckx have succeeded, and I'm perfectly satisfied. Both Nazareth and Loretto are in my prayers and I trust Badin is in theirs." His voice changed abruptly. "And now if you'll call the other Sisters to the chapel, I'll give them my blessing and ask their prayers for a safe voyage."

From the door Mother watched him cross the yard. A remarkable priest, Father Badin! His life story was an interesting one. In November, 1791, on the wharf at Bordeaux, France, he had met the two Sulpicians, Father

Flaget, now bishop, and Father David. They were on their way to America to assist Bishop Carroll in the care of his huge diocese, and Father Badin, still a subdeacon, accompanied them. After a long and stormy voyage the three clergymen had reached Baltimore.

Their first meeting with Bishop Carroll was memorable. Since they had arrived at night, they decided to wait until the next morning to call upon their new superior. Early the following day they set out for the episcopal residence and had gone but a short distance when they saw the Bishop hurrying to meet them. At first they were confused, mentally blaming themselves for not having gone directly to him on their arrival, but when they began to apologize, he waved their excuses aside saying, "It's surely little enough that I should come to welcome you since you have come fifteen hundred leagues to help me."

The next two years passed quickly, and on May 25, 1793, Bishop Carroll made Stephen Theodore Badin a priest, the first to be ordained in the United States. For a few months he went about Baltimore performing his priestly duties. Then one day Bishop Carroll sent for him. "The Catholics west of the Alleghenies have been pleading with me for a priest," he said, his keen eyes on young Stephen, "and I'm thinking of sending you to Kentucky."

"Kentucky!" Father Badin protested. "Why, there's only a handful of Catholics in that state. Besides, I'm too young and I speak English poorly."

"Well," counseled the Bishop, "let us make a novena to know God's will in the matter."

Each day the young priest prayed earnestly; on the ninth day he returned, confident that he would not go to Kentucky. The Bishop opened the interview with the words, "Well, Mr. Badin, I have prayed, and I continue in the same mind."

"And I too am of the same mind," Father Badin countered. "Of what use then was the novena?"

For a moment the Bishop looked at him and then said quietly, "I give no command, but I think it is the

56

will of God that you should go."

At these words the heavy weight of uncertainty lifted from the young priest's mind. "Then I'll go," he said gravely and knelt for the Bishop's blessing.

A few weeks later he left Baltimore on foot for Pittsburgh, and with Father Barrière, an older priest, he took passage on a flatboat with a company of emigrants for Kentucky. After landing at Maysville, the two priests walked to Lexington, a distance of sixty-five miles. There at the house of Dennis McCarthy, on the first Sunday of Advent, 1793, Father Badin said his first Mass in Kentucky. He remained in Scott County while his companion went on to Bardstown.

Four months later Father Barrière left for New Orleans, and Father Badin was alone in a diocese which stretched from the Great Lakes to Louisiana and embraced the states of Wisconsin, Iowa, Michigan, Ohio, Indiana, Illinois, Missouri, Kentucky, Tennessee, and half of Arkansas. Catholics were few in this region and widely scattered. As far as Father Badin was able to discover, there were about 25 in Tennessee, 50 in Ohio, 150 in Illinois and Indiana, and 300 in Kentucky. To visit these widely scattered families meant riding forty or fifty miles from one mission to another through rain and snow, through swampy lands and unbroken forests, and even through hostile Indian territory. Often his faithful horse had to swim rivers, out-distance wolves or wildcats, and rear away from rattlers or copperheads. But he spared neither himself nor his horse, and soon all over the area small log-cabin chapels furnished with hand-hewn altars and benches began to appear. He preached in season and out; he made friends and enemies; he saw other priests come and go. Only he, the vicar-general of this new territory, remained. For three long years he was alone, and once for twenty-one months he was without the sacramen of penance. In the winter of 1796 he suffered mentally and physically more than he thought he could bear and was beset with temptations to leave, but he stayed on.

Then in 1808 Bardstown became an episcopal see, and in November, 1810, his old friend and countryman, Father Flaget, was consecrated Bishop. Happily Father Badin spent the spring months of 1811 getting St. Stephen's into shape for the group Bishop Flaget was bringing with him, a group which included Father David and several seminarians. For about a year after their arrival the priests lived together. Since they were busy with the various missions, they saw little of each other; yet before the end of the year a rift had developed between Father Badin and Bishop over church property.

Finally the proto-priest agreed to go to Baltimore with the Bishop to attend a council and to get the advice of Bishop Carroll on the property dispute. Unfortunately, this matter was not settled. Father Badin did, however, have a joyful reunion with his brother Vincent, who, wanting to study for the priesthood in Bishop Flaget's seminary, arrived from France at this time and returned with him to St. Thomas's. Vincent was still there and would not be ordained for another three years.

Now after twenty-six years of hardship Father Badin was planning to return to his native land. Since the dispute over the property had never been dissolved and since his enemies among the laity were still bringing charges against him, he probably thought it best to leave the country for a while—perhaps for good. This move would certainly cause less talk and far less gossip than any other. Besides, he no doubt felt the need of rest after his long and arduous labors, and where could he better obtain it than with his relatives and friends in France?

Well, Mother Catherine reflected sadly, it would be Kentucky's loss.

CHAPTER SEVEN

1817-1820

The soft, plaintive call of a meadow lark made Mother Catherine slow her steps and listen for an answering trill. She was startled to hear instead a strong masculine voice proclaiming, "And to you, whose liberality has enabled the Bishop to erect in a country but lately over-shadowed by interminable forests, a cathedral church that would be an honor to the Catholic Faith of any people—" The voice faltered and stopped.

Mother Catherine smiled. Even in Kentucky, where anything could happen, one hardly expected to hear such a flow of words coming from a cornfield. "A temple," the voice resumed, "in which they and their children's children will meet and pay homage to the living God, and where, for generations to come, the great Sacrifice of the New Law will be offered up for the living and the dead."

Mother tried to recognize the voice. Father Badin? No, he was in France. Father Chabrat? No, the voice was too deep. Suddenly the cornstalks parted and out came a very absorbed young priest, entirely oblivious of Mother Catherine, who was in the path. She judiciously cleared her throat. Father Abell looked up, a startled and somewhat guilty expression on his face.

"Well, I'm certainly glad to see you," Mother Catherine said, paying no attention to his embarrassment, "for I was just beginning to think that even the corn had ab-sorbed some of the eloquence that is becoming common-place in this section."

Father Abell's face was the picture of confusion. "My main idea," he explained hastily, "was to get some distance from the seminary, Mother, and I hardly realized that I was so close to Nazareth. I do hope I haven't disturbed anyone."

"Not a bit," Mother laughed. "You're still quite far from the house. I was just coming back from the spring. No one else has heard you, I'm sure. But what's the reason for all the secrecy, may I ask?"

The boyish face relaxed into a grin. "You really startled me," he confessed, "because at first I thought you were Father David, and after the trick I played on him and Bishop Flaget last night, I'm not particularly anxious to meet him."

Mother Catherine shook her finger in mock seriousness. "Watch out, Father! Father David seldom misses anything."

"Well, in that case—," Father Abell made a gesture of resignation, "I may as well share my guilt with you so that when the time of reckoning comes, you can testify that I acted in good faith. But—it's a rather long story. Would you like to sit?" He motioned to a tree stump.

"Two weeks ago," he began, settling himself on a large stone, "Bishop Flaget sent me a message informing me that I had been appointed to give the sermon at the consecration of the cathedral and that I was to come to Bardstown to let him hear it." He plucked a long stalk of grass and twirled it in his fingers.

"I set out, and by the time I'd reached Elizabethtown, I had the sermon planned. Before I had time to jot it down, however, a messenger came to tell me that I was wanted by a sick parishioner. There was nothing to do but retrace my steps, and back I went.

"After anointing the lad, I set out for Bardstown the second time. It was a long, hard ride, but I finally arrived at the Bishop's house. As soon as I saw Father David, he asked me for a copy of the sermon. Of course I had none and I tried to explain that I didn't have time to write it, but that I did know what I intended to say and I thought it would be suitable." He smiled wryly. "But that didn't work. Father David demanded that I write the sermon at once.

"There was no way out. So from noon till dusk I stayed in my room noting down the main topics of the discourse but too exhausted to write everything out. After supper I took a blank roll of paper in my hand and approached my mentors. I proposed, then and there, to read them the sermon I'd prepared. For a moment I thought my ruse would fail because Father David said it would be better to submit the manuscript for reading and criticism first. I quickly objected, saying that since I had been clutching the bridle for such a long time, I was really incapable of writing legibly. Then I suggested that they keep their places and let me read them the sermon.

"Since neither raised any objection, I unrolled my blank paper and made a pretense of preparing to read. Of course in the dim light from the single candle on the table fully three feet away, I couldn't have seen a letter even if my writing had been as legible as print," he laughed heartily. "But since there was no sermon on the paper, of course it didn't matter, and strangely enough, neither Bishop Flaget nor Father David appeared to notice.

"I began my sermon in a key that was suitable to the size of the room and to the proximity of my judges. By degrees, however, I unconsciously raised my voice, not to its full pitch by any means, but loud enough to be heard beyond the wall of the building." He stood up and faced Mother Catherine.

"I recounted the vicissitudes through which the Church in Kentucky had passed during the thirty-four years of its existence. And I spoke of the crosses that had hitherto pressed down on the shoulders of both priests and people. I described the poverty of the churches in which for a third of a century the great Sacrifice of Calvary had been repeated in an unbloody manner for the salvation of God's people in the wilderness of Western America. I spoke of the joy with which the faithful Catholic people of Kentucky had greeted the Bishop who had been sent to them a few years before. I told of his hope and their own that was drawing near, when the Saviour whom they served would be provided with temples in some degree worthy of His exalted majesty. I gave my hearers a history of the undertaking that has now been brought to a happy consummation. I returned thanks to those who by their great liberality had enabled their Bishop to erect—" He stopped suddenly. "I forgot. You probably heard that before."

Mother Catherine nodded. "And how did your audience react to this eloquence?" she prodded.

"To tell you the truth," he confessed, "I looked at them only once—and that only after the delivery of a passage which I had endeavored to make particularly pathetic." He paused a moment as if to recapture the picture. "There they sat with their hands clasped, sobbing like children. I no longer felt that I had anything to fear. When I had finished, I asked if they were satisfied."

"Well?" prompted his listener.

Father Abell laughed outright. "Father David, after considering a minute, looked at me sternly and said, 'The sermon will answer.' "

"That means he thought it excellent," comforted Mother Catherine, rising carefully from the stump. "Father David is a master at understatement, and I imagine he wants to be sure your biretta will fit you for a long time to come."

"It will," Father Abell affirmed, brushing the dust off his cassock. "I still have to memorize my sermon or at least be sure my thoughts are in order for tomorrow. You'll pray for me, won't you?"

"Indeed, I will," Mother Catherine promised him, "and I know you'll do credit to Father David, but," she said laughingly, "don't ever tell him what you've just told me."

The next day when she was seated in the new cathedral

and was listening to the same words that she had heard issuing from the cornfield, Mother Catherine could not help glancing at the calm faces of Bishop Flaget and Father David and wondering if they would ever know that this sermon had never been written.

Exactly one week later, August 15, 1819, Mother and her Sisters were again in St. Joseph's Cathedral for another great event, the raising of Father David to the episcopacy.

Above them the full deep tones of the organ rose, gathered force, and burst into a tempest of sound which sent the notes swirling up to the high vaults of the cathedral. Suddenly they softened again as twenty seminarians intoned: *Ecce sacerdos magnus.* Down the center aisle Bishop Flaget, mitred and robed, walked slowly, at the end of the long procession, to the sanctuary where Father John Baptist Mary David waited, kneeling.

* * * * *

Mother Catherine had been right that afternoon three years before when she had guessed that Bishop Flaget had asked for a coadjutor. In fact, a letter to that effect had even then been on its way to Father Nerinckx, who was visiting in Rome at the time. The Bishop, feeling that the burden of his extensive diocese was too heavy to be borne alone, had requested the Kentucky priest to learn from Cardinal Pietro if Father David might be appointed his coadjutor.

The request had been granted and the Papal Bull, dated July 4, 1817, arrived at St. Thomas's in the late autumn. There had been great rejoicing by all except Father David. He was uneasy about the document because it stated that "Monsignor" had asked for help *ob provectam aetatem et adversam valetudinem* (because of old age and infirmity). On reading this, he had exclaimed, "No, it's not right for me to be appointed for that reason! Why, I'm two years the Bishop's senior and far less robust!"

The delicacy of his conscience demanded that this fact

be understood before his consecration, so he immediately wrote to Archbishop Maréchal of Baltimore, explaining the situation. The latter replied, assuring him that the appointment was valid.

After that question was settled, came the matter of money. Where would he find the money to buy the robes for the ceremony? As usual he turned to France, and as usual aid arrived. Now, two years later, all was arranged.

The cathedral was filled. In the front seats on the left side of the middle aisle were the somberly dressed Sisters, whose hearts were as glowing as the candles on the high altar. Today was their day too. This was their Father David who was being honored by the Church. And they were glad.

High above them in the choir loft were the seminarians, singing their hearts out in the motet which Father David himself had taught them and happy in the realization that the next triumphant *Ecce* would be for him.

Both groups watched prayerfully and intently as Bishop Flaget, assisted by the Reverend Charles Nerinckx and the Reverend Samuel Wilson, leaned over his friend and director to apply the sacred oil which gave additional grace to his already holy soul and new power to dispense the treasures of Mother Church. Both groups listened with grateful hearts to Father Chabrat's sermon eulogizing his former teacher. Their Father David was now Bishop, an honor of which they considered him eminently worthy; but one which, in the two long years of waiting, they had been afraid he would refuse. As the ceremony ended, Mother Catherine sighed in deep content; in some vague way she felt this consecration to be a mark of God's approval on the community which the new Bishop had founded.

For months after the cerermony the Sisters found themselves addressing Bishop David as "Father." Realizing their mistake, they would be embarrassed.

"Never mind, Sister," he would smile, "I still like the title 'Father' best."

No, nothing about him had really changed, not even his duties. He was still the Sisters' Superior and was consulted on all important matters. He continued to be pastor of the cathedral, and organist and director of the choir, training the seminarians in the Gregorian Chant and in the ceremonies of the Church. He heard confessions, went on sick calls, taught catechism, and managed, in spite of all this, to find time to write pamphlets of controversy and of piety. He still acted as rector of the seminary and taught the seminarians. And as if all this were not enough to keep him busy, he visited the four mission stations attached to the cathedral at least every month and frequently went to St. Thomas's to help with parish duties there.

It was two weeks after his consecration that he made his way slowly across the fields to the old farm. He paid no attention to the beauties of nature but walked with his head down, thinking. When he reached Nazareth, he found all the Sisters gathered in the community room. They were strangely silent, and as he entered, several looked pleadingly at him. He noticed the silent appeal and shrugged helplessly.

When all were seated, he stood facing them. "As you all know, my dear Sisters, we are assembled here today because Mother Catherine's term of office has expired." He glanced around at the solemn faces. "Privately, at the request of the Sisters, I have asked her to continue as the head of the community, but she has refused. Now, in the presence of all your daughters, Mother Catherine, I ask you to continue in office."

Every eye was upon her. Would she yield? Slowly she arose. Her eyes moved caressingly over the group before her and came to rest on her sister, Ann, who smiled encouragingly. Mother prayed that the words would pass the lump which threatened to close her throat.

"Father," she began, not even noticing the incorrect title, so intent was she on making him and her Sisters understand the motives that moved her to this decision. "Father, I have told you why I have refused. Our constitutions say that no one is eligible for a third consecutive term."

"And I have argued," he smiled a little, "that Blessed Louise de Marillac, directed by St. Vincent de Paul, continued at the head of her Sisters until death and that Mother Seton in Emmitsburg is doing the same."

Mother Catherine did not answer for a moment. How strange, she was thinking, that although younger than many of my Sisters, I really feel like their Mother! Maybe they do need me. But no. God's glory is my purpose in life. Wouldn't this be better promoted by putting the constitutions into immediate effect?

Unconsciously the old gesture, the slight lifting of the head, returned. "Sisters," she continued gravely, "Bishop David has given you the example of two women who, I am sure, will be canonized some day. They are far above me both in holiness and in age. Of course they should remain in office, but I am not necessary. I love the community as all of you do, and I am convinced that God would be more glorified by your putting the constitutions into effect than by your retaining me."

Sister Teresa had watched Mother Catherine intently during this speech. Suddenly she reached over and gripped her hand. A moment more and she was standing by her side. This was her place—beside Mother Catherine.

Her voice was low but it carried conviction. "Since Mother Catherine feels as she does, I believe that we, as loyal daughters, should follow her directions in this matter."

Glancing at the serious faces surrounding him, Bishop David saw reluctant compliance. "Then," he said slowly, "we will proceed to the election."

It didn't take long. Not much longer than the first one, he thought, as he tabulated the votes. At last he stood and read the results: Sister Agnes Higdon, Mother; Sister Ellen O'Connell, Assistant; Sister Ann Spalding, Treasurer; Sister Barbara Spalding, Procuratrix; and Mother Catherine, Mistress of Novices. He looked at Mother Catherine. She was smiling.

* * * * *

In the months that followed, Mother Catherine smiled even more frequently than usual for with the burden of governing removed, her heart was lighter than ever. Mother Agnes apparently fitted easily into the responsible office and her administration was marked by new and varied activities. The community, despite the deaths of Sister Mary Gwynn and Sister Martha Gough, was growing in numbers and was ready to extend its usefulness beyond the boundaries of St. Thomas's, thus gratifying Bishop Flaget's desire to establish elementary schools for the children in the surrounding parishes.

The Sisters prepared earnestly for these missions, spending many long hours at their books and their prayers, and many a jubilant recreation discussing their "mystery" missions, for no one except perhaps Bishop David knew where they would go. They did know, however, that they would have to travel on horseback, for most of the roads were too primitive for carriages. So with much laughter and countless suggestions, their ingenious minds invented several items which might be useful on the journey. One creation which met universal approval was an improvised satchel made from a tow apron sewed in the shape of a bag. This had the twofold advantage of being easy to carry and easy to reconvert into an apron after the trip was over.

Their very first mission, however, called for none of these new inventions, for it was at Bardstown, two miles away. In 1818, when Bishop Flaget and his seminarians moved from St. Thomas's farm to that thriving settlement, he asked for some Sisters to open a school. His request was granted and a year later on September 8, a house which stood within a few hundred yards of the new cathedral and which had once been a church-station was purchased from Nehemiah Webb. It was named Bethlehem Academy by Bishop David and was opened by Sister Harriet Gardiner, Sister Polly Beaven, and Sister Nancy Lynch.

Two years later several other Sisters went to Bardstown

to take charge of the wardrobe, the infirmary, the kitchen and the refectory at the seminary and at St. Joseph's College for Boys, where the Reverend George Elder was president.

Then, as if to take the place of those who had been called to work away from the center, three new members arrived at Nazareth. Two of them, Claire and Frances Gardiner, were Harriet's sisters, and the other, Agatha Cooper, was a close friend.

In December, 1820, the first call to a distant mission came. Sister Angela Spink, Sister Frances Gardiner, and Sister Cecily O'Brien set out to establish the Academy of St. Vincent in Union County, Kentucky, halfway across the state. The country through which they traveled was thinly settled, chiefly by Protestants to whom three nuns on horseback, accompanied by a priest, were a novelty and the subject of conversation for weeks. A night's lodging, however, was never denied, and the little company always met with a kind reception. Even then the Kentucky farmers had begun to establish their proverbial reputation for hospitality, and if the shelter offered was sometimes primitive, the generosity with which they gave it was princely.

The house intended for the Sisters' residence had been rented to Mr. and Mrs. Martin Hite, who were not prepared to give it up when the Sisters arrived. So, after riding a hundred and fifty miles on horseback, they had to clean a log cabin which had been used as a henhouse in order to have a place to spend the night. The hearth was not filled up either; so there again, as at Old Nazareth, they sat eating their supper on the edge of the floor, their feet dangling into space. The next day they found an old bench which they scrubbed until it was almost white and then used it for a table.

From the first, St. Vincent's was a hard mission. Sister Angela, endowed with almost masculine strength and incredible energy, felled stout trees, split fence rails, built fences, and helped the others to plough the fields and to reap the harvests. No pioneer women have more remarkable deeds to their credit than these Sisters. At last after years of labor their courage and endurance were rewarded and a thriving boarding school was permanently established.

In the same year the Sisters opened a mission in Long Lick, Breckenridge County, where the Reverend Robert Abell was pastor, but it did not flourish and was closed after approximately a year.

While these enterprises were under way, Mother Catherine was at home helping with the many tasks at Nazareth and working hard at the formation of the novices—who fitted perfectly into the classic description of novices. They burst into laughter for no reason at all, had their spells of homesickness, and broke everything they put their hands on, as do all good novices everywhere. To discourage this last fault, each culprit had to show the pieces to Mother Agnes, who at first gave a slight penance as a reminder of greater carefulness. But as this procedure did not always produce the desired results, Mother became more severe and often required the novice to wear a fragment of the broken glass or china suspended by a string around her neck until she was told to remove it.

This penalty seemed to work well until a new novice, Sister Martha Drury, chanced to break a dish and was required to wear a piece of it. One day watching the fragment bobbing up and down, she was suddenly inspired and mischievously rubbed it on a stone until she had shaped it into a smooth oval "medal." Sister Ellen, always ready for fun herself, abetted her by carefully printing on it the one word, "Diligence." Naturally the "Diligence Medal" attracted the attention of Bishop David and Mother Agnes. The latter was greatly displeased but decided to say nothing. After about a week Sister Martha laid the "medal" aside and forgot all about it. Not long afterwards, however, she happened to stumble over a large dish which Sister Teresa used to lay in front of the kitchen fire to keep the meat warm. It promptly fell to pieces. Sister Teresa was kind, but there was nothing to do but for Sister Martha to take the remains to Mother Agnes.

On her way she met Sister Mary, who was dissolved in tears.

"What's wrong?" she whispered.

Sobbing bitterly, Sister Mary opened her apron. In it reposed what was left of a pitcher. To her surprise Sister Martha laughed heartily. Sister Mary looked at her reproachfully.

"I couldn't help it," explained Sister Martha, choking up. "Do you know that that pitcher is a first cousin to the dish I broke? They're related!" She laughed again.

Suddenly her face sobered. "I'm afraid Mother will really be outdone when she sees two of us! Do you think she'll send us home?" Chastened by this thought, she knocked timidly.

"Come in," came Mother Agnes's brusque invitation. The guilty novices walked slowly to the table where she was working industriously. With feigned unawareness, Mother allowed them to stand there for some moments. At last she looked up and they, opening their aprons, showed her the contents.

Her eyes grew large. "This is too much," she said, looking straight at Sister Martha. "Everything in the house will soon be destroyed by our *diligent* novices."

Sister Martha flushed guiltily at the adjective.

"This broken ware must be shown to Bishop David at his next visit, and *he* will assign the penance."

The two culprits stood motionless, their eyes on the floor.

"You may go," she said coldly.

A moment later, however, there was the trace of a smile on her lips as she heard whispering in the corridor.

"What shall we do?" moaned Sister Mary, tears coursing down her cheeks.

"Don't worry," Sister Martha comforted her, "I'm not afraid of Bishop David, and you oughtn't be either. Why," she said, wiping Sister Mary's tears as she had so often done with the younger children at home, "Bishop David gave me my First Holy Communion and is like a father to me. No, indeed, I'm not afraid."

Her courage was contagious. "I'm not afraid either!" Sister Mary declared, suddenly brave. "Well—at least—," she faltered as fear possessed her again.

"I tell you what, Sister, I'll take your piece with mine and get a penance for both of us. You don't need to come."

Sister Mary could hardly believe her ears. "Oh, Martha, will you really? I'll never forget it—never!"

An impish light gleamed in the other's eye. "No, you won't," she promised smiling enigmatically.

All the next week Sister Martha picked up every piece of broken china or glass she could find and hid the fragments in a corner of the shed. One day when most of the teachers were busy in the classrooms, she visited the "crockery cemetery" and disinterred the gleaming bones of all the various dishes which had gone to an early grave. These she washed carefully adding them to her store.

The next day the Bishop came for instructions. Sister Martha sat quietly with the rest until he had finished. Then, excusing herself, she went out and piled all the bits of broken china on the big piece of the dish she had broken. Quickly she pulled a large sunbonnet down over her face, neatly concealing her features, seized her improvised tray and staggered with it past the Sisters to kneel at Bishop David's feet. "Bishop David," she said in a small subdued voice, "please give me a penance for breaking these dishes."

Speechless, the Bishop looked at the pile. She repeated her request. Finally he leaned over and pushed back the sunbonnet. "Martha, Martha," he admonished her in his deep voice, "you who ought to be careful about everything belonging to this house! Is it you who are thus heedlessly destroying the things entrusted to you?"

Trying to keep from laughing, Sister Teresa spoke up, "Father, she didn't break all those dishes. She broke only one, which was ready to fall to pieces anyway."

Every eye was on the penitent. "Please give me a penance," she urged still kneeling.

Bishop David's eyes twinkled but his voice was gruff. "Well, kiss the floor then."

Immediately Sister Martha obeyed, and as she leaned down, the load fell with a tremendous crash. Rising, she fled from the room.

For a moment there was an ominous silence. Then Bishop David's rare laugh broke the stillness and was soon joined by high light ones.

That evening Mother Catherine went to Mother Agnes to apologize for her novice's conduct. To her surprise, Mother Agnes merely smiled.

"Don't bother, Mother Catherine," she said, "I know Sister Martha." After a brief hesitation she continued, "However, you might go into the refectory about ten tomorrow morning. I heard a commotion in there this morning and went down, but when I arrived, Sister Martha and her companion, looking like plaster saints, were sweeping the floor. If I'm not mistaken, they were dancing on the same floor a moment before. That bears looking into."

Suddenly her eyes softened and she smiled. "Sister Martha surely is an imp, but," she admitted, "I guess we need imps to keep us from getting too serious. She needs to be corrected of course but don't be too hard on her. Actually she taught me a lesson today. There'll be no more showing of broken dishes to the Bishop, I assure you."

And Mother Agnes was as good as her word. Never again did any novice wear a crockery necklace and never again did anyone have to ask a penance of the Bishop.

CHAPTER EIGHT

1820-1822

It was October again. Trees in burnt yellow and flame stretched into a cloudless sky, making gay patterns against the solid blue. At a crude table in her small office Mother Agnes and Mother Catherine bent over for a last scrutiny of the plans for the new building, the third since the original log cabin had been enlarged. The first had been a small frame chapel; the second, a brick building which had replaced the clapboard school and which later housed the Sisters and the boarders. At present a larger school was imperative. For weeks the two Mothers had pondered over the situation and had worked to design a suitable structure. All they needed to go ahead was Bishop David's approval. And he had promised to come today.

Mother Agnes, who had gone to the front window, saw him dismount. "Here he is, Mother Catherine. Put the plan where he'll see it as soon as he comes in."

But although the drawing was in full view and Bishop David knew why they had sent for him, he talked at length about his catechism classes and his missions. The two Mothers answered politely and tried to show appropriate interest, but they exchanged perplexed glances as they became convinced that he was deliberately avoiding the subject of building. This was unlike the Bishop.

Mother Catherine could stand it no longer. Encouraged by an approving glance from Mother Agnes, she took the drawing from the table and handed it to him, remarking lightly, "This is our masterpiece, Bishop."

Almost reluctantly, he took the paper from her and went to the window. He scanned the plans closely for a moment and then stood looking out at the tall sycamore. The two Sisters watched him silently, more bewildered than ever. At last he returned and laid the paper on the table. There was a weariness in his manner which caught Mother Catherine's attention. Looking at him intently, she tried to fathom his expression. It was neither approval nor disapproval.

Then in a listless tone he broke the silence. "Mothers, I was afraid of this—," he hesitated for a word, then motioned to the paper, "this expansion." His eyes fell before their puzzled glances but he went on speaking. "In the past few weeks I have been engaged in a pursuit which I hoped would end gloriously, but instead—" He opened his hands in an elequent gesture of failure.

Mother Catherine moved in her chair uneasily. What was wrong? Why didn't he tell them?

Finally she leaned forward a little. "What is it, Bishop, please? Don't you want us to build?"

He liked the courage in that straightforward question, but he held back a moment, shaking his head slowly. "No, I don't want you to build, but not for the reason you think. If you erect a building on this property, you'll never really own it."

Mother Agnes looked startled, uncomprehending. "But —I—I don't understand, Bishop," she faltered. "Eventually, we will buy the property."

The Bishop avoided her eyes. "I'm sorry, Mother, but you can never own this property." He made a helpless little gesture with his expressive hands. "That's what I have been investigating this past month. And the bitter truth is that the will of the original owner, Mr. Howard, precludes the possibility of the land's ever being sold, even to a religious community. Believe me, until last month both Bishop Flaget and I were unaware of this, or we would never have let you build in the first place."

Mother Agnes drew in her breath sharply. Mother Catherine looked as if some one had struck her. There was an awkward silence.

Finally Mother Catherine spoke. "You mean," she

questioned, her voice barely audible, "that these buildings are not ours?"

"They are, but not the ground they stand on. I'm sorry," he finished lamely, stealing a glimpse of her face. It was ashen. Mother Agnes was staring at her fascinated.

"Then—we can't even—sell—the building?" Mother Catherine forced herself to say.

Bishop David dropped his gaze. "No," he said simply. There was no use trying to soften the blow.

At last the tightness in Mother Catherine's throat relaxed a little and the white lips moved. "Will you excuse me, please?"

Mechanically she knelt to kiss his ring and to receive his blessing, then left the room. Bishop David and Mother Agnes said nothing. They both knew where she was going.

There was nobody in the chapel when she entered like one walking in her sleep. She sank to her knees and dropped her head into her hands.

"But not the property—but not the property." The words seared themselves into her brain. All the labor . . . all the sacrifices of those lean years . . . all gone. The irony of it . . . the buildings theirs, but not the property. What good were buildings if one didn't own the land they stood on? They couldn't belong to the community. Everything a total loss. And whose fault was it? Hers. She should have found out before she spent community money to build. She was the Mother then. The fault was hers.

With an intense effort she put these thoughts aside and raised her anguished face to the tabernacle. "Just as you wish, dear Lord. Nazareth is yours. Catherine is yours."

The storm in her mind calmed. She knelt on, begging grace. Mother Agnes came in, prayed for a long time and left. Others came and went. Catherine was oblivious to everything. When at last she genuflected, her face had regained its color, and there was determination in her gaze. Talking things over with Sister Teresa a few minutes later, she even managed a smile.

"Well, I can't see anything to smile at," rebuked Sister Teresa glumly.

To her amazement Mother Catherine chuckled. "I just happened to think of your patron, Teresa of Avila."

"What's she got to do with this?"

"Nothing of course. But I understand perfectly now a remark made by her."

"A remark?"

"Yes. Once when she was on her way to start a new foundation, the wagon she was riding in turned over and dropped her neatly in the mud. Pulling herself out, she asked Our Lord, in that familiar way of hers, if that was the way He treated His friends. When He said 'Yes,' she retorted, 'Well, it's no wonder you have so few!'"

They both laughed.

"Yes, and she'd probably say on this occasion that He could at least have given a month's notice!" Sister Teresa added quickly.

They laughed again. Then Mother Catherine's face sobered. "But seriously, Sister, you must pray hard. Since it's apparent that God doesn't want us here, He'll let us know where to go. We must build," she smiled wanly, "on our own property this time."

"Don't worry, Mother," Sister Teresa consoled. "Saint Joseph is just the one for that job. He knows what it is to be looking for a home, and he'll find one for us, never fear."

And Saint Joseph thus commissioned was not long in finding the place they needed. Through Mr. Hynes, a Bardstown real estate agent, he informed Mother Agnes that two miles from Bardstown a farm of approximately four hundred acres was for sale. There were two buildings on the property, one brick and the other frame. Just what they had at St. Thomas's! And even Mr. Hynes had to smile when he gave them the final bit of information: the farm belonged to a Mr. Lapsley, a Presbyterian minister, who had often entered into public controversies with Bishop David.

The Sisters decided that this place was exactly what

they wanted, but since they had used their meager savings to build on the Howard property, there was no money to purchase it.

Evidently St. Joseph had thought of that as well. While the question of buying was being discussed, Father Chabrat arrived from Baltimore with some postulants. Among them was Scholastica O'Connor, a member of the wealthy Hill family of Baltimore. When very young, she had married Dr. O'Connor, a Catholic physician. Led by his example, she had become a convert and for a while was under the spiritual guidance of Father David. When her husband died a few years later, her relatives, offended that she had become a Catholic, refused to have anything to do with her.

She wasted no time in self-pity. Instead she decided that, if they would have her, she would join Bishop David's growing community. When she was accepted, her joy knew no bounds. Knowing how poor the Sisters were, she gathered up all her possessions and offered them with herself. Thus it was her money which bought the Lapsley property. Everything else she brought found a use too. Her silver graced the table in the priests' dining room, and her ebony clock stood in the hall to mark the time for the Sisters and boarders. Her rich clothes became beautiful vestments, and the family of slaves whom she had liberated and who had refused to be separated from her helped with the work on the farm.

St. Joseph had not failed them. Sister Scholastica had a new family and the Sisters had a new Nazareth.

Early in March three Sisters set out to prepare the farm for the others. With the help of two orphans and two Negroes, wheat and barley were put in and a vegetable garden started. The buildings were cleaned for occupancy, and the minister's study was fitted up for a chapel. In May, Sister Ellen joined the pioneers to start a day school for the children in the vicinity.

Finally, on June 12, 1822, they moved. Not until Mother Catherine saw the tables, benches, and stools loaded into carts, however, did she fully realize that they were really leaving. She had been too busy the last week, making arrangements, to take in the full implication. Now the realization came. While the rest were making the final preparations, she slipped away from the others and made her way to the frame chapel. There she offered herself to God again. Tears smarted in her eyes as she gazed fixedly at the tabernacle. She recalled the procession through the fields that day when He had first come to live with them. How easy His Presence had made everything! But, she reminded herself, He was not staying behind. Bishop David was bringing Him to the new Nazareth.

She rose reluctantly and went out. Almost automatically her feet turned to the spring, and she filled the gourd which still lay nearby. Sipping the cold water, she thought how often she had come here to draw water for the house. She looked around as if measuring every stone, then turned and walked rapidly down the path by the cornfield, smiling briefly as she recalled how she had met Father Abell rehearsing his sermon there.

Hastening past the tall maple, rich with leaves, she stood in the doorway of her old classroom. "This is silly," she immediately chided herself. "Why, it's only a building. All the pupils will be coming with us to the new farm."

A heavy step sounded outside on the porch and Sister Teresa appeared. Mother turned toward her. "I see you're bent on the same mission—saying good-bye."

Sister Teresa nodded. "Yes, and when I saw you pass the kitchen, I thought you wouldn't mind if I went along with you." She touched the window sill. "Even the walls look sad."

They stood silent a while. Finally, Sister Teresa sighed. "I thought I'd like to go to the cemetery. Our dead are the only ones who'll really stay behind."

They walked silently across the field toward the church. About halfway they stopped before a small plot surrounded by a low fence. Within were four grassy mounds sprinkled with daisies. As they prayed, both Sisters were reliving those early days when Mary Gywnn had been one of that light-hearted group who had climbed the fence on their way to the first election. She had seen the log school and the frame chapel go up and the foundation laid for the brick building. As she was never physically strong, however, the privations and hardships of those early days were too much for her. After months of suffering she died at five o'clock on the morning of the twelfth of August, 1818. Her death coincided with an occasion of great joy at the seminary—the ordination of Robert Abell, the first Kentucky student to be raised to the dignity of the priesthood. Hence seven Masses, a princely ransom, were offered for her soul by the assembled priests, and the procession to the cemetery was a triumphal one since all regarded her as a saint.

Two years later, in February, they had laid Sister Martha Gough beside her. A sister to Mrs. Howard, whose husband had given the land for the seminary, Sister Martha had not been young when she was admitted to the community. Mother Catherine remembered vividly the response she had given when asked her purpose in coming to Nazareth. "I've come at last to do what I had intended doing all my life," she had responded quickly, "to give myself to God and to my fellow men and to save my soul." God had evidently been satisfied with her desire, for He had called her to Himself after four short years.

Close by her grave rested Mr. Wesley, the saintly weaver, and Elizabeth Swan, Nazareth's first convert, whose greatest desire had been to enter the novitiate. At thirteen, however, she was seized with a fever, received her first Holy Communion, and died.

Sister Teresa glanced at the sun and tugged at Mother's sleeve. "Don't you think we'd better go back? The others must be ready to leave by now."

Mother Catherine turned immediately and together the two retraced their steps. Sister Teresa, stealing a glance at her companion, noticed the tired lines around her eyes. The last few weeks had been hard and bitter, but that they had not conquered her spirit was evidenced by the set jaw and the lift of the shoulders. The past was behind her. To it she had paid her last tribute. Courageously she faced the future.

Pride and open affection stood in Teresa's brown eyes for this twenty-eight-year-old woman who was a constant source of wonder to her. The almost luminous spirit of trust, faith, and courage which no trial could shatter always gave Sister Teresa a feeling of security and peace.

At the house they found Mother Agnes waiting. "Are you ready, Mother Catherine?"

"Yes, Mother. Are the others?"

"They're waiting for us." She waved her hand in the direction of the school. Thirty-five Sisters and several pupils were standing in a quiet, forlorn group, Sister Harriet in charge. "Father David will be here in a little while and will remove the Blessed Sacrament. Tomorrow I'll send Sister Frances and Sister Elizabeth with Abe and Terry to bring the things we are leaving today."

Mother Catherine made no answer but turned instead to the little group. From it broke the small figure of her sister Ann. As Mother Agnes and Sister Teresa watched, they walked together over the field. The rest followed. Across the Kentucky meadows they passed, a picturesque group, to their new home.

At the edge of the first field Mother Catherine caught Ann's hand in hers. Together they turned and looked back at the now deserted buildings. . . .

CHAPTER NINE

1822

"A penny for your thoughts!"

Mother Catherine did not start as Sister Ellen had thought she would. In fact, she did not even turn her head. "They're worth much more than that, Sister," she replied in a faraway voice, moving almost mechanically to one side of the stile and indicating a place beside her. Sister Ellen sat carefully, smoothing her voluminous skirts, and then followed Mother Catherine's gaze to the horizon where the crimson sun hovered over the silver poplars, and the shadowy line of the Knobs shimmered in a purple haze. In a nearby maple a robin chirped sleepily.

Mother's voice was soft. "What a glorious world God has created for me."

"For you?" Sister Ellen glanced at her curiously.

"Oh of course all of us share it, Sister, but I know that were I the only one on earth, He still would have made it every bit as beautiful just for me."

"Yes, I suppose He would," Sister Ellen agreed simply. "I guess I never thought about it in that way before."

It was useless to try to fathom Mother Catherine. When you thought you had catalogued her type of holiness as the down-to-earth, practical, American variety, she would upset your neat filing with something like this. The Mary in her was never lost in the activities of Martha.

"You know," Mother went on in the same dreamy tone, "when I look at a scene like this, I feel very insignificant, and then I remember that when all this is no more, *I* shall *be*. *That* makes me feel very important!" She turned to Sister Ellen with a little laugh. "That's rather confusing, I know, but it's the best I can do to explain how I feel at times like this."

They lapsed into silence. The sun was sinking quickly now, half of it already hidden by the tops of the hills. Wave after wave of crimson rolled across a sea of gold.

When the sun had completely disappeared, Mother Catherine rose reluctantly. "Well, this isn't getting down to the cabins. I promised Abe I'd have a look at Chloe. He's been worried about her."

Sister Ellen followed slowly. The steps of the stile were narrow, and she was less lithe and graceful than her companion. Down at last, she followed Mother Catherine through the pasture until they reached the gravel road that led to the four cabins which had been built a little distance from the Lapsley house. There were several Negroes sitting under the trees on crude benches, and a few children played nearby. In front of one cabin a group were singing, their voices hauntingly sweet and solemn in the gathering dusk. A little farther on a tall colored man stood listening, his back braced against an elm.

"Here I am, Abe," Mother Catherine called to him.

He hurried to meet her. "Ah sho am glad you come, Muthah. Ma lil gal sho em sick. Mirandy try ter git 'er ter eat suthin', but she don' wan' nuthin'." He shook his head sadly. "Eber since her Mammy done die, her bin mighty puny."

"Don't worry, Abe," Mother Catherine said reassuringly. "She'll be all right. It's probably some children's disease. Not many youngsters escape them, you know."

Lifting the latch she entered the dim interior of the cabin. Sister Ellen followed. At first everything lay obscured but when their eyes became accustomed to the gloom, they saw a little girl lying on a straw mat in one corner of the small room. She whimpered fretfully and struggled to a sitting position.

Mother Catherine went down on her knees and gathered the child in her arms, resting the hot head against her shoulder and placing a cool hand on the burning forehead.

"What's wrong with my Chloe?" she murmured, pushing the kinky hair back from the wet cheeks.

"I'se sick, Muthah. Ma face hurt!"

Mother ran an experienced hand under the dark jaws. "Mumps!" she exclaimed. "Why, Chloe, you're just going to have fat cheeks for a few days. Then you'll be all right, honey. But now you'll have to eat something." She paused for a moment and glanced up at Sister Ellen. "You know what? I'm going to get Sister Teresa to make her a nice bowl of chicken soup."

Chloe squirmed with delight, her black eyes rolling back and forth, the whites gleaming in the dim light. Sister Ellen laughed. "She'll eat chicken soup. You may be sure of that!"

"And right now," Mother Catherine spoke soothingly, "we'll fix you up nice and comfortable for the night." While Sister Ellen shook the straw mat, Mother Catherine held the child in her arms. Then wrapping her carefully in a blanket, she laid her down tenderly. "You be a good girl, Chloe, and I'll send that soup over immediately."

Outside Abe was waiting anxiously for them. "Go over to the kitchen, Abe," Mother directed kindly, "and ask Sister Teresa to give you a bowl of chicken soup. I think Chloe will eat that for you. She has the mumps, but there's no real danger."

Abe's white teeth flashed in a broad grin. "Tank yo', Muthah. Ah knows effen ah git yo', ebrythin' ud be fin'!" and singing softly to himself he hurried down the gravel path to the kitchen.

After watching him disappear, the Sisters retraced their steps. Suddenly in front of a large cabin with a great wooden chimney, Sister Ellen grasped her companion's arm. "Have we time to stop in the schoolroom? I've something to show you."

"Plenty. It'll be half an hour before it's dark."

Sister Ellen led the way into a long room furnished with rough tables flanked with benches. Two new stools were near the fireplace. She leaned over, picked up one and held it to the light. "Look, Mother, Andy is really learning to make furniture."

"He'll have to if the school continues to grow so fast," Mother Catherine said, crossing to a bench and sitting down. "Why, there's hardly space to seat the pupils in here, and even with the two new cabins, there's not enough sleeping room. The Sisters will have to give up their cabins and move to the loft over the wash house if any more come."

"Yes, soon we'll have to build a real school, a brick one!"

"You're right, Sister," Mother agreed quietly, but I'm glad it'll be Mother Agnes's responsibility, not mine. I haven't forgotten what happened to our first brick school at Old Nazareth."

"But you weren't to blame for that!" protested Sister Ellen, turning toward her. "Besides, this place is far better than the Howard farm. 'God often writes straight with crooked lines,' you know."

"Yes, I know," Mother Catherine affirmed ruefully, "at least I *ought* to know. But," she said, deftly changing the subject, "you haven't told me yet what you're going to do with the stools."

Sister Ellen picked up one and set it in the corner. "Do you know now?"

"I can guess!"

"And your guess is right. Sometimes my little girls get a bit too friendly on those long benches, and a solitary seat in the corner might help them—and me too," she added, moving to her desk. Eyes twinkling, she picked up a large slate and held it so Mother could see. On it was written over and over the brief sentence, "I must not bring snakes to school."

"Snakes! why that sounds like boys!"

"To tell you the truth, I believe Alice *is* more boy than girl. She has five brothers," Sister Ellen sighed, "so that explains it, I suppose. Anyway, yesterday she brought a little green garter snake and slipped it down Margaret Carroll's neck while I was hearing the spelling. You should have heard the scream."

"I don't blame Margaret. I hate snakes," Mother Catherine shuddered.

"So do I, but *I* had to get it out. And then it took me a half-hour to find the culprit. No one would *tell*, and Margaret didn't *know*. Tomorrow Miss Alice will have a new seat and a new view. She won't be able to do much mischief in the corner."

There was admiration in Mother's voice. "Leave it to you to find a solution! There isn't a pupil living who could outwit you, Sister Ellen." She rose. "Hadn't we better be going? It's getting dark now."

Sister Ellen fastened the log door, and together the two Sisters walked in a leisurely way toward the chapel. Above them in the maples the locusts had begun their harsh call, which sounded louder than ever in the twilight silence.

"These locusts are always screeching, 'heat, heat, heat,' " complained Sister Ellen. "And they're always right too. It was warm enough today to melt a stone."

"Cheer up. It will be cooler in a few more weeks, and in the meantime a cold drink from the well will help. No matter how hot it gets, the water there is always cold."

They moved slowly toward a large log cabin. Near it, at the top of a green mound, was a circular stone wall and above that a small roof to which was attached a coil of rope supporting a wooden bucket. Vigorously Mother Catherine turned the windlass. The bucket creaked down into the depths, then rose slowly, water spilling over its sides and falling with a tinkling sound. Sister Ellen filled a gourd and both drank from it gratefully.

"Good, isn't it?"

"Wonderful! And so cold!"

They went into the cabin. It was dark, the only light, the faint flicker of the lamp which burned before the tabernacle. They knelt briefly on the rough boards, made the sign of the cross, and went out quietly.

Sister Ellen was the first to speak. "The log chapel is a definite improvement over the Lapsley study, but we need more space."

"We really do," Mother agreed heartily, "and—well—it's not generally known, but Mother Agnes is planning a brick one very soon. For a while she was torn between it and an academy, but she decided in favor of the chapel when Bishop David advised her: 'Build first a house for your God, and He will help you build one for yourself.' The Bishop's right, too. God should come first."

"But what of the pupils? They really need more room."

"God will take care of them, you'll see. Besides, if I understand correctly, the new church will have additional space at the gable end. If entrances are made at the sides, this space can be converted into two rooms below and two above. That will help."

"When do you think the building will start?"

"In a few months, I hope. There isn't enough money yet, but by—," she stopped suddenly. "I thought I heard my name called."

They both stood still, listening. Sister Elizabeth appeared from behind the chapel. "Well, there you are, Mother Catherine! Where in the world have you been? I've been looking for you for the last half-hour."

"Oh, I'm so sorry. Is anything wrong?"

"I hope not, but Mother Agnes asked me to find you. She's waiting at the house."

"I'll come right away."

The three walked along in silence, wondering what the summons could mean. Mother Catherine went quickly up the steps to the tiny room which Mother Agnes had dignified with the name of office and knocked.

Mother Agnes smiled when she saw her visitor. "Why, I thought you'd gotten lost. It surely took Sister Elizabeth a long time to locate you."

"I went down to see Chloe. She has the mumps."

"Poor dear. I hope it doesn't spread to the other children, or we'll have our hands full."

"I don't think it will. I told Abe not to let her go out."

Mother Agnes indicated a stool for Catherine. "No

doubt you're wondering why I sent for you tonight. Of course I could have waited until tomorrow, but I thought you'd like to hear about this right away."

Mother Catherine leaned forward, her eyes bright with expectation.

"This afternoon," Mother Agnes went on, "Bishop David and I discussed the founding of a school at White Sulphur in Scott County. A Mr. James Gough has offered to donate his farm for this purpose, on condition that a small annuity be paid him while he lives."

"That sounds good, Mother. There are no schools near there and such a venture should be successful."

"I'm glad you feel that way about it, Mother Catherine, for we think it would be a good idea to take Mr. Gough's offer, and we also think—" she paused, "that you would be the right person to take charge. In fact, Bishop David wants the place to be called St. Catherine's after you."

Mother Catherine's heart missed a beat, and the hand that sought her rosary trembled. But when she spoke, there was no telltale tremor. "When do you plan to open the mission, Mother?"

"In April."

"And have you decided who is going with me?"

"Yes, there'll be three: Sister Bibiana, Sister Josephine, and Sister Mildred. I'll send for them later."

Mother Catherine's heart was heavy. Of course she shouldn't feel this way, but the thought that she would have to leave her beloved Nazareth had never occurred to her. Others had gone, but she had never pictured herself as a missionary. Leave Nazareth? She shook her head as if to rid herself of the thought. Then, as was characteristic of her, she viewed the situation from another angle. Why shouldn't she go? After all, the fact that she had been the first Mother of the community did not guarantee her a permanent place at Nazareth.

"I'll be ready whenever you say, Mother." She smiled bravely. "It won't take me long to get my things together."

Mother Agnes rose. "I'll miss you very much. But

Bishop David is right. The mission will be very difficult since the people in that locality are said to be prejudiced. Therefore, we must send Sisters who will be unusually understanding and kind."

The tightness in Mother Catherine's throat permitted only a faint "Thank you, Mother." With distinct relief she heard the ringing of the bell for the great silence. There was no need to say more.

The two Mothers walked side by side down the path. It was dark, but Mother Catherine could still see the white caps of the Sisters in front of her and hear the light footsteps of those who followed. In a daze she found her accustomed place in the chapel.

After prayers were over, she knelt longer than usual. Slowly the chapel emptied until she was alone. The sanctuary lamp seemed to beckon to her. She rose and went to the front. There, so close that she could have reached out and touched the tabernacle, she knelt again. A warm glow suffused her heart. Peace flooded her being. She knelt on and on.

Suddenly in the midst of her prayer, she seemed to sense, rather than to hear, footsteps in the aisle behind her. She turned. Sister Teresa was standing there.

"When you didn't come over," she whispered, "I got worried, so I thought I'd better come after you." She peered anxiously into the calm face.

Mother Catherine rose and took her fondly by the arm. "Always looking out for me, aren't you, Sister Teresa?" They turned at the door of the chapel and looked once more at the tabernacle, then fastened the latch and stepped into the night.

The moon was up. Around it clustered myriads of stars. Near the house a giant sycamore, its white limbs plated with silver, reached into the sequined sky. Suddenly Sister Teresa missed her companion and turned around. Mother Catherine was standing, her head tilted back, looking at the sky. Sister Teresa thought she heard her whisper, "For me," but that wouldn't make sense, and Mother Catherine's words always made sense.

CHAPTER TEN

1823

Sister Ellen stood on tiptoes, her plump fingers clutching the rail around the porch to steady herself. Finally she released her hold. "They're gone," she whispered and turned briskly to find Sister Teresa standing behind her. Laughing to hide the huskiness of her voice, she teased, "You being sentimental too? I thought everyone but me had gone long ago."

There was no answering laugh in Sister Teresa's voice. "I feel as though part of me went with Mother Catherine," she replied, not even looking up. "You know it's the first time we've been separated since we met in the log cabin at Old Nazareth; things won't be the same without her. But," she smiled wanly, "the people here seem to have acquired the habit of eating, so I'd better start dinner."

"And I'd better find out what my 'darlings' are doing in the classroom." Sister Ellen moved toward the door. "I left Margaret Carroll in charge, and though she is usually quite capable of managing any situation, sometimes things have a way of getting out of hand."

Halfway down the steps Sister Teresa uttered a smothered exclamation, "Sister Ann!"

Sister Ellen ran to the edge of the porch. Sister Teresa was sitting beside a small huddled figure, her arm around the bowed shoulders. Instantly Sister Ellen was on the other side. Neither spoke. Slowly the weeping ceased, and Sister Ann stood dabbing at her eyes with her handkerchief.

"Th-this is s-silly of me," she gasped between sobs. "I know I shouldn't."

"We understand," Sister Teresa whispered soothingly, brushing the dust from her habit. "I feel the same way myself."

"My sister wouldn't let me cry while she was here, and I guess the tears just wouldn't stay back any longer when I saw her turn and wave." The grey eyes brimmed dangerously again, but she blinked back the tears and said huskily, "It was just like her."

She turned to Sister Ellen, her voice steadier. "Are you going back to the school? I have to go that way, and I'll walk with you."

Together they started down a path between rows of daffodils which Abe had planted the first year and which had spread until they made a bright yellow border for the dull brown earth. Sister Teresa watched them out of sight and then, gathering her skirts around her, took a short cut through the long grass to the kitchen behind the big house. She was late already.

The little cavalcade which had caused all this activity at the Motherhouse was slowly making its way through the grove of locust trees which hid the Lapsley home from the road. Because of the narrow path the riders proceeded single file. Bishop David, with the assurance of a man who knows that he and his horse are one, headed the procession on the chestnut mare he always used for his long trips to the missions. He wore a heavy homespun coat and a woolen scarf, for although it was April, there was a nip in the air. That of course would soon disappear with the coming of the sun, but the morning so far had been cloudy. He looked at the sky with anxiety. The journey would be hard enough without rain. He had had plenty of experience with arriving at his mission drenched, but the Sisters. . . . He was not looking forward to that! As it was, they would have to depend almost entirely on the hospitality of friendly farmers for a night's lodging, and few of these houses had any extra rooms, let alone a place to dry these heavy homespun

90

habits. And then what would the Sisters do? But there was no use crossing invisible bridges. Perhaps it wouldn't rain after all.

He stopped his horse and waited for the others to come up to him. Mother Catherine was first on an old grey. She too was wrapped warmly, and her long skirts entirely hid the lower part of the side-saddle. Over her little white cap she wore a large black sunbonnet. She rode well, one hand grasping the reins and the other lightly touching the pommel of her saddle. Behind her came Sister Josephine looking perfectly miserable as she swayed with every movement of her skinny mount. Sister Bibiana and Sister Mildred had managed somehow to get side-by-side on the narrow path and were evidently enjoying themselves. Bishop David was too far away to hear what they were saying, but he could see Sister Mildred laughing, and he knew that Sister Bibiana was making some witty comment. She was famous for that.

At the top of a steep incline he waited for them. Pointing to a clear stream that cut through the undergrowth like a silver cord, he warned, "We'll have to wade this run. There's no bridge for miles."

"It looks narrow enough to jump," Sister Mildred remarked, standing in the stirrups and looking over her horse's head.

"I wouldn't advise you to try with that nag you're riding," rejoined Sister Bibiana in a low voice, quickly moving out of reach.

If Bishop David heard the aside, he paid no attention. "That run is deceiving," he warned, turning to Sister Mildred. "It looks narrow at this point, but it's wider than it seems and it's very deep and swift. It fooled me once! I'll never forget that day. I was on my way to St. Mary's, and since I was in a hurry, I decided to ford here rather than to go farther down. In the middle the current was so strong that it swept my horse off its feet and for awhile I thought we would both drown. But my mare was a good swimmer and kept going until her feet struck bottom again."

Sister Josephine paled visibly. "We won't try to cross here then, will we?"

"No, indeed, we'll go down about a half-mile. There it's much wider but only about two or three feet deep." He looked at the sky again. "I hope the rain will hold off until we can get to Mr. Blair's place."

"Are we going to eat there?" Sister Bibiana whispered hopefully to Mother Catherine.

"I imagine we will," Mother Catherine whispered back, "but if you're hungry, I can get you a little bread from the lunch basket."

Sister Bibiana flushed and shook her head. "Oh, no, Mother, I can wait as long as the rest of you—I—"

"Are you ready to move on?" called Bishop David, turning his horse and starting down the hill toward the stream.

The Sisters followed. Mother was first this time too. At some distance behind her Sister Bibiana's horse ambled along. As before, she managed to keep abreast of Sister Mildred except in a few places where the path was extremely narrow. It was at one of these places that the small wagon, piled high with their few belongings, became entangled with an overhanging branch. Suddenly there was a crash, and Abe, who was driving, called for help. As the rest of the group had disappeared around a bend, only Sister Bibiana and Sister Mildred heard his cry. They turned back and found him behind the wagon struggling valiantly with the headboard of a bed. It was not heavy but awkward. Soon, with the aid of the two Sisters, it was back on top of the load.

Abe flashed them a grateful smile. "Ah'll fix hit so's hit won't get ketched by a branch agin," he promised, swinging up to his seat, where he found a rope and fastened the headboard firmly to the rest of the load.

The Sisters remounted and cantered briskly for a while to make up for lost time. Soon they came in sight of the others, who had not even missed them.

They slowed down. "I didn't know we were bringing

a bed along," Sister Mildred remarked, letting the reins fall loosely on the horse's neck.

"Neither does Mother Catherine!" Sister Bibiana glanced quickly up the path to be sure she was not within earshot of the others. "She thought she was rid of that bed when she left Nazareth, but Bishop David insisted that it be brought along for her. I know she'll have a 'delightful surprise' when she sees it."

"Why'll that bother her?" Sister Mildred asked innocently. "I wouldn't mind having a bed instead of a straw mat."

"No, not *you* perhaps!" Sister Bibiana looked at her companion in mock reproach. "But Mother hates having anything different from the other Sisters. This is the bed Sister Martha brought to Nazareth with her. When she saw that the other Sisters slept on straw mats, she gave it to Mother to dispose of. For a long time the bed remained empty, reserved, Mother Catherine explained, for the sick."

"But since no one had time to be sick—," prompted Sister Mildred.

Sister Bibiana laughed. "Very, very true! But it didn't remain empty forever because Sister Teresa told Bishop David about it, and he ordered Mother to use it. A couple of years later, when Mother Agnes took office, Mother Catherine thought that she could pass it on to her, but by that time there were two other beds and Mother Catherine, much to her dismay, had to keep hers. Poor Mother, she really thought she had left it behind this time—but there it is."

When they reached the ford where the others were waiting, Sister Bibiana moved her horse close to Sister Mildred's. "Don't tell her," she warned.

"I won't," whispered Sister Mildred, "but for her sake I hope it falls off again—in midstream this time."

Mother Catherine turned to look at them. "What in the world are you two up to? You seem to be in a conspiracy of some sort."

The two young Sisters looked uncomfortable but were

saved from thinking up an answer by Bishop David who was eager to get on the way. "Mother Catherine," he called, "you come right after me. We'll go single file, in case the creek is deeper than I think or there are some holes that I don't know about. I'll go first, and you can tell about the depth from watching me." His horse stepped daintily into the cool water, paused a moment to take a drink, then moved on, and was soon on the other side. The others followed carefully.

About an hour later Bishop David stopped. "There's the Blair farm. You can see the top of the house over that clump of trees. Seems like it's just in time too." He pointed to a huge black cloud right overhead. "That promises a storm before long."

"April showers!" commented Sister Josephine, whose joy at seeing a respite from traveling loosened her tongue.

"April showers or not," Bishop David grumbled, "you'll find them wet enough."

Large drops were beginning to fall as they reached the door of the large cabin, and Abe urged his horse on until the cart was safe under a rude shelter. Then slipping the tired animal out of the traces, he seized the reins and followed Bishop David to a lean-to behind the cabin, where the farmer's draft horses greeted the newcomer with excited neighs.

Inside the cabin Mother Catherine and the Sisters firmly resisted the offers of food because they knew that the family could ill afford to feed five strangers, but they gratefully accepted some milk and sage tea. By the time they had finished their frugal lunch, the rain was pelting down, and Mother Catherine suggested a rosary in gratitude for the shelter. The dreary afternoon passed slowly. By the time the rain stopped, it was too late to go on; so arrangements were made for the night. In a small room separated from the kitchen by a log partition were two beds. The farmer and his wife insisted on giving up these to the Sisters while they and the children slept in the loft. Father David settled himself comfortably in the kitchen.

The long journey and the rain had made the travelers

drowsy, and as soon as their weary bodies relaxed, they slept soundly. Some time during the night, however, Mother Catherine, who was nearest an outer door, awoke and at first felt that she was dreaming when she heard the door creak and a slice of sky became visible. She lay paralyzed, her eyes dilating as she watched the crack widen, then narrow again. Then a strange sound like muffled breathing reached her ear. For an instant she was tempted to waken the other Sisters. But she decided against that. They were so tired!

She lay rigid, her ears alerted for the least sound. Nothing! The slice of sky was still faintly visible. Evidently, the door was still open. Whether that was good or bad she couldn't decide. At least the noise had stopped. No, it hadn't. There it was again. She held her breath and listened. Distinctly she heard a groan and the sound of a heavy body settling itself on the earthern floor. Then quiet again. What could it be?

Another look through the partly opened door convinced her that dawn was breaking. At least so far nothing had actually happened, and she was glad she hadn't disturbed the others.

After what seemed hours a faint light began to creep across the floor. Slowly and cautiously Mother raised herself on one elbow and looked around. Nothing. She became braver and sat up. At that Sister Bibiana stirred and opened her eyes. When she saw Mother Catherine, she sat up too. Mother put her finger to her lips, and Sister Bibiana nodded wisely. Then Mother looked around the room again. Nothing. Suddenly she heard it. The breathing! It came from under her bed. Only Sister Bibiana's frightened eyes kept her from slipping between the bedclothes and hiding. Grasping her crucifix firmly in her hand, she leaned over the side of the bed and looked underneath. She came up struggling for breath, her hands pressed against her mouth to prevent any sound. Then she motioned Sister Bibiana to look. Sister leaned over obediently and straightened up immediately, her eyes twinkling. Then they both sat convulsed with silent laughter. Beneath them a big fat pig was sleeping soundly.

At breakfast Mother Catherine told her story to the amusement of all. Then the travelers, after thanking the farmer and his wife sincerely and promising prayers, set off again much refreshed. The rain had cleared the air. The sky was blue, patched with white; the whole countryside, fresh and vibrant with life.

Once more the horses followed the trail which led through a thick grove where the sun penetrated only fitfully and where long graceful ferns grew in profusion in the dense shade of red maples. The Sisters carefully pulled their large sunbonnets over their small white caps, for every slight breeze tilting the wet leaves produced a pseudo-shower. From the maple grove they entered a stand of evergreens where the air was heavy with the aromatic scent of pine. Mother Catherine was the first to see the little patch of ladyslippers, a dash of living pink, rising like the promise of spring from the dead brown leaves, and her voice was happy as she pointed it out to the others.

The day went slowly now, for the trail was harder to follow. Sister Bibiana and Sister Mildred no longer rode abreast, and Sister Josephine was beginning to show real fatigue. No one said very much, even when they stopped beside a wooded spring for a meager lunch of bread and cheese. The novelty of the ride was beginning to wear off, and all were eager to see the end of the journey. That night they spent at a cabin inn and had there been a friendly pig, no one would have heard it, for they slept too soundly. There were bugs and spiders, and even mice. But no one noticed until morning when it was too late to bother!

The travelers started out early and by afternoon they had emerged from the woodlands into miles of rolling meadows, where the riding was easier and where they could move abreast to say their rosary. After that there were hymns, Bishop David's deep voice blending musically with the light tones of the Sisters'. The miles slipped by. Finally they came to the first house in White Sulphur. Mother Catherine's heart beat faster as they passed it. What would St. Catherine's look like? Would it be near the parish church of St. Pius? Would the school be ready? Would the people be friendly? Before she could voice any of these questions, Bishop David, who had gone ahead, stopped his horse and motioned them to hurry.

When they reached the top of the small incline where he was waiting, he pointed out a new location, almost dwarfed by a huge elm. Close to it was a well, much like the one at Nazareth with its protecting roof and stout windlass. On every side stretched acres of undulating meadows, rich with a bluish grass and dotted with myriads of dandelions. Above, the sky was clean. Not a cloud marred the wide sweep of blue.

Mother Catherine's horse tossed its head impatiently and stretched its long neck to crop the yellow flowers. She sat quietly. So this was St. Catherine's, her new home! It was certainly good to be here at last. She drew in her breath slowly, pulled firmly on the reins, and moved toward the cabin. The others followed.

CHAPTER ELEVEN

1823-1824

Deep in thought, Sister Josephine followed Mother Catherine along the narrow, winding footpath which led to the new log school at White Sulphur. As she walked through the sere brown leaves, her mind was busy with other days and other Octobers. Absorbed in her reverie, she did not notice Mother's abrupt halt and nearly ran into her. Recovering her balance, she was startled to see that Mother Catherine's face was pale and her eyes large with fear. Sister Josephine gazed in the same direction and gasped. The log door of the school was swinging crazily from one leather hinge.

Quickening their pace, the Sisters reached the threshold and stood paralyzed. Benches, tables, and stools had been hacked and broken, the fragments so small that they could be used only for firewood. In one corner was what was left of the few slates they had scrimped to buy. In another, tacked to the logs, was a piece of brown paper bearing in large wobbly letters the order, "Papist witches leave our children alone. Get out."

Sister Josephine looked stunned. "W-what are we going to do?" she faltered.

"Do?" Mother Catherine expostulated through set teeth. "Why, the first thing we're going to do is clean up this mess."

She caught up a piece of broken stool and tossed it out the door. Then moving swiftly across the room, she pulled the crude message from the wall, crumpled it, and thrust it into her pocket. Sister Josephine stood there, watching. At last she pinned up her long sleeves and began half-heartedly to help Mother gather up the pieces and throw them outside. They worked steadily until the front of the room was cleared of debris.

Finally Mother Catherine stopped. Her face was still red from indignation and exercise, but her voice was much calmer. "When the children come, they can help us. This will be a good object lesson on poor citizenship. Imagine a thing like this happening in our land of the free!" She pointed to the rubble.

"But what can we do about it?" questioned Sister Josephine, rather timidly.

"Nothing," Mother answered quietly. "That is, nothing material. Prayer is the only thing that'll open their eyes."

"But why, Mother, would people want to harm us? We try to help them. What have we done to deserve such treatment?"

Mother Catherine did not answer immediately. When she did, there was a trace of sadness in her voice. "There's no answer to your 'Why?' Sister. We aren't the first to be punished for doing good, nor will we be the last. For some reason those who do good are often persecuted. Perhaps because they are a constant rebuke to those who do evil." Thoughtfully she ran her finger over a deep gash in what was once the top of a desk. "Ignorance, I feel, is at the bottom of this," she added, pushing a piece of broken slate with the toe of her shoe, "and our job is to dispel ignorance."

"Y-you mean we're going to stay here?" Sister Josephine's voice trembled in spite of her effort to control it.

"Why, of course, Sister, we can't give up because of a little thing like this. The children need us."

"B-but everything is destroyed."

"It won't take Abe long to replace the benches, and perhaps we can help a bit too."

There was a slight noise in the doorway. The Sisters started involuntarily, then relaxed when they saw five of their pupils huddled together watching them, their eyes wide, their mouths open.

Mother Catherine forced herself to smile. "Put your

things down and help us pick up these pieces of wood and carry them outside. Hurry now," she urged as they stood immobile. "The one who makes the biggest pile gets a holy picture."

That did it. Instantly they came to life, scrambling over each other to pick up the scraps of wood and edging each other in the narrow doorway to get out first. Mother watched them, her eyes twinkling. It wouldn't be long until the clutter would be out. Then her face sobered. What would replace it? It was all very fine to speak so encouragingly to Sister Josephine about Abe remaking the benches and stools, but who would pay for them? She had no money. Neither had Father Chabrat. And then if they did fix things up, what would prevent the persons who destroyed them from doing it again? And worse. She shuddered. No, you mustn't think about that, she warned herself. Surely no personal harm would come to the Sisters. No one would go that far.

"What in the world!"

Turning swiftly, Mother Catherine looked into the shocked faces of Sisters Bibiana and Mildred, who had just arrived.

"Just a minor cyclone, Sisters," she explained dryly. "Nothing to worry about." Beckoning them to one side of the room, she showed them the note she had found.

"Well, of all things!" Sister Bibiana's face was flushed. "Witches indeed! I'd like to tell the person who wrote that a thing or two!" She was so vehement and her face so red that the others laughed.

"If the culprits could see you right now, they would die of fright!" Mother said banteringly, placing her hand lightly on the other's shoulder. "But since they're not here to get a piece of your mind, we'd better go on with the work. Sister Josephine, you gather up all the smaller children and take them on a walk. You two," she motioned to Sister Mildred and Sister Bibiana, "go get Abe. I'll stay here with the older ones and finish this."

The Sisters were already on their way when she called to them, "Tell Abe I said to get the wagon. And bring some benches and stools from the house. We can manage without them until he can make some more."

She faced Sister Josephine, her lips a thin line. "We must have something here for the children. It won't be enough, but I'm determined that we'll have some benches in this school this very day in case the persons who did this come back to see what happened." Her voice was firm with no trace of fear. "There'll be no need then to write an answer to their note."

When the Sisters returned to the convent that evening, they ate their supper sitting on a log which with Abe's help they had dragged from the woods behind the cabin.

"Ah'd lak ter fin' dat white trash dat tear up yo'all's school," he muttered darkly when they told him what had happened. "Ah'd fix'm." He made a significant gesture with his fingers across his neck.

"And I'd help you," bragged Sister Bibiana viciously. Abe laughed delightedly at the blood-thirsty little Sister whose black eyes sparkled with indignation, and his amusement cleared the air.

After the evening visit to the chapel Mother Catherine and Sister Josephine went to the rectory where they told Father Chabrat of the destruction. He tried to make light of it, but Mother Catherine saw he was worried. "Perhaps you'd better stay home tomorrow," he advised at last. "Without benches and slates you can't do much anyhow."

"And let them think they've driven us away?" demanded Mother Catherine in surprise.

"It might be wiser under the circumstances."

"We're not afraid."

He looked at her admiringly. "No, I can see you're not, but one never knows just how far a thing like this will go." He thought an instant, stroking his chin meditatively with his long brown fingers. "But if you really want to return, I think you'd better take Abe with you. I've a little lumber that he can have to make some

101

more benches, and he can work at the school just as well as here."

"Thank you, Father," Mother murmured gratefully. "That's a perfect solution. Abe'll be our bodyguard, and I'm sure nothing will happen with him along."

They started back to the convent in much better spirits.

*   *   *   *   *

Sister Josephine thought she heard someone calling. At first the voice was very faint; then it became louder . . . louder . . . louder . . . LOUDER . . .

"Sister Josephine! Sister!" A strong hand was grasping her shoulder and shaking her. She awoke with a start to find herself staring into Sister Mildred's face. Above her she saw rafters. Then slowly it dawned on her that it was morning—her first morning at St. Catherine's. Nothing had happened at the school, for it hadn't even been opened. Her heart was suddenly light with relief, and she felt like crying and laughing at the same time. It had been a horrible dream, but it *was* only a dream.

Having dressed quickly, she climbed down the rude ladder to the main room of the cabin, and as soon as she appeared, Mother Catherine began the morning prayers. Meditation was not quite finished when there was a loud knock on the cabin door. Sister Mildred opened it. The gentleman introduced himself as Mr. Jenkins, one of the parishioners, who had been sent by Father Chabrat to act as their guide to the parish church.

It was a delightful morning for an early walk through the woods to St. Pius, and the Sisters found it easy to continue their meditation. Above them birds chirped and warbled, squirrels scampered in and out of their path, and once they caught sight of a fawn poised by a woodland stream. Finally at a bend in the path they saw a cross through the leafy branches of a huge elm, and a little later they were standing before the oaken door of St. Pius church, pleasantly surprised to find it such a fine brick building. They admired the lovely white altar, the white-ash floor and altar railing, and the dark walnut pews with their odd button-latched gates.

Bishop David was already vested for the Mass, which Father Chabrat served. Later the roles were reversed. After the two Masses, the Sisters returned to the convent carefully noting landmarks on the way so that they would be able to return for a visit in the afternoon without a guide.

About ten o'clock, while they were unpacking supplies they had brought with them, Sister Josephine told her dream. No one interrupted during the telling, and even when she had finished, they were silent a minute or two.

"You certainly have an imagination which works overtime, Sister," Mother Catherine finally remarked dryly. "When you went to sleep, you were probably thinking of what Bishop David told us about the trouble the various pastors have had here at White Sulphur."

"Dreams never come true, though," Sister Bibiana interposed quickly.

Although they all agreed with her and laughed, they found themselves thinking of what Bishop David and Father Chabrat had told them of the stormy history of St. Pius. The people of this parish, under its original pastor, the Reverend Stephen Badin, had built the second Catholic church in Kentucky in 1794. It was a frame building situated on a knoll near the home of Courtney Jenkins on the old Limestone Trail and was dedicated to St. Francis. From the beginning there had been trouble about the property, which was in the hands of the laity. This system of lay trusteeism was in force in many sections of the United States at this time, for Bishop Carroll, realizing that laymen had to sustain the clergy and to build the churches, felt that they should have some voice in the administration of the parish. Such was the democratic spirit of the new country. Unfortunately the trustees were not always imbued with the true spirit of the Church and from this system came many disputes and scandals.

In the White Sulphur congregation dissensions arose from time to time among the members themselves and between certain factions and the pastor. Perhaps for this reason Father Badin moved in 1795 to Nelson County about three miles from the Hayden Farm where Father De Rohan had erected Holy Cross, the first church in Kentucky, and had built there a chapel which he called St. Stephen's in honor of his patron saint. For several years after this, St. Francis Church at White Sulphur was only one of Fatherr Badin's missions.

Disputes over this church property were still going on when a convert from the Congregational ministry, the Reverend John Thayer, the first American priest to work in the state of Kentucky, came to White Sulphur to take up his duties as pastor of St. Francis. Almost immediately he encountered disfavor with some of his congregation because of his zeal in behalf of slaves and his unusual political views. After two years he left, and White Sulphur reverted to mission status under Father Badin.

During this second mission period a movement was inaugurated by the trustees to govern the affairs of the parish by a constitution. Accordingly, when Father Badin arrived on his mission rounds, he was requested to deny all spiritual assistance to those parishioners who had failed to abide by the new regulations. He refused and partly succeeded in curbing this movement. Yet after he had gone, the trustees showed their authority by selling the church property without even consulting him.

The Dominicans were then given charge of St. Francis. In 1809 Father Angier was named pastor. Seven years later he was succeeded by the newly ordained Reverend Samuel H. Montgomery, O.P. During all this time the trustee trouble continued, but in the first few years of Father Mongomery's pastorate, there was comparative peace. Encouraged by this cooperation, he decided to replace the old frame church. He selected a site about two miles away and erected a fine brick church which he named St. Pius.

In 1822, however, Father Montgomery found himself involved in difficulties resulting from his manner of dealing with a parishioner who had attempted to secure a piece of church property for his own use. The priest's efforts to protect the rights of the parish made this man an enemy who rallied to his side a group of thirty-seven malcontents, some of them men of social standing and influence. The dissenters maintained that their grievances were due to unjustifiable acts on the part of the pastor. Although the majority of the congregation came to the defense of Father Montgomery, his usefulness as pastor was undermined. He was recalled by the Dominican provincial and was not replaced.

Distressed by these events, Bishop Flaget in 1823 appointed as pastor the Reverend Guy I. Chabrat, the first priest whom he had ordained in the Diocese of Bardstown. Father Chabrat set about his new assignment with his characteristic zeal, endeavoring to impart to the congregation a truly Christian spirit, but he too had trouble. Thinking that a school might help the general spirit of the parish, he asked Bishop David for the Sisters of Charity of Nazareth.

He was sorry that he could not help the Sisters financially, but Mother Catherine assured him that she was used to poverty. She had seen its face many times at Old Nazareth and now after the long association of years, she found it lovingly familiar. Hence she did not flinch at the destitution which marked St. Catherine's. From the beginning she and the other Sisters figuratively and literally rolled up their sleeves and pitched into the work with a gaiety that was bound to be contagious. Abe found a neighboring farmhand to help him build a cabin school. Later he fitted it out with benches and—because Mother Catherine had not forgotten Sister Ellen's technique—a couple of stools. Meanwhile the Sisters plowed and planted in the fertile soil behind their home, and even felled small trees to use for fuel. Sister Josephine, not quite so robust as the others, assumed the work of the house, the spinning and weaving as well, with the rest helping her when the work outside was done.

Every morning the Sisters walked nearly two miles to St. Pius, where they made their meditation and assisted at Mass. Then again in the late afternoon they went back for adoration. It was hard to be without a chapel where they could visit their Divine Friend often during the day, but even this deprivation Mother Catherine found familiar from the first year at Old Nazareth.

By late August the Sisters were ready for pupils. But the day they opened the school, there were only five girls to greet them. Where were the other thirty-five who Father had promised would come?

Mother Catherine was worried as she looked at the five well-scrubbed little girls standing near the door. Would it be possible to carry on the work with this handful of pupils? Four Sisters and five pupils—one and one-fourth apiece. Glancing down, she met Nancy Hite's big blue eyes looking up at her. Instantly she smiled. "Well, Nancy, we won't worry, will we? If no one else comes, we'll have a fine school all to ourselves." Taking the child by the hand, she entered the building. Sister Josephine followed with flaxen-haired Alice Greenwell, Sister Mildred with tiny Mary Wathen, while Sister Bibiana brought up the rear with Barbara and Stella Blandford.

The morning flew by. At noon the children sat on the grass under a shady redbud to eat their lunch while the Sisters ate their dry bread and apples at the rough table inside. Afterwards they went for a walk with their charges through the woods behind the school, found a cool stream, and let the children wade to their hearts' content. Then back to the classroom for a few more lessons and dismissal.

The following day there were four new children; the next, six. For a long time after that the number remained stationary. Father Chabrat came over to tell the Sisters that the old quarrel over church property had broken out again, and the faction which opposed him would do nothing for any project he had begun. He also warned Mother Catherine and the Sisters to be very careful in their conversations with the pupils and their parents lest they think that the Sisters had taken sides. In that case harm could come to the school.

One morning not long after this, when Mother emerged from the path at the clearing in front of the school, she saw a group of men standing near the door. Her heart missed a beat. Who were these people? Was Sister Josephine's dream to come true after all? She squared her shoulders and stepped ahead of Sister Bibiana who was watching her anxiously. The men, seeing her coming, began to talk among themselves. Then one broke away and approached her. As he came closer, she saw that he was smiling and her set face relaxed.

"Are you Mother Catherine?" he asked.

"I am," she replied in a gracious tone.

"I'm Henry Greenwell, Alice's father. She's been telling me how much she loves you and the school, and since I had a little time this week, I thought that I'd get some of the other fathers to come up here and see if there's anything you need."

"What we need more than anything else right now is pupils," Mother answered quickly.

Mr. Greenwell looked thoughtful. "Well, we may be able to do something about that. We'll go around to the various farms and advertise."

"That's very kind of you," Mother murmured. "Very kind."

"Not at all!" Mr. Greenwell cleared his throat to hide his embarrassment at her gratitude. "It's the least we might do for those who have come so far to help us and our children."

By now the two were surrounded by the others. Mr. Greenwell introduced the men to Mother Catherine and the other Sisters; and it was not long before they were all talking easily, the proud fathers and the proud teachers.

That morning the Sisters taught to the sound of hammering, and before the day was over, the classroom was resplendent with four desks, one for each of the teachers, a luxury they had not expected to have for many a day.

It was a happy group of Sisters who said goodbye to their new friends that afternoon. Evidently other things besides pupils and furnishings had been discussed by the men, for Mr. Greenwell told Mother that Mr. Hite, Nancy's father, had offered to go to Lexington for slates and that Mr. Blandford, Stella's father, who was not a Catholic, had planned to send one of his slaves to help with the work around the farm.

Thus for a while at least it seemed as if St. Catherine's was going to prosper, for within a month about forty children were enrolled and there were prospects of several more. Few of the children could pay tuition, however; and although some contributed farm produce, others could not give anything. Still, the Sisters knew now that they had friends, and in spite of hard work and poverty, they were very happy. Mr. Greenwell and some of the other men of the parish came around periodically to see if there was anything they could do. As a result, the Sisters were spared much of the heavy work in the fields and were able to do more spinning and weaving. This enabled them to stay at St. Catherine's because they could sell or trade some of the cloth they made.

The school, however, did not increase as the Sisters had hoped. When a child had learned to cipher and to read a little, she was usually kept at home to help on the farm. Thus instead of more pupils, there were fewer. Some new girls came of course but not enough to make up for those who had "graduated."

As winter set in, the Sisters suffered much from the north wind which battered at their little cabin and swept in through the cracks in the logs. On blustery cold mornings each one wrapped up in the woolen shawl which Mother Catherine had knitted for her and stepped over the threshold into the snow. Sister Bibiana seemed to be the only one who really enjoyed these icy expeditions. Her eyes danced when she opened the door and saw the pure unbroken drifts which had formed during the night. "I'll lead," she would offer gleefully. And off she'd go placing each foot carefully—not, as she was so often tempted, in the deepest drift—but in the shallowest spots so that the others could follow Indian file in her footsteps.

When all had reached the school at last and were removing their buskins, she was already lighting the shavings in the fireplace with a piece of flint, her cheeks rosy and her breath white. Still wrapped in their shawls, they would watch the feeble blaze grow until it succeeded in thawing them out sufficiently to prepare for their pupils. At noon they remained inside listening to the merry shouts as snowballs whizzed through the air. Finally, in the late afternoon when the sun was setting behind the pines, they started home again, the snow crunching under their weary feet.

And then, before they realized it, it was spring with the plowing and planting again. A year had passed! On the fourteenth of April Mother Catherine made a tiny cake to celebrate the event. Summer came with a rush, the short vacation flew by, and the Sisters were back in school for the next term.

Everything, it seemed, would be the same this year. But on September 30 they found Father Chabrat waiting for them at the convent when they returned from school. In his hand he held a letter which had been brought from the Motherhouse by a special messenger, who, not finding the Sisters at home, had asked him to see that Mother received it.

Her hand trembled a little as she took the message and studied the name on the envelope. It was not Mother Agnes's writing, but no doubt it was an important letter from her. A change? She hoped not. The Sisters were all so congenial and able for the life here. Moving toward the light, she broke the red wax seal. The others pretended to talk, but they watched her out of the corners of their eyes. She unfolded the paper, read it several times, and then put it down on the table. The Sisters were openly curious by now, but still no one said anything.

Finally Mother Catherine spoke. "I'll have to leave for Nazareth as soon as possible."

"Nazareth!" they echoed.

"Yes, Mother Agnes died—" she consulted the letter while they stood as if rooted to the spot, "six days ago."

"Mother Agnes!!!" they exclaimed together. "What happened?"

"She went out into the fields to help with the harvest and must have over-exerted herself. She died within a few hours."

Sister Josephine was the first to recall Mother's original statement. "But why do you have to go to Nazareth?" she queried, her troubled eyes on her superior's white face.

Valiantly Mother Catherine struggled to control her emotion. At length she answered quietly, "Bishop David has called me back to replace Mother Agnes."

CHAPTER TWELVE

1824

The old wagon jogged up and down, its wheels creaking with every rotation, protesting loudly against the dust and the deep ruts which marked the winding road. It was hot. For miles now the three travelers had been riding through fields, with only an occasional tree to give a bit of shade. Sister Mildred, sitting beside Mother Catherine, was silent, wrapped in her own thought. Abe sat up front, a huge straw hat protecting his eyes from the sun, his dark hands loose on the reins. Probably asleep, Mother Catherine thought. She envied him a bit. It would be nice to sleep away some of this discomfort. Moving a little on the hard plank that served for a seat, she pulled the black sunbonnet closer to her face to shade her smarting eyes. Her mouth was dry, her habit like a wrap of fire. Her feet burned in her heavy shoes. She looked compassionately at Sister Mildred and then turned her thoughts to another midafternoon centuries before when One whom she loved had suffered thirst and heat and. . . .

Suddenly it was less hot. She looked up to find that they had entered a thick grove. A moment later Abe stopped and turned. "Hit's not much fudder," he encouraged, noticing their fatigue. "Ah reckon dere's a sprin' roun' yer. Want fer me ter fin' hit?"

Mother nodded. Abe let the reins fall, slipped over the side of the wagon, and disappeared into the grove. He returned grinning from ear to ear. "Ah done fin' hit, Muthah, en hit sho am col'."

He helped the Sisters down and led the way to a spring surrounded by the greenest grass Mother had ever seen. Leaning down, she cupped her hands and drank thirstily, motioning to Sister Mildred to do likewise. Nothing else, she thought, could ever be as good as this spring water. Abe lay in the grass for a few minutes and then stood up. "I'se gwine back ter de wagon, but yo'all tak yo' time."

She smiled at him gratefully. Abe was so understanding. When he was out of sight, the Sisters removed their black sunbonnets, cupped their hands again, and splashed the cold water over their dusty faces. Then using a brush made of leaves, they dusted each other off, laughing gaily at their bedraggled appearance.

When at last they emerged from the woods, they looked refreshed and ready for the rest of the drive. Abe, who had been stretched out full length under a gnarled oak, sprang up as they approached, gave them a look of approval, and helped them ceremoniously into the old wagon.

How Mother had dreaded this trip and how sorry she was that Sister Mildred would have to make it twice! Two long days in this rickety wagon that Father Chabrat had so kindly lent! Now her ride was almost over, and she was ready to meet what lay ahead. Her thoughts wandered on and on—so far that Abe's words came to her as if from a great distance. "We's mos' dere, Muthah."

She shaded her eyes and looked about her. Sure enough, there at the next bend was the grove of locusts which hid Nazareth from the road. Her heart began to pump violently. Her eyes strained to penetrate the walls of trees. Then she saw it—the cross on the small steeple of the new church which Mother Agnes and she had planned two years before. Finished now! The blood rushed to her face with the excitement.

They were on the other side of the trees when she saw the first Sister, a blob of black and white. Almost immediately the blob disappeared only to be replaced by a dozen more. They grew larger by the second. Suddenly

Mother Catherine and Sister Mildred were in the midst of a sea of faces, all welcoming them at once, all eager to point out the improvements. When things finally quieted down, the travelers started for the chapel with Sister Ellen and Sister Ann.

The interior was cool and dark. Mother Catherine drew in her breath when she saw the sturdy oak benches and the kneelers. Only in the cathedral had she seen anything better. But she did not waste her time in admiration. Walking quickly down the middle aisle to the communion rail, she knelt.

For a long time she remained motionless; then she genuflected slowly and joined the others outside. To her surprise, instead of leading her to the house, they moved to a side door of the chapel. Then she remembered that the plans had called for a few rooms at the gable end of the new building. Proudly the Sisters led her down a small corridor and flung open a door. Within was a small room with a bed, a cherry stand, and a chair. The luxury of it!

She turned to Sister Ellen. "Mine?" she faltered.

"Yes, Mother. Be sure to let us know if there's anything lacking." She opened the door. "I'll leave you now with Sister Ann. I must get back to my girls." It wasn't until Sister Ellen had left and Sister Ann had answered all her eager questions that Mother Catherine discovered how tired she was. Every inch of her body ached, and she turned her back to the bed lest it tempt her. Then suddenly in the midst of her fatigue she realized that she had only seen Teresa—that she had not spoken to her. That would never do!

"Come on, Ann, I've got to go to the kitchen to see Sister Teresa. She couldn't wait to speak to me—not if she wants us to have something to eat. So I'll go to her."

Together they crossed the lawn to the house where Sister Teresa greeted Mother Catherine with eyes brimming with glad tears. Sister Ann took over the kitchen tasks while the two friends talked and reminisced.

The rest of that day was a blank in Mother's mind.

She had eaten, had talked, had answered and had asked questions. Then the oblivion of sleep, deep and restful.

The bell the next morning at four startled her. She could not think for a moment where she was or what it was. Then she remembered. Nazareth! In the chapel during Mass she offered again all her days to Christ as He offered Himself to the Father.

During the morning she began to go through the stack of mail which had accumulated after Mother Agnes's sudden death. She looked at each piece quickly. The first contained a bill. She frowned and picked up the next—another bill! Without even bothering to find out what it was for, she attacked the next and the next, growing more disturbed. Ten bills! Mother Catherine sat quietly trying to compose herself. Then she went through the bills systematically. Most of them for materials used in the construction of the chapel, and all of them were from two companies. That was strange! In her own experience she had discovered that business men, knowing that the Sisters were poor, insisted that bills of this sort be paid when the supplies were delivered. Surely they had not made an exception in Mother Agnes's case! Well, it would be only a matter of checking the receipts. Sister Eulalia, the new procuratrix, would know where they were.

Mother smiled when she thought of this young Sister, whose effort to speak English had produced so many amusing phrases. She was Bishop Flaget's niece and had learned of the Kentucky community through his letters. Intrigued by the courage of the pioneer group she had volunteered her services and after crossing the ocean had come down the Ohio on a flatboat to join the Sisters at Nazareth. When Sister Frances, who had been procuratrix, was sent to St. Vincent's, Sister Eulalia was appointed to that office.

Mother Catherine didn't have far to go to find Sister Eulalia. She was right in the next room dusting as if her life depended on it.

"Sister, please come in here and see if you can tell me about these bills."

Sister Eulalia hung her dust cloth on the back of a maple bench and hastened after Mother Catherine.

"These, I mean, Sister." Mother handed her the stack of bills. "They're paid, I hope."

Sister Eulalia's black eyes darted from one to the other while Mother Catherine waited anxiously. Looking up, Sister murmured, "*Je ne sais pas*," accompanying her words with an expressive French gesture.

Even if Mother Catherine had never heard that phrase before, she would have understood, so eloquent was the motion of the hands and shoulders. But Sister Eulalia immediately added the English. "I don't know, Mother. I've been procuratrix only a month and since I have—" she paused, searching for a word, "have—difficulty with the English at times, Mother Agnes took care of these things herself."

"Do you know where Mother Agnes kept her accounts?"

Sister Eulialia looked at her blankly. "Accounts? I do not know that word."

"Money books? Where did Mother Agnes keep her money books?"

The dark eyes lighted. "Yes, I know." The little nun went directly to a wooden chest in the corner and opened it. "Here!" she exclaimed triumphantly.

Mother thought the book looked very familiar. When she had opened it, she knew why. It was indeed an account book, but the last entry was in her own hand. She handed it back to Sister Eulalia. "This is the one I left. Where is the one Mother Agnes kept?" They looked again, but there was no other.

"Perhaps," offered Sister Eulalia, "Sister Frances knows."

"But she's at St. Vincent's and it'll take time to hear from her." Mother took her old ledger and paged through it again slowly as if still hoping to discover the missing accounts.

"Well," she sighed, "there seems to be no other solution, so I'll write her immediately. We must find that record or the receipts. Otherwise, these bills will have to be paid again."

Suiting action to her word, Mother sat at the small desk, and soon only the scratching of the quill broke the silence. Sister Eulalia watched the strong, sure fingers and felt a certain security. With Mother Catherine at home again, all would go well. Of course this book which was so very important was missing, and Mother seemed unduly worried about that, but in the end it would be found. In the meantime—well—Mother could always manage to solve a problem. When everyone had been so worried about losing Old Nazareth, hadn't she, Sister Eulalia, said that Mother Catherine would find a way? And she had found it. Why, the whole community was far better off now than they ever had been at Old Nazareth. Oh, Mother would find the book all right.

But Mother Catherine did not find it. Sister Frances wrote that Mother Agnes had paid all bills herself. Consequently, Sister had supposed that she had kept all the receipts and accounts, but if they were not in that room, she had no idea where they would be. Sister had added as an afterthought that since Mother Agnes had had a phenomenal memory, possibly she felt such records were unnecessary.

The room was small, and it did not take long to dispel any hope of finding the receipts there. When Mother questioned Sister Ellen and the other Sisters about the bills, they were positive that Mother Agnes had paid them; but since there was no written proof, there was no alternative but to pay them again. Mother learned to dread Wednesday, the day the mail-coach came to Bardstown, for then new bills joined the pile. In all they amounted to over four thousand dollars, an enormous debt for the impoverished community.

It took two years of the strictest economy to liquidate the debts and, to make sure that there would be no doubt

116

about the payments in the future, Mother Catherine kept a duplicate ledger.

Had unpaid bills been Mother Catherine's only concern at this time, she would have considered herself fortunate. But something far more precious than money—something far more irreplaceable—was at stake, the life of Sister Columba. If she died, she would make the fourth in less than a year. What was the loss of money when compared with the loss of these wonderful women?

Sister Scholastica O'Connor had died of turberculosis in March after a long illness in which not one word of complaint had ever crossed her lips. It had been her little fortune that had purchased Nazareth, her slaves that had helped till the land, and her household possessions that had given the convent the only sembance of comfort it possessed. She had given all these and herself joyously.

Her death was followed by three others in quick succession: Sister Agatha Cooper on June 3, Sister Polly Beaven on August 13, and Mother Agnes on August 24. Mother Catherine's heart was heavy as she thought of what the years had done to the first six members of the community. Mary Gwynn and Polly Beaven had slipped away to heaven, Betsy Wells had left Nazareth, and of those who had elected her Mother only Sister Teresa and Sister Harriet remained.

The latter was in Vincennes, Indiana, where she had been sent by Mother Agnes in April, 1824. Her letters were cheerful, but they could not hide the fact that she was having the same difficulties which Mother Catherine had encountered at White Sulphur. In addition, the little group in Vincennes was spiritually impoverished. Poor Father Camponier, in his determination to raise the standards of his parishioners and to give them a decent church and a school, traveled all over the country from Louisiana to Canada to raise funds. While he was gone, the Sisters were deprived of Mass and Holy Communion for months at a time. This Sister Harriet and her companions minded far more than any material deprivation; and this too Mother Catherine understood although in her religious life she had never experienced such spiritual poverty.

She breathed a prayer for the Sisters in Vincennes and turned her mind again to Nazareth, where death was threatening to take one of the most beloved Sisters at the Motherhouse—the young and beautiful Sister Columba Tarleton. Strong of soul, but delicate of body, this Sister could not stand the rigors of the life and like Sister Scholastica and Sister Polly had contracted tuberculosis. Every day promised to be her last. When the Sisters went to stay with her at night, she always insisted that they lie down on a mat rather than sit in the hard chair. Naturally, worn out with the day's labor, they were soon asleep. Her own night was one of wakefulness and suffering, but when her nurse awoke in the morning refreshed, Sister Columba greeted her with a smile. All the Sisters felt that she was a saint.

Mother's reverie was interrupted by a timid knock, to which in spite of her anxiety she answered with a cheery "Come in."

It was Sister Teresa, a little out of breath. Mother glanced at her sharply. Understanding the look, Sister Teresa hastened to reassure her. "Yes, Mother, it's about Sister Columba, but not what you fear."

Mother relaxed. "What is it then?"

"Just this. You know Sister Columba has no appetite these days. Well, this morning when I went up to see her, I asked her to tell me something she thought she would like. She smiled as she always does and said, 'I wish I had a partridge. It seems to me that I could eat that.'"

"Partridge!" Mother exclaimed. "Why, it's not the season for partridges."

"Yes, I know, Mother," Sister Teresa agreed quickly. "But she'd never mentioned anything before, and I felt bad that when she did, I couldn't get it for her."

"It's hard, I know, but a partridge—that's impossible."

"That's exactly what I thought, Mother, but when I got to the kitchen, there on the doorstep was a beautiful one. At first, I couldn't believe my eyes, but there it was.

And even more wonderful, it remained perfectly quiet until I caught it!"

They were silent, each thinking her own thoughts. "Well," Mother Catherine said finally, "if *we* love her so much, it's not strange that God does too. I dread to think of the day when she'll be taken from us."

Sister Teresa moved a few steps toward the door and turned. "I cooked the partridge and sent it up by Margaret Carroll. Those two are kindred spirits. Sister is always happy to have Margaret, and Margaret feels honored to be with her."

"You're right, Sister, and *if* you can keep a secret,—"

"If?" Sister Teresa's eyes sparkled. "Why, Mother Catherine, you know I never tell anything except to my pots and pans, and—they're safe!"

Mother laughed. "Yes, indeed, they are! I often envy you your pots and pans. They do more than keep secrets, I warrant you."

"But the secret, Mother?"

"It's this. Sister Columba has already told me that Margaret is going to enter our community next year, and —," her voice broke, "Sister has asked that Margaret be given her name. I've promised."

"Does Margaret know she asked you?"

"No, and I think Sister would have let Margaret ask me herself except she was afraid the child would think it bold to *ask* for a name."

A week later, on the twenty-fourth of October, the Sisters stood at an open grave, the sobbing Margaret between Mother Catherine and Sister Teresa. Only the comforting realization that each new grave meant a new intercessor in heaven strengthened Mother Catherine to face the future.

* * * * *

One fine spring day after the noonday visit to the Blessed Sacrament, Mother went to see the garden. It had rained the night before, and the young plants looked green and sturdy as they pushed up into the sunlight. The ground was so soft that she did not hear the footstep behind her and started involuntarily at Bishop David's exclamation, "So here you are!"

She turned to face him, genuine pleasure in her face. "I'm so glad you came, Bishop. We've missed you the last few days."

He regarded her kindly. "I've good news for you. Wednesday I rode to Lexington and asked Henry Clay if he would give out the testimonials for our first graduation."

"Since you said you have good news, he must have agreed."

"He's a fine gentleman, Mother Catherine, and mark my words, the country will hear more from him in the future. We talked for more than an hour, and I could have listened all day." He smiled wryly, "And you know that's not characteristic of me."

"I hope he'll talk to the girls too."

"Oh, he will. He's coming a day early in time for the examinations."

"Examinations!"

"Oh, yes, I forgot to tell you. Bishop Flaget and I have decided that the public should know what a fine education the girls receive at this school. Public examinations seem to be the answer to that, and we should have them." He glanced at her solemn face. "That is, unless you object."

Mother Catherine fingered her rosary. It would be hard, she thought, and the Sisters already had too much to do; but Bishop David was right; the public should know what was going on at Nazareth Academy. She looked up brightly.

"Why of course, Bishop, if you and Bishop Flaget think it best."

"I'm glad you see our point. However excellent the training, a school will not prosper unless sufficient evidence of its work is presented to the public. Parents do not willingly confide their children to teachers whose skill has not been tested. If the results of their work are not shown, the sphere of activity which Providence may have designed for such instructors will be limited. Here," he waved his hand in a broad gesture encompassing the level acres around them, "here is room for hundreds of scholars, and at present we have but thirty."

As Bishop David spoke, Mother Catherine's gaze was fixed on the distant Knobs, her eyes bright with a vision. She had no difficulty seeing the fulfillment of the Bishop's words—she had seen it years ago when she first rode over a stubble field to the log cabin of Old Nazareth. From the very beginning she had seen a vision.

CHAPTER THIRTEEN

1824-1825

With a quick motion Eliza jerked the ends of the long blue sash which encircled her slender waist. How in the world did anyone expect a girl to tie a bow behind her? These white dresses and blue sashes were a bother anyhow. And the examinations that you had to wear them to were worse. Why did grown-ups have to think up such things?

All those rows of people watching you when you stood to face the examiners from St. Joseph's. Lucky thing Henry Clay hadn't been able to come after all. Imagine the questions *he* would ask! Eliza shivered at the thought. Two whole days of questions, questions, and more questions. You were so nervous that even your pigtails shook. It was nice though when you looked down at Sister Ellen and saw her smile. Then you knew she was proud of you. Well, she won't be so proud today unless that bow gets tied right.

With determination Eliza tried again, her tongue caught between her small, even teeth. The result was no better. She could feel that one loop was still too much longer than the other. Exasperated, she jerked it untied and was just about to stamp one small buttoned shoe when she heard the faint jingle of beads. She paused. Nazareth girls simply did not stamp their feet when Sister Ellen was around. Of course she could ask Sister's help with the bow, but she'd rather not. More than likely, Sister thought her a baby already and would probably call her one if she saw her now.

She tossed her head at the thought. A baby! Why she was ten already. And ten made anyone a young lady ... well, most anyone. A young lady always looked and acted the part, Sister Ellen said.

That's why the bow just had to be perfect. She, Eliza Crozier, and her best friend, Nancy White, were to act as ushers at the first graduation at Nazareth. For days they had practiced curtsies and had escorted each other primly to nearly every chair in the assembly room. And now to think she couldn't even tie a bow!

Well since there was no other way out, she would just have to find Sister and ask for help.

Then she noticed a girl sitting in the far corner of the room. Although she couldn't see her face, Eliza thought she recognized the fair head bent studiously over a paper.

Her eyes lighted up. Lou!

"Lou, come here—please," she added hastily for Sister Ellen's benefit, just in case she happened to be within hearing distance.

The girl continued to read.

"Lou!"

Slowly the girl turned around.

"Oh, I'm sorry," Eliza gasped when she saw Margaret Carroll, one of the older students and the prettiest girl in the school. Panic seized her. A graduate was almost as far above her as the Sisters were. They were idols to worship at a distance. "I—I—I thought you were Lou," she faltered.

The fair-haired girl smiled. "That's all right. Naturally, you wouldn't expect to see me here. Sister Ellen told me to find a quiet corner to go over this welcome speech— and," she added mischievously, "I thought I'd found one."

Eliza flushed. "I'll be quiet now," she promised.

"But what did you want? You sounded desperate."

"Nothin'."

Margaret Carroll laughed. "Well, if you can scream that loud for nothing, I wouldn't want to be around when you *did* want something. Come," she coaxed, "what is it?"

Eliza studied her shoes for a while, and then squaring her thin shoulders, faced the older girl and held out the ends of the offending blue sash. "I just can't tie this right."

"It won't take long to fix *that*," Margaret assured her. A few movements of her deft fingers and the deed was done.

Eliza looked at her with admiration. "You know," she uttered shyly, "you were wonderful at the examinations yesterday. You didn't miss even one question."

Margaret patted the small, smooth head. "Why should I? With such wonderful teachers as Mother Catherine, Sister Ellen, and Sister Elizabeth, I should be able to answer anything. You did very well too."

Eliza was ecstatic. Here she was, Eliza Crozier, talking with one of the seniors just as if she were her sister. The mere thought of it went to her head and made her bold.

"When are you going to cut your hair?"

Margaret looked at her startled. "Cut my hair?"

"Oh, you know what I mean. You're going to be a Sister, and Sisters always have their hair cut."

Margaret looked at this small piece of humanity with new respect. "So, I'm going to be a Sister. How do you know that?"

"Well, one day before Sister Columba died, Agnes and I were arguing about her. Agnes said that she was a saint, and I said she was just a teacher. I knew I was right 'cause saints always have a bright line around their heads and Sister Columba didn't have any. Well, Agnes said that maybe Sister had gotten one since she'd got sick. We hadn't seen her for about two months, so we decided to find out."

"But how could you see her? She was in the Sisters' Infirmary."

"Oh, that was easy. We waited until all the Sisters had gone to prayers and then we slipped up the steps to her room. We weren't going to go in," Eliza explained carefully, "just peek."

"Well, did you see her?"

Eliza shook her head, disgusted. "No, the door was open, but there was a screen in front of it. And we didn't dare go close enough to look through the crack 'cause there was talking in there. We could hear everything though," she confessed archly.

"And pray tell, what did you hear?"

"We heard you—only we didn't know it was you then —telling Sister Columba that you felt that God wanted you to be a Sister of Charity and that you wanted to take her name."

"But how did you know it was I?"

"We heard you say that you were going to get Sister a cold drink, and we waited 'round the corner 'til you came out."

Suddenly Margaret grasped the little girl firmly by the arm. "And how many people have you told about this?"

"N-nobody, 'cepting you. And you won't tell we went up there, will you?" she asked, her eyes pleading.

"Not if you promise not to say a word about what you overheard."

Eliza made a quick movement over her heart. "Cross my heart and hope to die."

"Eliza, you shouldn't—" the final words were lost as Mary Lee, another older girl, came flying into the room.

She had no eyes for anyone except Margaret. "Did you hear the news? Henry Clay *is* coming after all."

"He is?"

"Yes, Mother Catherine just got word that he's in Bardstown at St. Joseph's and will be here this afternoon for the graduation." She caught Margaret and swung her around. Eliza looked on with disdain. Grown-ups acted so silly.

"That'll be an honor, won't it?" Margaret's face glowed at the mere thought. "Just imagine! I'll receive my diploma, the very first one given by Nazareth Academy, from the Secretary of State of the United States of America!"

"And I'll receive a testimonial from the same hands," Mary added gleefully. "Oh, I can just hear Mama telling her society friends in Yazoo about the commencement." She drew herself up and put an imaginary monocle to her left eye. " 'Oh yes,' " she drawled, " 'my daughter, Mary, received a testimonial in July from Nazareth, a very select school conducted by the Sisters of Charity, and Mr. Henry Clay gave out the awards.' Oh," she laughed, "I can just hear her. Dear Mama is so proud of us all, and she just *loves* to have something to brag about. Why if *I* were going to receive a diploma, she'd never stop!"

Margaret's eyes clouded. There would be no mother or father at her graduation. Her father had died in Louisville several years before of a fever he had contracted while taking care of Father Philip Hortsman. Two years later her mother had become seriously ill and had died of the same ailment. Since then Nazareth had been her home and the Sisters, her father and mother.

Mary, noticing the change in expression, guessed the reason. "And won't your guardian, Mr. McGillyCuddy, be proud of you when he hears your valedictory?" she hurried on. "And your sister Esther? She's coming over from Loretto, isn't she?"

To Mary's relief Margaret's eyes began to shine and the old smile returned. "Oh, yes, Esther will be here and has permission to stay with me for a week after, and Mr. McGillyCuddy's here already."

"That's wonderful, and now," Mary took her friend by the arm, utterly ignoring the silent Eliza, "we'd better go down."

"No," Margaret shook her head. "I have to stay here and go over this speech. Sister Ellen's coming back to hear it once more."

"Speak of the angels," laughed Sister Ellen coming in through the door behind them. "I'm ready for that speech right this minute." Suddenly she spied the small Eliza. "And what are you doing here, young lady? You should be downstairs!"

"Y-yes, Sister, I'm going," Eliza stammered and started for the door. When she reached it, she turned, caught Margaret's eye, and put her finger to her lips. Margaret nodded slightly and Eliza, relieved, scurried down the steps, glad to have gotten off so easily. Generally Sister Ellen went to the bottom of things.

"And what do you want, Mary?"

"I just came up to tell Margaret that Henry Clay's coming after all. Isn't it wonderful?"

"Yes, it will be a great honor for Nazareth."

"I hear he's an eloquent speaker, Sister. Have you ever heard him?"

"Yes, once."

"Tell us about it, Sister, please," Margaret begged. She loved this Sister with her fund of stories.

"Well," Sister Ellen began slowly, "my father, a few years before his death, took me to Washington to see our democracy in action. As we entered the gallery of the House of Representatives, Henry Clay, who was then Speaker of the House, rose to give reasons for a war with England. At that time he was a tall, slender, fair-haired man in his thirties, who looked like a school-boy among greybeards. But when he began to talk, his persuasive voice, his logic, and his convincing arguments made everyone forget his youth." She paused, remembering that scene.

"Father had been a pacifist, but after he heard Clay, he was all for the war with England. As for me, all I could think of was Patrick Henry and his speech urging the Revolution. 'War Hawk' they called Clay then, and a good name it was for him at that time."

"It's too bad that he didn't win the election. He would have made a good president," Margaret said soberly.

"If he had, he wouldn't have been coming here," retorted Mary, "and just think what an honor it is to have the Secretary of State at Nazareth!"

"Yes, and think what a disgrace it will be for us if Margaret here doesn't deliver that speech of hers well! And she won't if we stand around talking." Sister Ellen opened the door. "You go on downstairs, Mary, and I'll be along as soon as Margaret has gone over this a time or two."

* * * * *

Dinner was a solemn affair that day. Everyone was too excited to talk and too nervous to eat much, so the meal was soon over, and all hurried away to make the final preparations for the great event. Margaret slipped into the chapel to ask Christ to help her to do honor to her school, and then edged carefully to the door of the assembly hall, taking care not to be noticed by the audience. Eliza, dignity itself, was escorting parents and guests to the seats reserved for them.

Finally Sister Ellen rang the little handbell which was to warn the older girls that their turn had come, and with Margaret at the head, they marched slowly down the aisle and up onto the dais where Bishop Flaget, Bishop David, and Mr. Clay were already seated.

Margaret's throat was dry when she rose to welcome the guests, and her tongue almost refused to move. All the audience saw, however, was a slender, graceful girl, poised and confident, curtsying gracefully to the distinguished visitors. Her voice was deep and pleasant; her welcome, sincere. Excitement lent roses to her cheeks and stars to her eyes and above her a ray of sunshine from a window caught the gold of her hair. Away in the back of the hall Eliza nudged her friend, Mary. "Isn't she beautiful?" she whispered. "And to think," she added dolefully to herself, "she's going to be a *Sister!*"

When Margaret had finished her welcome speech, there was a burst of applause. Then Henry Clay, a little stouter than Sister Ellen remembered him but straight as a soldier at attention, rose to take the young speaker's place. His fair hair was beginning to grey at the temples, and time had etched fine lines on his long, thin face, but his eyes had lost none of their fire nor his chin any of its determination. The sonorous tones of his voice held his audience spellbound while he paid Margaret, her teachers, and her school gracious compliments. Then he went on to point out that there was an important place for women—educated women—in the state of Kentucky and in the nation. Margaret saw Mother Catherine nod slightly in agreement with this and caught herself smiling, for Mother had said the same thing dozens of times. She never grew tired of impressing on her young charges the necessity of developing their spiritual and intellectual talents to the utmost in order to serve God and country better.

At last the great moment of the presentation of awards arrived and Margaret, as if in a dream, found herself face to face with this great man. As he handed her the treasured diploma, he bent low over her hand, looked at her earnestly, and said in his deep voice, "Kentucky will always be as great as its women." Margaret smiled and thanked him graciously, swept him and the Bishops a low curtsy, and left the stage, walking on a cloud. After the older girls had been given their testimonials, the younger ones came to receive their sealed reports from the distinguished visitor.

Eliza drew her breath audibly as she took hers, for she still was not sure whether she had merited good notes or bad. She looked up to see Henry Clay studying her. "It can't be that bad," he encouraged, and in her embarrassment she gave him a tottering little curtsy and hastened off the stage, her face as red as her ruby pin.

All the parents remained in place until the Bishops and Henry Clay had left the room, and then they rose *en masse* to claim their precious children. Eliza felt her hand seized by her sister. The next moment was smothered in a parental embrace. Desperately she clutched the fatal report. "Let's get out of here, Mother, so we can open this. I just *have* to see what is on it."

Her mother smiled indulgently. "Very well, you lead the way. After we see the report, we can come back to greet the others."

As she passed a practice room near the hall, Eliza saw Margaret, her cheeks still flushed, her face radiant, talking to Mother Catherine.

Eliza stood still and stared. "She's telling her," she muttered.

"What did you say, Elizabeth?" queried her mother.

Horrified, Eliza clapped her hand over her mouth. She had almost told the secret. "It's just Margaret talking to Mother Catherine," she blurted.

"But why are you so excited over that?" persisted her mother.

Luckily for Eliza, Nancy appeared with her parents, and over the introductions the question was forgotten. At last outside on a bench underneath a shady linden, Eliza's mother broke the red wax seal of the report and unfolded the long paper. Eliza watched her face anxiously. Finally she relaxed. The report was good—at least better than the last one. Slipping around behind her mother, she looked over her shoulder at the telltale paper in Mother Catherine's exquisite handwriting.

SCHOOL OF NAZARETH

Note on Miss Eliza Crozier

April 14th to July 20th, 1825.

In class	Attentive, less giddy than formerly
Conduct in the study room	Do*
In recreation	Agreeable
Application in the study room ..	Tolerably assiduous
Reading	Very Good
Writing	Improved
Arithmetic	Progressing
Plain sewing	Not assiduous
Grammar	Very Good
Composition	Emulous
History and Geography	Very Good
Logic, Rhetoric	
Natural Philosophy	
Ornamental Needlework	Good
Embroidery and Tapestry Work.	
Drawing and Painting	Considerably Improved
French	
Music	Good
Politeness	Improved
Health and Growth	Very Good

* (Abbreviation for ditto.)

Eliza has for the last session given universal satisfaction. She is less volatile and more emulous than formerly. She acquitted herself with honor at the last examination and appears much excited by the plaudits she received on that occasion.

With esteem and respect,

C. Spalding

CHAPTER FOURTEEN

1828-1829

Mother Catherine stood at the window watching the snow cover the small bushes and shrubs near the new brick building. Without turning she murmured in a low voice, as if talking to herself, "It's wonderful to look out there and see the new academy. Sometimes it seems like a dream." Her voice faded away. Sister Ellen continued her writing, her pen gliding swiftly over the page in time with the rhythmical tick of the grandfather clock in the corner. Mother spoke again, louder this time, "I'll never forget how cooperative the Sisters were while it was going up."

Sister Ellen paused to glance up at her. "Of course they were cooperative!" she said emphatically. "Everyone was convinced we needed a new academy if we were to provide properly for the girls and have a place to sleep ourselves."

"I know, but human nature being what it is, I expected to hear more complaints."

"Did we disappoint you, then?"

Mother swung around. "Oh, no! You know what I mean, Sister Ellen. I was only too happy that there were no complaints, but even *I* haven't forgotten some of the things we did to save money." She walked to the desk and sat down. "Remember the shoes Sister Eugenia made during that time?"

"Remember!" Sister Ellen exclaimed. "My feet'll never forget them. I'm certainly glad we've passed the stage of homemade shoes. You never knew when you were going to be spiked by a nail."

"But we had our blessings too!" Mother Catherine added quickly. "We were able to put every cent into the building because the Bardstown merchants never pressed us to pay even one bill during that time. They were most generous with groceries too."

"Yes," Sister Ellen admitted, smiling. "Food's one thing we don't seem able to get along without, even when we're building."

"Hardly," Mother agreed dryly. "But that's all behind us now and the academy's paid for. Furthermore, since Bishop David seems to be resigned to our wearing the white collar, some of our troubles are over for a time at least."

Frowning a little, Sister Ellen put down her pen, carefully folded her letter and slipped it into an envelope. "You know," she said diffidently, "I could never understand the Bishop's protest over the collar, but at the time I refrained from asking because I knew the subject was painful to you. Since you mention it, however, I would like to know what did happen. That is," she added hastily, looking sharply at Mother Catherine, "if you don't mind discussing it now."

"No, not a bit," Mother assured her quickly. "The storm has passed and the bitterness with it." She studied the frankly curious expression on her companion's face and began. "For several years a group of Sisters had been talking about wearing something white around the neck, maintaining that most religious did so. Finally they won me over to their view, and I allowed several Sisters to design a collar that they thought suitable."

"But you asked the Bishop's permission first, didn't you?"

"Certainly, but evidently he forgot that I had, and the fact that he saw several styles of collars probably turned him against them. Of course we were merely trying them out to see which type suited best."

"And then the trouble began?"

133

"If you want to call it that." Mother's face was serious. "Looking back over the whole affair, Sister, I'm convinced that the devil stirs up these silly storms in a teapot to keep our eyes on our own tiny world when we should be looking at the vast world around us. Really we shouldn't pay any attention to such trifles, for they keep our minds and hearts small and aren't worthy of our splendid vocation. After all, what difference does it make what we wear? It's what we *are* and what we *do* for Christ that counts."

Sister Ellen unconsciously fingered her own linen collar, "Exactly, but since the Bishop was so opposed how was it that he finally gave us permission?"

Mother thought a minute, then said slowly, "Well, when I found I couldn't come to an agreement with Bishop David, I wrote to Bishop Flaget, giving him my reasons for wanting the white collar, but offering to adopt or reject it as he pleased, for I realized then how unimportant the whole issue was. Evidently he showed the letter to Bishop David, who decided that, after all the misunderstanding it had brought, the collar would really be more of a penance than a source of vanity for us."

"But it *is* becoming, isn't it?"

"I think so, but hardly worth the commotion it caused."

They lapsed into silence, Mother reading a letter and Sister Ellen going on with her writing. After a while Mother began to straighten her desk, arranging the answered letters in one pile, the unanswered in another. Glancing up, she found Sister Ellen watching her quizzically.

"No, I'm not finished," she confessed, a trifle abashed, "but I can't keep my mind on letters today. I keep thinking of the charter and praying that we'll get it."

"Oh, we will."

"You sound very certain."

"Well, knowing Bishop Flaget as we do, we can be certain that if anyone can get it for us, he can."

"Yes, that's why I had all the Sisters making a novena

that he would come home from the Bishops' meeting in Baltimore in time to accompany Bishop David to Frankfort. But people in general are still prejudiced, and our legislators are no exception."

"That's true, but they respect and admire Bishop Flaget, and they know he's Henry Clay's friend. That'll help."

"I hope so!" Mother reached for a fresh sheet of paper. "When I think I have a great deal to do, I always console myself by thinking of Bishop Flaget. It's wonderful how he manages to fulfill all his obligations."

"It certainly is," Sister Ellen nodded thoughtfully. "And even more wonderful how he manages to do so many other things as well. Did he tell you about his visit with Charles Carroll after the Bishops' meeting?"

"Yes, indeed. He said he was very much impressed with the ninety-two-year-old patriot and felt highly honored to shake a hand that had signed the Declaration of Independence." She stopped suddenly. "Speaking of shaking hands reminds me that I haven't told the Sisters yet about the meeting between Bishop England and Bishop Flaget. Father Reynolds was there and told me the story, but when I'm with the Sisters, I always forget to pass it on."

Sister Ellen looked up eagerly. "There's no time like the present!"

"I said 'Sisters,' " Mother teased, "not 'Sister.' "

"I'm almost big enough for two!"

"You win," Mother laughed. "It's short anyway and won't take a minute, but please remind me to tell it again to the whole group."

"I will, this very night."

"Good!" Mother leaned back in her chair. "It seems that Bishop Flaget had never met Bishop England. When he was introduced, he bent over the Bishop's right hand and kissed it, saying in his best French manner, 'Allow me to kiss the hand which has written so many fine things.' Not used to this type of compliment, the Bishop of Charleston was nonplused for a moment, but recovering himself, he took both of Bishop Flaget's hands in his and kissed them saying, 'Permit me to kiss the hands which have done so much.'"

"Leave it to the Irish!" declared Sister Ellen gleefully. "No Frenchman could have done better!" She paused, then continued more soberly. "Seriously though, that story certainly bears out what we've heard about Bishop England and what we already know about Bishop Flaget."

"Yes, God has surely blessed us with wonderful leaders." There was a note of exultation in Mother's voice. "It must have been a consolation to Archbishop Whitfield to know he has shepherds like them to lead his people."

There was a hesitant knock. Sister Ellen opened the door and found Eliza at the threshold. The girl curtsied. "Mother Catherine is wanted in the parlor. Father Reynolds is here."

"Thank you, Eliza," Mother called to her. "I'll be right down." As she passed Sister Ellen, she took her by the arm. "Would you like to come too? I imagine it's about the charter!"

Sister Ellen needed no second invitation. Together they hurried down the narrow steps, beads jingling and skirts rustling, but when they reached the little parlor, they were the essence of dignity.

Father Reynolds stood in the doorway smiling a little at the question in Mother Catherine's eyes. "I won't keep you in suspense," he greeted them. "We've received the charter!"

The Sisters exchanged delighted glances and their hearts sent up a prayer of thanksgiving, but neither interrupted him. "The Bishops returned with me this morning," he continued, struggling out of his great coat and handing it to Sister Ellen, "but they were too tired, and the weather was too bad for them to venture out. I offered to tell you about it."

"Do," Mother exclaimed, her eyes dancing, "but first, let's sit down."

They settled themselves in the straight, hard chairs. "Now tell us everything," Mother pleaded.

"From the very beginning?"

"From the very beginning."

Father laughed, "I warn you it's a long story."

"We don't mind."

"Well then, you shall have it in detail. But if you get bored, don't blame me!" He paused as if collecting his thoughts. "We arrived in Frankfort on Friday morning, December 18, and went immediately to the House of Representatives. Shortly after we had seated ourselves in the gallery, the bill for the incorporation of Nazareth under the title, 'Literary and Benevolent Institution,' was read. The Speaker, who as you know is Mr. Crittenden, Nancy's father, put the question whether the bill should pass. It was carried with only one dissenting voice. The Bishops and I were in high glee at the progress it was making. But as often happens in such cases, our joy was premature. A Mr. Morehead rose to present a similar bill for Loretto Academy. This was too much for a certain Mr. Rucker from Caldwell County. He said that he feared the House was proceeding too fast, that he was opposed to the ascendancy of any religious sect, and that he felt a bill of this kind was placing some property in Kentucky under the control of a foreign power."

"A foreign power?" Sister Ellen echoed, raising her eyebrows.

"Yes. He reasoned this way. The Bishop was, by the bill, constituted Moderator of the Board of Trustees and as the Bishop is chosen by the Pope of Rome, a foreign power, the Pope might dispose of the property according to his pleasure." He chuckled. "Logical, anyway!"

Mother Catherine laughed outright. "As if the Pope would ever want this land! I wonder why it is that so many people seem to think that the Pope is just waiting for a chance to come to America."

Father Reynolds shook his head. "They just don't understand. That's all."

"What happened then, Father?" Sister Ellen urged.

"Mr. Calhoon, from Breckenridge, saved the day by making a long speech saying that he had been informed that the legislature of Maryland had already granted a charter to the Sisters at Emmitsburg; evidently then it was not contrary to the Constitution to do the same for Nazareth and Loretto. But Mr. Rucker declared he dreaded to think of the power which such a bill would give the Pope. He was abetted by a Mr. Ball, who rather sarcastically expressed his satisfaction that the issue had given Mr. Calhoon the opportunity of making speeches. With that the Speaker called attention to the fact that personalities should not be indulged in. To stop the controversy, he immediately called for a vote of yeas and nays. We held our breath at that but relaxed when we heard only one loud 'Nay' shouted by Mr. Rucker."

"He was consistent anyway," Mother Catherine commented dryly.

Sister Ellen's eyes were bright, and she moved to the very edge of the chair. "Was that all?"

"Oh, no," Father Reynolds shook his head. "We were less fortunate in the Senate than in the House. First of all, we had to wait three days for the bill to be introduced. Even then the Senate was busy until late; and before our bill could be discussed, an adjournment was proposed. Mr. Ben Hardin, however, stood up to inform the group that three reverend clergymen were in attendance on behalf of the bills to incorporate two institutions. Consequently he moved that the Senate continue with the order of the day. After this motion was agreed to, Mr. Hardin gave a long eulogy on the merits of Nazareth and the reasons why the Sisters had applied for a charter. Right after he had finished, Dr. Rudd rose to support him and to urge the grant of a similar charter to Loretto. Since Dr. Rudd had heard the objections to a foreign power raised in the House, he first assured his listeners that the authority of the Pope was purely spiritual. Then to prove that Catholics are good citizens and loyal to their country, he gave the example of Archbishop Langton, who wrestled from King John the great Magna Charta. And to demonstrate that Catholics are not prejudiced, he told how the Irish O'Connell sought the relief of the Protestant Dissenters even before the Catholics of Ireland had obtained their own emancipation."

Father Reynolds's brown eyes twinkled as he turned to Sister Ellen. "You should have been there to hear your family name praised so in the Kentucky Assembly."

"There's reason enough!" she retorted quickly.

Having no answer for that, the priest continued his account. "Dr. Rudd is quite an orator, so I took down his final words to read them to you." Fumbling in his pocket, he produced a dog-eared notebook. He flipped the pages quickly. "Ah, here it is. 'Aren't Catholics found to be good citizens, whether called to sit in the councils of their country or to fight her battles in time of peril? The Catholic who should prove false to his country would merit the severest censures of the Church. According to the great charter of our liberties, Catholics enjoy the same rights as other citizens, and I trust therefore that the Senate will grant the just request now made.' With that he sat down, and I was about to clap when Bishop David caught my eye and shook his head."

"It was perhaps wiser to be quiet," remarked Mother Catherine. "But that was a brave speech for anyone to make in the Senate these days."

"And then?" prompted Sister Ellen.

"The rest passed quickly. The senators voted and the motion was carried by thirty-one 'yeas' and only four 'nays.' And so, Mother Catherine, in the year of Our Lord 1829 you will receive the charter which will make this institution the 'Nazareth Literary and Benevolent Institution.'" He rose to go. "And may it last as long as Kentucky!"

"Amen," Mother Catherine rejoined solemnly.

All three were silent as they walked to the door. It was still snowing and the wind was high. Father Reynolds said goodbye, pulled his coat collar up over his ears, and made his way slowly to where his horse was waiting.

After he was out of sight, Sister Ellen turned to her Superior. "Now that you have the building, the collar, and the charter, what's next on the agenda?"

"Perhaps we'll just rest on our laurels."

Sister Ellen shook her head. "Not you! I'm willing to wager that you have another project in mind right now."

Mother sank into the chair she had vacated a short time before. "To tell the truth, Sister, I hadn't thought about anything much until the mail came this afternoon. But since I read this," she opened a much-folded piece of paper, "I've decided it's high time that I went out on a visitation."

"I knew it," Sister Ellen said triumphantly. "I knew there would be something. Where are you planning to begin?"

"Saint Catherine's in White Sulphur." Mother's voice was worried. "The Sisters are having a hard time there. I had hoped things would become easier as the years went on. But," she tapped the letter, "it seems that's not to be. They're still living on clabber and hoe-cakes, and to make matters worse, Sister Monica, who knows so much about farming, fell from a horse and broke her leg."

"Oh that *is* too bad," murmured Sister Ellen sympathetically. "Bad for her of course but even worse for the other Sisters. It'll be hard to get along without her."

"Yes, I had hoped when I sent her there that she would make things easier for the other Sisters by supervising the farm work, but now—" Mother Catherine's voice drifted to a stop. There was no sound except the whine of the wind outside. Almost mechanically, Mother arose and walked slowly toward the hall. In the doorway she stopped and turned to Sister Ellen. "Will you please send Sister Claudia to me? I've decided to take her to replace Sister Monica."

"But you won't go in this weather!"

"Oh no, we'll have to wait a while, but Sister Claudia will be glad to know in advance. It'll give her a chance to plan."

* * * * *

Months later George drove the Nazareth carriage to the front of the academy and sat patiently waiting for his passengers. Like all Sisters, Mother Catherine and Sister Claudia would take a long time to make their farewells, but George didn't care. He enjoyed sitting, doing nothing. When the Sisters came at last, he cracked his whip importantly, and the carriage rolled down the avenue.

The first part of the journey passed pleasantly enough. Mother regaled Sister Claudia with tales of her first trip to White Sulphur with Father David at the head of the calvalcade, and then of her long, lonely trip back to Nazareth.

"And now after four years I'm going back to St. Catherine's," she mused, looking with unseeing eyes at the passing scene. "I hope I can help the Sisters there."

"From what I gather," Sister Claudia said sincerely, "just seeing you will be a help to them, Mother."

"In that case, I'd better leave them a picture." They both laughed.

Their enjoyment was cut short, however, when suddenly the carriage jerked to a stop and the Sisters were almost thrown to the floor. Sister Claudia clung desperately to the side-strap to keep from jostling Mother Catherine. The latter, hastily opening the door which on her side was almost level with the ground, stepped out. George had already climbed down from the driver's seat and was inspecting a broken axle.

"I might have known something would happen," Mother murmured resignedly. "It's impossible to travel to St. Catherine's without some difficulty." She turned to the distressed driver. "Never mind, George. We can't be too far from a settlement, and you'll be able to get the axle repaired there. That is, if you can get the carriage that far."

"Ah think ah kin, Muthah," George said hopefully. Pulling a heavy rope out from under the driver's seat, he fastened the wheel to the broken end of the axle in such a way that it supported the carriage, but wobbled like the legs of a newborn calf.

141

Mother took one look. "Sister Claudia and I will walk."

"Yass'm," George grinned and climbed into the coachman's seat.

Luckily it was only a mile to the nearest blacksmith, and the man promised to repair the axle right away. After a two-hour wait Mother Catherine turned to Sister Claudia. "Would you mind walking a little way?" she inquired. "When the carriage is ready, George can follow us, and we'll ride."

"Of course I wouldn't mind, Mother," Sister Claudia assured her, and off they went walking carefully to avoid the ruts.

An hour passed, and still no welcome rumble of carriage wheels. It was beginning to get dark. Looking about for a place to rest, Mother spied a large rock near the road, and the two hikers sat down wearily. What had happened to George was the question uppermost in their minds, but before they could voice it, they heard the crunch of wheels on the loose gravel. George drove up and ceremoniously ushered them into the back seat of the carriage.

"It's too late to go much farther tonight, George. Do you know where Mrs. Boston lives?"

"No'm, ah don'."

"Is she the English lady who came to Nazareth the first year I was there to enroll her two daughters, Jane and Sarah?" Sister Claudia asked, trying to place the name.

"Yes, indeed. I do wish I knew exactly where she lives, for I'm certain she'd gladly put us up for the night, George," Mother beckoned to the coachman. "Go into that house across the way and ask if they know a Mrs. Boston."

She had hardly finished speaking when a woman emerged from the very house which she had pointed out, threw open the white gate in the picket fence, and hurried to the carriage, crying, "Mother Catherine! Mother Catherine!"

"Why, Mrs. Boston!" Mother exclaimed, embracing her. "How did you know it was I?"

"I didn't at first, but when I saw the carriage stop, my curiosity got the best of me. I peeked out to see who it was. Of course it was too dark to make out your face, but I heard your voice. That's one thing I could never be mistaken about." Slipping between the Sisters and taking each one by an arm, she ushered them gaily into her comfortable home.

Morning came all too soon, and Mother Catherine and her companion were off, Mrs. Boston waving goodbye to them from her white-columned porch. Noon the same day saw them turning off the main road to the narrow, dusty path which led to St. Catherine's.

Sister Mildred, working outside near the convent, saw them, and an instant later all the Sisters were at the carriage welcoming the two visitors. Sister Josephine clung to Mother Catherine as if she would never let her go again. Mother's solicitous eye took in the pallid faces into which even joy failed to bring a warm flush and the thin bodies which the full habits could not conceal.

After supper the group gathered around the fire. Sister Monica, her leg in a crude splint, lay quietly on a hard cot, her pain forgotten in the joy of having Mother Catherine. She knew that somehow, some way, Mother would help them out of their difficulties. Even now Mother was listening intently as Sister Bibiana talked, her knitting growing with her story. "And to make matters worse," she sighed, "last week Mr. Hudson, whom we engaged to help Sister Monica with the farm, let the cows into a clover field and two of them died."

Mother Catherine frowned. "The money you made from the sale of milk was your chief support, wasn't it?"

"Yes, and now we have only enough milk for ourselves —none to sell."

"Do you have any help?"

"Just a little twelve-year-old Negro boy, but," Sister Bibiana shrugged expressively, "he's forever into some mischief, and he runs away periodically."

"Remember the time you sent him to the Rhodes farm for some butter?" Sister Mildred broke in, her eyes twinkling.

"I certainly do. And the horse came back without bridle, boy, or butter!"

The home Sisters laughed. The visitors looked puzzled. Turning to Mother Catherine, Sister Bibiana hastened to explain. "At first we concluded that the horse had run away and had killed the child perhaps, but later, in an adjoining field we found the bridle and the butter—what there was left of it—hidden under some bushes. We knew then that Master Ben had taken off again. Sure enough a few days later a note came from Frankfort informing me that he was lodged safely and securely in their jail."

"Did you get him back?"

"Yes, by paying a small fine of course. After that Ben swore he'd stay home, but after a week or two he ran away again. He tried the Lexington jail that time." She shook her head. "There's only one Ben."

"Well, at least you can't accuse him of running away during February and March, Sister," commented Sister Monica from her cot.

"No, he was safe in bed then," Sister Bibiana nodded, smiling at her. "But that didn't help the situation any."

"What was the matter with him?" Mother was all attention.

Sister Bibiana took a couple of stitches in the stocking she was knitting before she answered. "After we hired Mr. Hudson, he took care of Ben. Knowing the boy's running-away habits, he locked him up in the house one Sunday morning while he went to Mass. When he came back, he found no Ben, only a shoe by an open window." Her needles clicked disapprovingly. "Though the window was high, Ben had jumped out, losing a shoe in the operation. It was very cold, and the ground was frozen. Consequently, when Master Ben was found a few days later, his bare foot was so badly frost-bitten that we were afraid it would have to be amputated. But Sister Josephine nursed him through."

"Is he all right now?"

"Fine—physically, but any day I expect to hear that he's gone again."

There was a pause in the conversation. Mother looked thoughtfully at the Sisters grouped around her. "St. Catherine's doesn't seem to be prospering, does it?"

"No, I'm sorry to say it isn't," Sister Bibiana admitted reluctantly.

"Then I don't suppose any of you would mind going to Lexington?"

They looked at her startled. "Lexington!"

"Yes, Lexington. For several years Father McMahon has been asking for Sisters for his parish there, but I had none to give him. So the last time he came, he suggested that you move there from White Sulphur. Since he has charge of both missions, there wouldn't be any problem. Besides, he assures me that there'll be plenty of pupils and that you'll be warmly welcomed by the people."

"Have you told him we'll come?"

"Not yet. I wanted to see you first. Now I'm convinced that you'll be better off in Lexington, the sooner the better."

Sister Bibiana put down her knitting. "Mother, I think you're right. St. Catherine's is not growing here. It needs transplanting."

"Good! Then that's settled," Mother said cheerfully but she avoided their eyes, and they knew she was hiding her hurt from them. After all White Sulphur *was* her foundation. There was an awkward pause. At length Mother continued, "As soon as I return to Nazareth, I'll consult Bishop David. I imagine it'll be August before the transfer can be made, but in the meantime I'll try to make things easier for you here."

And she made good her promise, staying with the Sisters more than a week, doing any task which presented itself—nursing Sister Monica, helping milk the cows, even working in the fields. When the Sisters protested, she reminded them, "If I am called Mother, I must be willing to wait on my children."

Recreations those evenings were a delight, for Mother had a keen sense of humor and a real gift for storytelling. One of her favorite subjects was the elderly ladies who were being taken care of at Nazareth. About these women Mother had many interesting stories. One evening with the help of Sister Claudia she re-created, in her own inimitable way, a conversation between Mrs. O'Brien, who was very deaf, and Mrs. Wescott, her friend, who was very loquacious. Mrs. O'Brien heard everything wrong and answered accordingly, while Mrs. Wescott shouted louder and louder never repeating nor stopping until her store of news was exhausted. Then she would leave happy, completely undisturbed that Mrs. O'Brien had understood nothing.

Another evening Mother told them about Aunt Polly, who was a neat sewer and made habits for the Sisters. Her chief fault was a mania for collecting firewood. When the Sisters were at prayers, she would creep out, gather some wood in her apron and hurry back, adding the new load to the wood already stacked under her bed, in her closet, and around her room. When the collection was so large that there was no space for Aunt Polly, Mother Catherine talked long and earnestly with the old lady and at last got her to promise to remove it. Later Mother looked into the old lady's room and found to her relief that the wood was gone. When, however, she went next door to visit blind old Granny Speak, she found that good woman sitting in her chair in the middle of the room behind a veritable barricade of firewood. Aunt Polly had merely moved her "loot" next door.

Not a member of the Nazareth group of old people, but a neighbor, was Mrs. Rapier who came each morning to the Sisters' chapel for Mass. Sometimes, Mother told them, she came so early that the doors were still locked, and then she sat on the step and waited patiently. The Sisters often found her there shivering, her clothes wet and frozen on her, but she did not seem to mind, and what was more amazing, she never came to any harm.

This story of Mrs. Rapier would always remind Mother Catherine of a similar one about Sister Frances, who on her way to St. Vincent's was caught in a heavy rain. Later the temperature dropped. When at last poor Sister Frances reached her mission and attempted to get down from her horse, she found that her clothes were frozen and she couldn't move. A farmer finally came to her rescue by lifting her from the side saddle and carrying her like a sack of meal into the house where she gradually thawed out.

Stories like these and Mother's presence created in the Sisters a new spirit and revived their hopes, and it was a sad little group that gathered to see her off. Their hearts lightened, however, when she called back to them, "Next year I'll come to see you in Lexington."

CHAPTER FIFTEEN

1830-1831

"Yes," Mrs. Degallon said with finality, laying down her handsome fan and facing her mother almost defiantly. "Jack and I have decided to send Selina to Kentucky to school. We heard from some friends that the Sisters finished a new building for boarders in 1828. That was almost three years ago, and since then any number of girls from the South have gone there."

"But, Sarah, dear, that's so far. Isn't there any place here in Mississippi you can send her?"

"You know there isn't, Mother."

Mrs. Degallon looked at the older woman reproachfully. "Mother, you don't think we would send Selina off to any school without finding out all about it, do you? Jack had business in Louisville, so he decided to go out to see the place for himself." She went to a small desk and extracted some papers. "And here's his report."

Fumbling in her purse for her pince-nez, Mrs. Shelby scanned the letter closely, then held it out to her daughter. "You'll have to read it for me, Sarah. I'm afraid I can't make out your husband's writing."

"That's not strange, Mother," Mrs. Degallon smiled, taking the letter from her, "even *I* have difficulty reading his scribble. I'd merely tell you the contents, but Jack gives so many details I think you'd enjoy hearing his description of the place. As you know he never does things by halves."

She unfolded the closely written pages and spread them on the table before her. "He stayed in Bardstown overnight and went to Nazareth from there, but I'll skip that part."

Her eyes skimmed rapidly over the first pages. Finally she began to read:

A short and pleasant ride through the woods brought us to the convent. As we approached it, nestled in a grove of locust trees, we were surprised to see a spacious edifice, sufficient to accommodate a hundred and fifty boarders, occupying the foreground. A pretty chapel is in the rear. These buildings form a quadrangular mass with an area in the middle around which extend covered piazzas. On the left stands a neat lodge for the chaplain, on the right a building in which a number of orphans are received and sheltered from the heartless world. A small frame building, the Lapsley house, which was first used by this community stands close by the new buildings, a relic of ancient days reminding us of many privations nobly endured by the Sisters.

She paused and drew a long breath.
"I see what you mean about Jack and details," smiled Mrs. Shelby, leaning forward in her chair and opening her jeweled fan. " He surely writes an interesting letter though. Do go on."
Moving closer to the light, Mrs. Degallon continued.

Passing over the well-kept lawn, we entered the hall. Mother Catherine appeared and with admirable courtesy received us. The simple and modest habit of black, the unsullied white cap, the unworldly spirit, and the smile of benevolence on her countenance proclaimed her at once a Sister of Charity—a daughter of St. Vincent. With great kindness we were conducted through the institution. We noted its general character and in every department found a pervading order, elegance, and ability. The refectory with its neat, comfortable arrangements; the well-ventilated dormitories; the books and appropriate apparatus for a complete and liberal education. The study hall, with its silence and assiduity of labor, and the drawing room, with many and various specimens of taste and elegant accomplishments, were among the objects which arrested our attention and won our unequivocal approbation and praise.

We visited also the spring house where a beautiful fountain gushes forth with great purity and copiousness into a cistern of wrought stone and supplies the many wants of the institution.

"Was there any place he missed?" chuckled Mrs. Shelby. "It's a good thing those Sisters are excellent housekeepers! Be sure you tell me several days in advance if Jack decides to visit my plantation," she added mischievously. "I had no idea he was so observant."

"But that's not all. Listen to this."

On our return to the parlor, Mother Catherine had some of the young ladies perform on the piano, and we were gratified to hear selections from several modern composers, among them Felix Mendelssohn and the late Ludwig van Beethoven. The girls also knew about the two famous young pianists, Frederic Chopin and Franz von Liszt, a fact which shows that the good Sisters keep their pupils abreast of the times and that they recognize good music. The impromptu concert was concluded with a beautiful *Ave Maria* which I had never heard, but which Sister Joanna, the music mistress, told us was written by Franz Schubert, who died just a few years ago. You must get a copy of that hymn for Selina. The girl who sang it had a lovely soprano voice and was well-trained.

"No wonder Jack is such a good business man!" exclaimed Mrs. Shelby, fastening her pince-nez on the narrow bridge of her aristocratic nose. "He's not fooled by appearances. He wants to see the results. But," she added irritably, "he doesn't mention what the girls study besides music. Music's all right of course but Selina needs other things as well."

"Oh, but I haven't finished," protested Mrs. Degallon, hastily picking up the letter again. "Listen!"

Before our departure, we availed ourselves of the opportunity to make some inquiries concerning the course of instruction and the general routine of education and scholastic duties. The course, we were informed, embraces reading, writing, arithmetic, English grammar, geography with the use of globes, ancient and modern history, with chronology and mythology, rhetoric, botany, natural philosophy, plain and fancy needlework, lace and bead work, drawing and painting in water colors and crayons, painting on satin and velvet, music on the piano and guitar, exercises in polite English literature, and the French language taught with care and correctness.

She paused to catch her breath. "There, does that answer your question?"

"Indeed it does," Mrs. Shelby agreed wholeheartedly, "and it also explains why you have decided to send Selina to Nazareth."

"Send me to Nazareth!" echoed a youthful voice in consternation.

The two women swung around to face the French window where Selina stood like a framed portrait of a girl in blue, her small head poised proudly on her long neck, her billowing skirts almost touching the wood on either side. Her arms were full of flowers, and her large straw hat dangled from a blue velvet ribbon about her neck. The summer breeze blew her dark curls about her flushed face and carried into the room the fragrance of magnolias and roses.

For an instant she stood there, her great dark eyes fixed anxiously on her mother's face. Then she was at her side. "Mother, what do you mean?"

Mrs. Degallon gathered her daughter into her arms and kissed her tenderly. "Selina, honey, we had no intention of telling you like this, but now that you've heard part of it, I might as well tell you all. Your father and I have decided that you must go to a real school and finish your education."

"But Miss DeVaux can teach me." The red lips pouted.

"Not the things you need to learn so that you can manage a plantation some day." Mrs. Degallon patted the girl's shoulder. "No, honey, there is no other way. Your father and I have talked it over many times. You must go away to school." Her voice was soft but firm.

Selina began to sob. "Come now," her mother said brusquely. "You haven't even spoken to your grand-mother."

Obediently Selina swept a curtsy and valiantly fought back the tears. Mrs. Shelby took her hand. "Don't worry, Selina. You won't have to leave for a month yet, and think of the wonderful trip you will have up the Mississippi on the *Washington*!"

Selina's face brightened. "That's Captain Shreve's two decker, isn't it?"

"Indeed it is! And on the last trip from New Orleans he made Louisville in eight and a half days."

"That's wonderful! Do you think we might go even faster?"

"Maybe. And you'll come home in the summer," encouraged her mother. "Furthermore, I'm going to see Mr. and Mrs. Granger. They've been looking for just such a place to send Cynthia."

"Oh, if Cynthia goes, everything'll be perfect. Why, she's my very best friend!" Selina's face dimpled into a smile.

"That's better," approved her mother. "Now sit down here, and I'll let grandmother see the rest of the things your father sent about the school. Here," she said as she held out a circular, "are the requirements for entering."

Mrs. Shelby looked over the printed pages. "Hum-m, maps, slates, paints, embroidery, books, stationery, bed, bedding. These would be hard to send," she said anxiously, looking up.

"But I read somewhere that the pupil can get them at Nazareth if she comes from a distance."

"Oh, yes, here it is. That's all right then."

Absorbed in their conversation, neither woman was paying any attention to Selina who was playing quietly with a Maltese kitten on the rich Phyfe sofa. Suddenly she stood up, dropping the surprised animal to the floor. "Mother!" she cried running across the room, "I just thought of something! What kind of clothes will I take to Nazareth?"

Annoyed at the interruption, Mrs. Degallon looked disapprovingly at her small daughter. Children should never break into their elders' conversation. Selina needed a lesson in politeness—well, she would get it—next time. At present she could be excused on the grounds that she was excited, too excited to mind her manners perfectly, and besides, she had taken the news of going away to school very well.

Mrs. Degallon stared at her daughter until she saw a slight flush of embarrassment color the oval cheeks. Satisfied, she flipped a page and found the caption, *Wardrobe*. "Here it is," she said looking up to see if her mother was ready to listen. Then without even glancing at Selina, she began to read:

> For winter each young lady shall be supplied for everyday with two dresses of common merino, maroon in color.

Selina tossed her head. "But I don't like maroon. I like blue."

Mrs. Degallon paid no attention to the second interruption other than to dart a look of reproach at her daughter, who quickly lowered her eyes.

> And for Sunday, one dress of French merino, mazarine blue—the body and sleeves for the latter dress to be trimmed with black velvet.

She stopped reading. "Does that suit you better, Miss?"

"That should be very pretty," her daughter acknowledged sheepishly.

Also a plain mantilla or cape of heavy cloth, snuff color. For summer she shall also be supplied for every day wear with three dresses of purple calico, the Manchester-Hoyle prints, small figures.

Selina frowned, but said nothing.

For Sunday and particular occasions two dresses of buff-colored French percale made with a spencer of the same. For exhibition day she will likewise need one dress of white India muslin made with a spencer of the same and a sash of blue ribbon to be worn with this dress. Aprons for every day of a black silk or lustre and a sunbonnet of maroon color, delaine of light material. The bonnet for Sunday, the Quaker scoop, is trimmed with mazarine blue. It is especially requested of the parents not to furnish their children with any jewelry, save a plain breastpin and earrings.

Mrs. Shelby looked fondly at her grandchild. "It sounds as if you are going to be a very busy little girl for the next few weeks getting fitted. But if your Mother can spare you, I want you to come to the *Elms* with me for a while. And," she whispered in Selina's ear, "we might have a going-away party for you."

Selina's eyes danced. "Granmama, you're wonderful!" She hugged the older woman, then turned to her mother. "Mother, can I go?"

"May I."

"Well, *may* I then?"

"As soon as your wardrobe has been planned, you may. I think I can get Miss Mather to come tomorrow to take the measurements, and I'll have Aunt Mabel send the material from New Orleans."

Hearing the sound of wheels on the pebbled drive, Mrs. Shelby rose to go, and Selina and her mother accompanied her across the wide front porch with its four Doric columns and down the circular steps to where a liveried coachman waited. He helped his mistress to take her place in the fashionable victoria, then climbed to his high seat in the front, flicked his long whip over the two perfectly matched Morgans, and drove off with a flourish between the rhododendrons which lined the drive.

* * * * *

Mrs. Degallon's letter of application reached Mother Catherine the day following Bishop Kendrick's consecration, which took place on June 6, 1830. That was a memorable day, memorable because on that occasion in St. Joseph's Cathedral were gathered six princes of the Church—Bishops Flaget, David, England, Fenwick, Conwell, and Kendrick. For the Church west of the Alleghenies this ceremony marked the end of its infancy.

Mother Catherine was glad that such honor had come to Bardstown and to Father Kenrick in particular, but she was sorry to lose the zealous young priest who had replaced Father Chabrat at St. Pius and who had been extraordinary confessor at Nazareth for several years.

He was very much devoted to the Sisters and to their pupils, and on the evening of the consecration itself he had come to Nazareth with Bishop England to say goodbye. The girls honored him with a program. After it was over, he rose to express his thanks but was so overcome with emotion that Bishop England had to speak to the girls in his place. Later, however, he recovered sufficiently to give the Sisters a touching address on perseverance in the religious life.

Mother reached for the copy Sister Ellen had made for her and read it over slowly:

As this is the last time I shall have it in my power to address you, my dear Sisters in Jesus Christ, I think it proper to entertain you this evening on a subject of all others most important for you; I mean that of perseverance in the holy state you have embraced. This is momentous for you, for after having entered such a state of life, you are bound at the peril of your salvation, to continue in it. . . .

If you are unhappy at any time, my Sisters, is it not precisely because you neglect your duties, because you neglect your rules and the particular virtues of your state? Our Saviour bids us remember Lot's wife, who when she was commanded with her husband to go out of the city which was to be destroyed, left it unwillingly; obeying with reluctance, she turned to look back to see if what the angel had threatened had actually happened. She was punished instantly by Almighty God and thus was made an example to the world. . . .

In all ages and in every country where religious houses have been, persons who, after making a fervent novitiate and spending years happily in the exercises of their state, have indulged in a fatal security, have imagined that perfection followed as a matter of course without much effort on their part, have grown careless in the performance of the duties belonging to their profession, have neglected prayer, neglected to invoke the light of the Holy Ghost, have lost all relish for the spiritual life, have become unhappy and believed they had no vocation, and now they find it absolutely necessary for their salvation to return to the world. I do not say that a case never happens in which it has become expedient to leave this state after having embraced it; but it is rare and extraordinary; it very seldom occurs. . . .

Beloved Sisters in Jesus Christ, I exhort you to have thoughts worthy of your sublime vocation. Think not of the world you have left; but think of heaven think of Jesus Christ, of His passion; meditate seriously on the maxims of religion; apply them to your conduct and correct what you may find defective. Make them your guide and your support in every occurrence in your life. . . .

Mother put the paper down and closed her eyes. Once more she could see Bishop Kenrick standing there, his eyes searching into their souls, his earnest voice exhorting them to stand firm. She would never forget his words nor his kindness.

* * * * *

A year later, in August 1831, Mother Catherine's third term of office was completed, and she was assigned with Sister Clare Gardiner, Sister Appolonia McGill, and Sister Serena Carney to a new mission in Louisville.

While the Sisters were jogging along toward their destination in the lumbering stage coach, Father Robert Abell, who had known Mother Catherine at St. Thomas's, was pacing the small front room of a frame house adjoining St. Louis Church on Fifth Street. He had many things to do, but he knew that if he started any of them, the Sisters would have no one to welcome them when they arrived at their new convent. That must not happen. Especially since Mother Catherine herself was coming. He wondered, half smiling, if she would like the name, "Presentation Academy." He hoped so, because that was the name he had selected for the new school to be conducted in the church basement.

The rumble of wheels on the dirt road brought him hurrying to the window. At last they had come! Mother Catherine introduced him to the Sisters. He fairly glowed with satisfaction. Four Sisters! He had been promised only three! It didn't take him long to show them the tiny house and the large church basement which had been fitted up for a school. Then he left. The rest was the Sisters' problem!

From the beginning Mother loved Louisville and delighted in its history, much of which she had learned from Mr. McGillyCuddy, Margaret Carroll's uncle. Louisville, he told her, was founded in 1778 when George Rogers Clark, the great hero of the Northwest Territory, landed on Corn Island in the Ohio, built a fort there and one on the mainland, and drew up plans for a settlement. Two years later he asked Thomas Jefferson, then governor of Virginia, to which state this land belonged, to sign a grant for the establishment of a town to be named Louisville in honor of Louis XVI, the royal friend of the Americans who were at that time engaged in their fight for freedom.

After the Revolution many men destined to become famous in American history came to this new settlement just above the falls of the Ohio. Among the first was Daniel Boone, who transacted the first bit of banking business in this district when he deposited six beaver skins with John Sanders, the proprietor of a crude sort of exchange. This famous Indian scout and pioneer was followed by Colonel Taylor and his small son, Zachary, who in the years to come was to gain fame as a general in the Mexican War and as the twelfth President of the United States.

Royalty arrived in 1797 in the persons of Louis Philippe and his two younger brothers, the Ducs de Montpensier and Beaujois, both exiled by the terrors of the French Revolution. It was this same Louis Philippe, "Citizen King," who, after returning to France and to his throne, sent Bishop Flaget a beautiful clock and several paintings for the new cathedral at Bardstown.

The turn of the century brought two famous duelists to the pioneer town. Aaron Burr, former Vice-President, remained in Louisville several weeks on his way West in 1805, just a few months after he had killed Alexander Hamilton. Four years later Henry Clay, the youngest senator in the land, turned a vacant lot near the Ohio into a field of honor when he challenged Humphrey Marshall to a trial by arms. Unlike Burr's encounter this duel ended happily, for Clay was but slightly wounded and the contest was called off.

By far the strangest visitor to this river port was the *Orleans* built by Robert Fulton in Pittsburgh. One midnight in 1811 this boat, belching black smoke, steamed noisily to the Main Street Landing, awakening everyone who lived near the waterfront and terrifying them with its ear-splitting din. When some of the braver citizens investigated the racket, they were welcomed on deck by the New York captain, Nicholas J. Roosevelt, whose name was to become familiar to countless Americans through his famous descendants, Theodore and Franklin D.

From this time on, steamboats were a common sight on the town's waterfront, and during the War of 1812 they transported men and supplies up and down the Mississippi. Four years after the great victory of New Orleans, in which many Louisvillians played an active part, General Jackson came by steamer from that gulf port with James Monroe, the President. They spent several days at Washington Hall, the city's finest hotel, where they were entertained at a public dinner and a ball. Among those present at the festivities were two celebrated citizens, George Keats, the brother of the great English poet and proprietor of a flourishing lumber business; and John James Audubon, the world-famous ornithologist, painter, and naturalist.

But of all the distinguished visitors the Marquis de Lafayette, friend of Washington and of all Americans, was the most welcome. Arriving on May 8, 1825, he was received by the City Trustees and hundreds of citizens who turned out to greet the illustrious Frenchman. Processions were formed, arches erected, and bevies of young girls strewed his pathway with flowers. After the general acclaim the Marquis remained in the town for several days reliving the War of Independence with some of his old American officers, particularly Colonel Anderson.

Hardly had the excitement of Lafayette's visit died down when New York's governor, De Witt Clinton, promoter of steam navigation and builder of the Erie Canal, came to Louisville to inaugurate the Portland Canal. This million-dollar project actually got under way in March, 1826, and was completed in 1828.

Other less welcome visitors also appeared from time to time. Among them were smallpox, yellow fever, earthquake, and floods. Despite these uninvited guests, Louisville soon outstripped her neighbors in size, and early in February, 1828, was incorporated as a city. Portland, a neighboring settlement, declined to become a part of the new municipality, but Shippingport, by the consent of her people, was included.

In 1831 when Mother Catherine and the other three Sisters arrived, Louisville was thriving. There were sixty-five stores and many small establishments such as tin shops, furniture factories, and hat stores. Business on a larger scale included a wool factory, a cotton mill, two pottery concerns, a steam grist mill, two iron foundries, a planing mill, three breweries, two lead factories, and fifteen brick yards. All of these were in one small area from Main Street to Jefferson and from First Street to Eighth. In this section the streets were paved with cobblestones, and most of the residences scattered among the business establishments were of brick, two stories high, shaded by large maples and beautified with shrubbery and flowers. But here and there a grey and weathered log cabin reminded the passerby of the city's not-too-distant pioneer past.

Beyond the main district stretched the country with its muddy roads and uncultivated fields. It was while walking in this country area on Fifth Street near Walnut in 1829 that Father Abell had seen just the three lots he needed for his new church. The small brick building of Gothic design which Father Badin had erected on the corner of Eleventh and Main Streets in 1811 was too far away from the Louisville congregation and too small. When this church was built, John and Louis Tarascon, the leaders of the French colony and the donors of the land, had envisaged great things for Shippingport. Now their dream had ended and there was need for a new church nearer the center of Louisville. This spot on Fifth was ideal.

Less than a year later the new St. Louis's raised its modest spire to the sky. One day shortly after its dedication in 1830, Father Abell suddenly conceived the idea of using a frame house which stood nearby for a convent. Sisters—he mused. Why hadn't he thought of that before? The house would be ideal for a dwelling, and the basement of the church could be fitted out for a school.

Happy with this marvelous idea, he had gone to Bishop Flaget as soon as he could and had discussed the matter with him. Then armed with the prelate's permission, he had hurried to Nazareth at the very first opportunity and had sought out Mother Catherine. She had been delighted to see him and they had talked happily about the early days at St. Thomas's, laughing again over the secret of the unwritten sermon, which he had confided to her so many years before in the cornfield near Old Nazareth.

Father Abell explained the reason for his visit and described the possibilities of a school in Louisville. When he finally rose to go, he had Mother's promise of Sisters. Neither of them dreamed at the time that Mother herself would be one of the missionaries. But here she was at Presentation!

And what Father Abell had promised her about the school had come true. Pupils came in droves—some rich, some poor, some Catholic, some not. The first parochial school was not to be passed by lightly.

And teaching was not to claim all Mother's attention. One evening in November, a man came to tell her that a family of non-Catholics, by the name of Jenkins, had lately arrived in Shippingport from Pennsylvania and were in great trouble. Taking Sister Appolonia with her, Mother Catherine went immediately to a miserable hovel where on a cot she found a woman who had just died, a tiny baby still lying in the crook of her arm. Clinging to the cold hand was a golden-haired girl of five, and kneeling by her mother's side and weeping uncontrollably was a delicate girl of sixteen. The father, listless with discouragement, sat at a table, his chin cupped in his hands, his eyes staring off into space.

Mother Catherine took in the situation at a glance. No one here was capable of doing anything. A hasty visit next door brought kind neighbors. With their help she saw to it that the woman was prepared for burial and the children washed and fed. Her heart ached to take the little ones home with her, but the older girl refused to part with them, assuring Mother Catherine that she could keep the family together.

Every day Mother Catherine went to see how the family was getting along. When the brother, a boy of eighteen, who was unaware of his mother's death, finally returned from Indiana where he had gone to purchase a farm, he too refused to separate the family. Less than two weeks later, however, the girl, overfatigued with hard work, died in her sleep of a heart ailment. That night the father and brother begged Mother Catherine to take the two little girls to the Sisters' home.

Thus Mother's dream of an orphanage began to materialize. Her little Penn Babies, as she called them, were not destined to be alone long because people soon learned that there was a welcome for needy children on Fifth Street.

One day less than a month after the Penn Babies were installed in the Sisters' home, Sister Clare knocked at Mother's door. There was a soft "Come" and Sister entered. Mother was busy with her accounts.

"I'm sorry to disturb you, Mother," Sister Clare murmured apologetically, "but Miss Mallon stopped by about ten minutes ago and asked me to tell you about a German family in Portland. The parents died shortly after landing, leaving two girls and a baby boy. Do you think we can take them in?"

"Think!" Mother rose immediately, gathering the scattered papers into a neat pile with one swift movement of her hand. "Sister, we *must* take them in. Get your cape, and we'll go right now." As Sister Clare hastened up the stairs, Mother called after her, "And bring some flannel too, Sister. We'll probably need it."

While the young Sister was collecting clothing, Mother Catherine filled a wicker basket with food that had been intended for the Sisters' dinner. "We won't starve," she said, smiling to herself as she pictured Sister Serena's amazement when she discovered the loss. "Besides, there will be two less for dinner."

At the back door Mother met Sister Clare, and together they set out for Portland. They walked nearly a mile in

162

silence, each busy with her own thoughts and prayers. Suddenly Mother Catherine stopped short. "I just remembered," she said, looking ruefully at the bundle in her arms. "My name's on this clothing. That'll never do."

The Sisters looked at each other in dismay. Suddenly Sister Clare's face brightened, and she reached into her bulging pocket. "I just remembered I've a pair of scissors with me," she said, brandishing them triumphantly. "We can cut off the name if you wish."

They were in the country now, so they stopped on an unfrequented path, cut the telltale marks from the garments, and then hastened on.

Another half hour and they were in Portland, where after a few inquiries they found the shack where an elderly couple were sheltering the orphans. While Mother Catherine and the woman prepared a meal, Sister Clare quieted the crying baby, a mere skeleton covered with sores, and wrapped him tenderly in a small blanket brought for that purpose. Leaving the rest of the food and clothing for the old couple, Mother Catherine gathered the ends of her apron in one hand, placed the well-wrapped baby in it and carried him to the convent. Sister Clare walked beside her with the two little girls, a tiny hand in each of her own.

The people they met on the street stared at this novel sight, but the Sisters paid no attention. When they reached Fifth Street and home, Sister Clare arranged a bed for the two little girls in the Sisters' community room. Mother Catherine, however, refusing to let the baby out of her sight, placed him in a wicker basket in her own room and cared for him herself. There he grew strong and healthy and in a few months was adopted by a Reverend M. Gernadine.

As the years went by, Mother Catherine, leading a child by the hand or carrying an infant in her arms, became a common sight, and the people of Louisville began to speak of the Sisters' orphanage. Gradually contributions, most of them small, were sent by kindhearted people, and Mother Catherine's heart sang as she saw the bright, rosy faces of the children—loved and wanted.

CHAPTER SIXTEEN

1832

The feeble light struggling through the rich, stained glass windows of St. Louis Church came to rest on the white caps of a dozen Sisters who knelt motionless at the ornate altar rail. Before them on the steps of the altar stood a grey-haired prelate and a dark-haired priest.

A half-hour earlier in their community room the Sisters had welcomed Bishop Flaget, who had hastened from a visitation in Detroit on hearing that the dreaded cholera which had been ravishing central Europe in the summer of '31 had now invaded his beloved Louisville. He was pleased when Mother Catherine told him that, since Presentation would be closed during the plague, the Sisters had, under Father Abell's direction, offered their services as nurses. They were accepted immediately, and Mother Frances had sent Sisters Martha Drury, Margaret Bamber, Hilaria Bamber, and Martina Beavin from Nazareth to help. For several days the prospective nurses had been studying the instructions issued by Doctors Drake, Richards, McDowd, Bonner, and Woodward at a special meeting of the Cincinnati Medical Society. Now they were ready for the actual work. After a short discourse the Bishop invited the Sisters to the church saying, "Come now, my children, offer yourselves to God."

And so they knelt there with Bishop Flaget and Father Abell, each absorbed in prayer for the sick and prayer for themselves because each was aware of the danger of falling prey to the fearful disease. Slowly Bishop Flaget came to the Sisters. One by one he blessed them, resting his hands lightly on each white cap. Each Sister kissed his ring, genuflected, and left the church.

Waiting for them at the convent was Father Abell, who for weeks, day and night, had acted as nurse, physician, and priest at the bedside of his parishioners and of non-Catholic neighbors as well. He held up a paper. "Here's the list of the families which have been stricken in this area. Each Sister will take one or two names and visit these homes today. And," fumbling in his pocket, he pulled out another paper, "here are some things you should take with you."

He handed the second list to Mother Catherine. "Mother, please see that each group has all these."

Slowly and distinctly she read out: "Laudanum, spirits of hartshorn, ether, essence of peppermint, spirits of turpentine, calomel in powder, capsicum, powdered mustard, box of soda powders, whiskey, bags for sand, brushes, and old flannel."

As she read, the Sisters took the articles from the table where they had been placed and put them into the tow bags that had served to carry their own few possessions to the mission.

"I'm glad we had enough," Father Abell said in a relieved tone, his dark eyes scanning the quiet group. "Now, I know that you have studied the rules for caring for cholera patients, but hearing them again won't hurt anyone. Mother, will you read them through? But, before I forget," he added hastily, "these instructions are to be carried out only if you can't get a doctor. If a doctor leaves orders, then of course follow them. All right! Mother, will you begin?"

Before complying, Mother Catherine looked at the serious faces before her and forced a cheerful note into her voice. "Why not make this an oral test? All of us have studied the directions. Let's see if we can remember them. If we have to refer to a paper while taking care of our patients, I'm afraid they'll lose confidence in us."

"As usual, you're right, Mother!" Father Abell exclaimed approvingly. "Suppose you ask the questions."

"Since that's the very easiest part of any examination, of course I will," Mother assented lightly, striving hard to relieve the tension. "Here's the first. What is the initial step in taking care of a cholera patient, Sister Appolonia?"

The answer came instantly, "Bathe the patient's feet in a hot salt bath, then cover him with blankets and place bags of hot sand around the legs."

"Good. Sister Martha, go on from there."

"Make a mustard poultice about as big as your two hands, and apply it over the pit of the stomach."

"Next, Sister Margaret."

"Give your patient a drink of warm weak lye made from the fresh, clean ashes of the fireplace, and put two or three heaping teaspoons of flour of mustard seed in it."

"Right! And if the patient is seized with violent spasms, Sister Martina?"

"You should prepare a cold drink and put into it a teaspoon of laudanum, twenty or thirty drops of spirits of hartshorn, the same amount of ether, and a little weak lye. Repeat the dose in a half-hour if needed."

"And if your patient should complain of thirst, Sister Hilaria?"

"Make a drink from the powdered soda and add a little whiskey."

"And if the doctor still does not come and the patient gets worse, Sister Serena?"

"Give ten grains of calomel, mixed with a little sugar in a small amount of whiskey and make more mustard poultices, sprinkled with powdered capsicum for the inside of the thighs, above the knees."

"What could be used in place of these, Sister Dorothy?"

"Flannel bandages dipped in hot spirits of turpentine."

Turning, Mother Catherine handed the paper back to Father Abell, her free hand gripping her sidebeads. They were comforting in her fingers. "I think we passed," she said at last. "Now we had better be on our way, and may God keep you safe, my Sisters."

Love for them rolled over her like a wave. She kissed each one, then took Sister Appolonia by the hand. "Come,

Sister. We have work to do. Goodbye, Father. We'll report to you this evening."

Once outside, the two Sisters walked north toward the river—their destination, Market and Eighth Streets. Praying silently, they passed through the deserted thoroughfares. After a while they came to a two-story frame house set back some distance from the street. Sister Appolonia checked the name on the gate with her list and nodded. The two Sisters went up the path to the door and knocked. There was no response. After waiting a little while, they went to the back door and repeated the knock. Still there was no answer, but this time Mother Catherine was sure she heard a feeble cry. Lifting the latch, she walked in. There on the floor of the kitchen near the wide hearth lay the distorted body of a stalwart Negro evidently dead, and in a corner another lay twitching in agony. Not pausing to remove their wraps, the Sisters went to the assistance of the dying man. His tortured eyes lighted up when he saw them, and he tried to smile at Sister Appolonia, who was already on her knees rubbing his cramped hands, while Mother Catherine prepared some laudanum to relieve his spasms.

After he had been given the drink, he made a desperate attempt to say something, mumbling unintelligible words over and over again. At last Sister Appolonia thought she understood. " 'Help Massa.' Is that what you're saying?"

The slave nodded and then the parched and twisted lips ceased to move. Suddenly another spasm seized his tormented body. He writhed in pain, moaned feebly, and then lay quiet.

The Sisters straightened his still form and went into the next room. It was empty. A narrow stairway led to the upper part of the house. They went up quickly. There on a large four-poster bed lay the body of a woman, her long black hair spread carefully over the white pillow, the sheet pulled up to her neck. From the next room came the sound of weeping. The Sisters, following the sound, found the bereaved husband bending over a cot where a six-year-old boy lay racked with pain. On the other side of the room in a canopied bed a girl of ten was moaning. At first the man merely stared at the Sisters; then dropping into a chair, he buried his head in his hands. Without a word Mother Catherine removed her cape and the large black scoop which covered her white cap. Sister Appolonia did likewise.

The man looked up. "You'd better get out," he gasped between the dry sobs which shook his body.

"We're not going to leave you, sir," Mother Catherine told him gently.

His head snapped up. "But you may get the cholera." He nodded in the direction of the next room. "She died of it this morning." His voice broke. He covered his face again.

Going over to him, Mother laid her hand on his shoulder. "Don't worry. We'll help you and nurse your little son and daughter."

First, the Sisters made the two children as comfortable as possible. Then they went to the nearest house to ask someone to go for a doctor and to report the deaths. By evening the bodies had been removed, the doctor had come, and Mother Catherine had cooked a hot meal.

Early the next day when the Sisters came bringing nourishing food, they found the little girl worse. By mid-afternoon it seemed certain that she was not going to recover. After a whispering consultation with Sister Appolonia, Mother Catherine approached the father. "May I ask you, sir, if your daughter has been baptized?"

He looked at her piteously. "You mean she's going to —?" He broke off suddenly as if unable to say the word. "N-no, she hadn't been baptized yet, nor the boy either. In our religion we wait until the children are twelve."

"I understand. But would you object to our baptizing both of them now? I think it would be better."

The man got up and walked back and forth in the room. The Sisters watched him compassionately. Finally he faced them. "Do what you think best. I'm not of your faith, but I can refuse you nothing—not after what you have done for me. My friends and even my relatives have deserted me, but you, strangers, have stayed by me and have risked your lives." His voice grew husky with emotion. "I can never repay you, but what I have is yours."

While Mother Catherine poured the waters of salvation over the heads of his dying son and daughter, he stood by with bowed head. A few hours later he too was stricken and notwithstanding the prompt attention given him he died, worn out from the vigil he had kept. Miraculously the children recovered, and when they were well enough to be moved, Mother took them home with her.

Each morning for weeks the Sisters went out on their errands of mercy and in the evening returned exhausted but happy. Gradually, as the plague subsided, the walls of the convent figuratively bulged with orphans. Sometimes it seemed impossible that another could be cared for, but still when a new child was brought to the door, Mother Catherine, trusting in Divine Providence, always accepted the little stranger.

Meanwhile at Nazareth the Sisters had dismissed their pupils and were using the school as a hospital. In addition, as in Louisville, many of the Sisters went to the homes to take care of the plague-stricken, and several contracted the cholera from their patients. Among them was Mother Frances, who never fully recovered from the ravages of the disease. Others gave their lives. Sister Patricia, whose two sisters, Sister Margaret and Sister Hilaria, were nursing in Louisville, was the first to die a victim to her charity. Bishop David was with her in her last hours, rubbing her cramped hands and comforting her with his blessing. Sister Joanna Lewis, a talented musician, and Sister Generose Buckman, who taught art at the academy, died shortly after.

Although Bishop Flaget seemed at first to be immune to the disease, he finally succumbed. After recovering, he wrote to his brother in France:

For several weeks I seemed to laugh at the pestilence, being almost constantly in the midst of those who were infected with it, speaking to them, consoling them, rubbing their hands and feet when circumstances required this service. In brief I regarded myself as invulnerable. But my Lord Cholera, whose march is guided by an omnipotent and Invisible Hand, laughed at my bravados; he struck to the right and to the left the victims which were marked out for him, waiting patiently for the day when he could, all at his ease, lower my colors, and make me feel the entire weight of his formidable arm. He could not have chosen better the time of avenging himself of my boastings and making me know who he was and what he could do, for it was precisely when he appeared to have retired from the country that he cast himself on me, with arms uplifted, and struck me so heavy a blow, from the very beginning, that all my friends and even the physicians believed me to be in a struggle with inevitable death.

I had then recourse, on the spot, to my old coadjutor Bishop David, who had been my friend for forty-five years and my confessor for nearly thirty. With a soul filled with grief and a charity more than human he heard me, he enlightened me, he consoled me, and, above all, he relieved me from a thousand details which would have been necessary for any other confessor less acquained with my conscience. . . .

From that moment I enjoyed a peace which the world could not impart, and which the Lord Cholera himself could not trouble. I left to my confessor the charge of administering to me the last Sacraments at the moment he might judge most suitable. But a favorable crisis having occurred at the end of three days, I was no longer in a condition to require their reception.

* * * * *

When the plague had finally subsided and classes had been resumed at Nazareth, there were only thirty pupils present. But before the end of the school year the number had increased to a hundred. At Presentation Academy in Louisville, Mother Catherine and her little band, all of whom had been spared, also resumed teaching, but memories of the cholera were ever present in the twenty-five orphans who were still with the Sisters, sharing their food, their lodgings, and their love.

Naturally the care of these children added greatly to the expenses of the convent, and so it happened that one fine spring morning Sister Clare found Mother Catherine poring over her accounts, with a worried expression marring her usually cheerful face. Making ends meet was becoming more of a problem day by day. Sister Clare watched until the pen stopped, then coughed discreetly.

Startled, Mother looked up quickly. "You frightened me. I didn't even hear you come in," she smiled.

"No, like a miser you were absorbed in your money books!" Sister Clare jested, closing the door quietly behind her.

Without rising Mother motioned her to a chair. "You know, Sister, this is one time I wish I were a magician. Perhaps I could manage then to stretch ten dollars into a hundred. But," she added hastily, "I'm not complaining. God always provides."

"How did you come out yesterday? I saw you leave with Nora and I knew you went begging."

"As usual the merchants were generous, Catholic and non-Catholic alike, and I think I've almost enough to pay our bills this month."

"Did you visit Mr. McGillyCuddy? He has three nieces at Nazareth now, you know."

Mother chuckled. "I never miss him, poor man. And I always leave him for last because I'm sure he'll give me something. Yesterday, when I told him that we had lived on potatoes for the last week, he was almost angry with me for not coming to him before. He immediately sent his office boy, a bright freckled-faced redhead, to the grocery. And when I got home, there were enough provisions for a week on the kitchen table. God bless him!" She closed her book. "Now if only someone would give us another cow and a new building, I believe we could manage very nicely."

"You're not asking for much," Sister Clare commented dryly. "But it's a new building we need, all right. There's a gentleman downstairs right this minute with his orphaned niece whom he wants to leave here. I could have told him there wasn't any room, but I thought better of it."

"It's a good thing you did," Mother Catherine said in mock severity. Then to Sister Clare's surprise she added, "Tell him we'll take her.'

"But, Mother, there's not another bed and not even space to put one if we had it," Sister Clare protested.

"Don't worry, Sister. We'll get her in somehow."

Sister Clare threw up her hands in resignation. "That's what you always say."

"Well, we always manage to make room for one more, don't we?"

"Yes, Mother, we do," Sister admitted reluctantly. "But —"

"And we'll do it this time too. I'll go down and talk to the gentleman and I'll find a place for the child. You'll see."

As Sister Clare started out the door, Mother called her back. "And I'm telling you a deep, dark secret. Today I am writing to Nazareth and asking them to help us buy the lot on the south side of the church. That would be an ideal place for an orphanage."

"Y-You mean we'll build one?" Sister Clare's grey eyes opened wide. Mother nodded.

"With what?"

Rising, Mother grasped the astonished Sister by the shoulders and shook her playfully. "You doubting Thomas! With Faith, of course!"

* * * * *

Before the end of 1833 the house which Mother Catherine always called the Faith Building was ready for occupancy. Emblazoned in bold letters on the wall above the front door was the name: St. Vincent's Female Orphan Asylum.

Now that Mother Catherine had a real orphanage, she

felt that she should ask for information from an expert in this type of work. Consequently, she wrote to Sister Margaret, a Sister of Charity of Emmitsburg, who was in charge of St. Peter's Orphanage in Cincinnati. The latter gave her excellent advice and a regular schedule for the little ones. Soon all the girls who were old enough were helping with the work in the kitchen and the refectory and doing their share of the sweeping, washing, and ironing. After the house was in order, the children spent the rest of the day in study and in play, and the evenings in sewing and knitting. Their handiwork with that of the Sisters was displayed in a large press with glass doors. The sale of these articles together with the sewing supplied by clothing stores and private families helped to keep the wolf from the door.

Generous friends also came to the aid of the Sisters. Miss Rosaline Mallon, who was very much interested in the orphans, often helped Mother pay her bills; and after her marriage to Dr. Jack Smith, she started a permanent fund for the support of St. Vincent's. Another friend, Mr. Hohan—in whose funeral procession some years later four hundred orphans walked—not only gave money, but, what was just as important, kept Mother Catherine informed on all affairs which pertained to the orphanage and to the general welfare of the Sisters.

CHAPTER SEVENTEEN

1833-1838

An errand of information brought Mr. Hohan to the orphanage early one Friday afternoon in February. As he stood at the door waiting for the Sister portress to come, the wind from the Ohio River tore at his tall hat, threatening to send it flying into the street. But his mind was too much occupied with what he had to tell Mother Catherine to worry about his hat or about the bitter cold.

He heard the bolt being drawn, and Sister Alice appeared in the doorway.

"Come in," she welcomed, shivering a bit as the icy blast struck her. "My, but it's cold."

"Yes. We'll probably have snow before the day's over," Mr. Hohan remarked, handing Sister his hat but making no move to take off his coat. He knew by experience that it was never very warm in the orphanage. "Is Mother Catherine in?"

"Yes, indeed! I'll get her for you." Sister Alice conducted him into the meagerly furnished parlor, asked him to be seated, and then disappeared down the dark hall.

Left to himself, Mr. Hohan sat stiffly on the uncomfortable chair and looked around. There were no curtains at the windows, no rugs on the floor. The furniture, what there was of it, was of the cheapest, and from where he sat he could see the glass press with its homemade wares to sell. He didn't like that press. Never had. It always made him uncomfortable by silently reminding him that the Sisters and the orphans had to work too hard.

A light footstep, and Mother Catherine was smiling at him from the hall. He rose quickly and bowed.

"This *is* a surprise!" Mother greeted him. "I thought you were out of town this week." She motioned him to be seated. "I'm glad you aren't and that you stopped by to see us."

Mr. Hohan was about to remark that he would like to buy some new furniture for the parlor, but somehow since Mother had entered the shabby room, it didn't look quite so stiff and poor. He decided to say nothing about that but to get to the purpose of his visit right away.

"You know I'm always happy to stop at the orphanage," he assured her with sincerity, "and I would like nothing better than to have a visit with the orphans, but time doesn't permit today." He pulled a newspaper from his pocket and pointed to an article on the first page. "I've something here that I'd like you to read."

Mother took the paper from him. Watching her face closely as she read, he saw the smile vanish from her eyes and her lips set in a stern line. When she had finished, she handed the paper back to him without a word.

Mr. Hohan waited.

Finally Mother broke the silence. "Thank you for calling this to my attention," she said. "I'd never have seen it otherwise."

"What are you going to do about it?"

Mother Catherine hesitated, then said slowly, "I'm not sure yet. It will take some praying first, but I *will* do something. You may be certain of that." She paused, her mind groping for a solution.

When she spoke again, there was a note of indignation in her voice. "When two years after our nursing of the cholera victims a group of bigots dare to print an article calling our work 'mercenary' and asserting that the city's account books testify that we were well paid for our services, I think something *should* be done."

Satisfied with the results of his interview, Mr. Hohan stood. "Yes, something should be done and done quickly. One of my non-Catholic friends told me some time ago that the subject was mentioned frequently from the pulpit of his church, but I didn't say anything then, for I thought the matter would die a natural death. However, when I saw this," he pointed to the article, "I knew that it was about time I called it to your attention."

"May I keep the paper please? I'd like to show it to the Sisters who did the nursing."

" Yes, of course. Let me know what you decide to do, and if I can help in any way, you may be sure I will."

Mother Catherine's serenity had returned, and she was calm as she accompanied him to the door. "I suppose I shouldn't get too much upset over this when we have so many good friends in Louisville, but I promise you," she said with determination, "this shall be settled once and for all."

After Mr. Hohan had gone, Mother read the article again slowly. Then folding the paper carefully, she thrust it into her copious pocket and made her way to the chapel. After praying long and fervently for guidance, she went to her office. Sitting at her desk, she pulled out a drawer and took a sheet of paper. She carefully tested the nib of a quill and began to write. For ten minutes there was no sound except the faint scratching of the pen. Finally she stopped and scrutinized what she had written. Then letter in hand, she rose and hurried through the empty hall into the little girls' dormitory in search of Sister Susan. She found her combing Sally's curly red hair. "Could I see you for a minute, Sister?"

"Surely, Mother." Sister Susan patted Sally on the head and came out into the hall.

"Sister, do you know if we have seventy-five dollars in the house?"

"Seventy-five dollars!" Sister looked as startled as if Mother had asked if she had an elephant. "Well—w-we sold several articles yesterday, and this morning Miss Mallon sent us the results of a cake sale her group had for us; so we have something, but"—the mere thought of such a sum was overwhelming—"seventy-five dollars!"

Less than two minutes later she was back. "I'm sorry,

Mother. We have only ten and we need groceries to-morrow."

"Well then, I must borrow it," Mother Catherine said grimly.

Sister Susan looked at her superior in amazement. She had never seen Mother Catherine like this before. In answer to her unasked question, Mother pulled the newspaper out of her pocket, unfolded it, and pointing to the article, said, "Read this!"

When Sister Susan finished, her face was flushed. "How could anyone write a thing like that?" she demanded.

Mother Catherine merely shook her head.

"What are you going to do?"

"I've already done it," Mother replied with a faint trace of satisfaction in her tone. "But I have to have seventy-five dollars to give it force." With that she thrust the letter into Sister's hand. "Read it aloud, please. I want to hear how it sounds."

Almost mechanically Sister Susan obeyed. "To the Mayor and Council of the City of Louisville, February 10, 1834." She glanced briefly at Mother's tense face and continued, pronouncing each word carefully:

Feb. 10, 1834

Gentlemen:

At that gloomy period when cholera threatened to lay our city desolate and nurses for the sick poor could not be obtained on any terms, Rev. Mr. Abell in the name of the Society of which I have the honor to be a member, proffered the gratuitous services of as many of our Sisters as might be necessary in the then existing distress, requiring merely that their expenses should be paid. This offer was accepted—as the order from your honorable board inviting the Sisters will show. But when the money was ordered from your treasury to defray those "expenses," I had the mortification of remarking that, instead of the term "expenses" of the Sisters of Charity, the word "services" was substituted. I immediately remonstrated against it and even mentioned the circumstance to the Mayor and another gentleman of the Council, and upon being promised that the error would be corrected, I remained satisfied that it had been attended to, until a late assertion from one of the pulpits of the city led me to believe that it stands yet uncorrected on your books, as these same books were referred to in proof of the assertion. If so, gentlemen, pardon the liberty I take in refunding to you the amount paid for the above named expenses, well convinced that our Community, for whom I have acted in this case, would far prefer to incur the expense themselves than to submit to so unjust an odium.

Gentlemen, be pleased to understand that we are not hirelings; and if we are, in practice, the servants of the poor, the sick, and the orphans, we are voluntarily so. But we look for our reward in another and better world.

> With sincere respect, Gentlemen,
> Your obedient servant,
> Catherine Spalding,
> Sisters of Charity.

Sister Susan looked up at Mother with an admiration powerless to express itself.

It was Mother who broke the silence. "That will do, I think."

"Do! It's perfect!" Sister Susan exclaimed, enthusiastically finding her voice at last. "That is," she added dolefully, "all except the seventy-five dollars!"

"Put on your shawl, Sister. We'll take this to Mr. McGillyCuddy. He'll be glad to lend us the money, and as soon as Nazareth hears about it, I know Mother Frances will manage to repay him somehow. This is an error which must be corrected at all costs."

The letter had the desired effect. The next day the mayor returned the seventy-five dollars enclosed in a letter of apology, expressing regret for the negligence which had resulted in such false impressions and assertions, and assuring correction of the city's books. Mother was jubilant over the outcome.

Sister Appolonia's only comment was, "Well, I'm glad he sent the money back. Nazareth can certainly use it."

Yes, the Sisters could find many uses for that money and much more, for although the new orphanage, the Faith Building, as they were still calling it, was only three years old, it was already so overcrowed that Mother Catherine was forced to look around for a larger home. On the corner of Wenzel and Jefferson Streets she found a new three-story tavern which belonged to James Marshall. He was eager to sell it because he had used all his money, and the interior was still not finished. For Mother this building was ideal because there were enough rooms to house the orphans and the Sisters, and the rest of the building could be completed to her own specifications later.

And so on one September morning in 1836 Barney Cochran, while painting a house on Jefferson Street opposite the new tavern, saw a strange procession. Carefully placing his dripping brush in the paint can suspended from the ladder, he stopped work and stared.

Suddenly he experienced a minor earthquake and heard the irate voice of Pat O'Malley coming from below. "What's the matter wid ye? Loafin' on the job?"

Instead of replying, Barney grinned and motioned his boss to come up. Pat groaned as he thought of the ascent, but his curiosity got the better of him. As soon as he was half way up, Barney pointed over the roof of the house to the tavern yard. "Look what's goin' into the new tavern!"

Shading his eyes against the glare of the sun, Pat looked in the direction Barney pointed and saw a group of children shepherded by six women dressed in black. "Shure, an' if that ben't the funniest thing," Pat said, scratching his head in perplexity. "What's them wimmen and young wans doin' goin' into a tavern? Ould man Marshall do be havin' quare customers."

Barney looked down on him, "Didn't you know that Marshall sold the building? He didn't have enough money to finish it."

"Well, now, shure an' I wouldn't be knowing that."

Just then an old lorry loaded with furniture drove up, and the Sisters and their charges swarmed around it, unloading the smaller pieces and carrying them inside. The Sisters had removed their black scoops, and their little white caps gleamed in the morning sun.

Pat almost upset the paint bucket in his excitement. "Ye know who that be, Barney, me lad?" Then without waiting for an answer, " 'Tis Mother Catherine, herself, God bless her, and them's the orphans, I do believe. Shure an' manny's the day I seed her on the strate wid a babe on the wan arm and a colleen ahoulding onto her skirts, taking them home to the orphanage wid her. 'Tis a place next to St. Louis's Church she had for a couple of years."

He shaded his eyes and looked steadily at the little stream of children and nuns, moving from the lorry to the house with loads far too heavy for them. " 'Tis movin' out here she must be now, begorra," he mumbled, starting down the ladder.

Idly Barney watched Pat descend and then reached for his paint brush. Suddenly there was a bellow from below.

"What do he think ye be doing with that brush, man? That kin wait. Git down here and lend a hand to the ladies."

With the help of the two painters it was not long before the lorry was unloaded and the tavern-orphange made as comfortable as any place can ever be on moving day.

That evening when the children had been put to bed, the Sisters sat down for the first time. But their hands were still busy mending the well-worn garments of their small charges. Sister Julia was working industriously on a faded green-black stocking.

"You know," she laughed, putting her finger through a large hole in the toe, "I believe Sarah gets the prize for wearing out stockings. Yesterday's pair had one hole half this size; today's has two twice as big."

"Shows she's improving with age," Sister Xavier commented dryly with a roguish twinkle in her eyes.

"And that her toe's a day bigger," Sister Clare added, making sure that Sister Julia was still busy rewarding the first speaker with a withering look.

As always Sister Sophia came to the rescue. "Cheer up, Sister Julia, Sarah'll be able to do her own darning in a few more years."

Sister Julia threw up her hands in mock dismay. "And by that time there'll be ten others, I imagine." She threaded her needle. "Well, it's all for God, I know, but —I don't think I'll ever like to darn stockings."

"Here. I'll exchange," Mother Catherine offered, reaching into her workbasket and selecting a very wrinkled and worn pinafore.

Sister Julia declined hurriedly. "No, thanks, Mother, I'll stick to the stockings. Those pinafores are so worn you have to patch the patches." They all laughed.

Mother Catherine waited until she could be heard. "Sisters, now that Sister Julia has openly refused a change of occupations, I'll tell you something. Tomorrow we'll have five more girls and," she added mischievously, "no doubt they'll be even better at wearing out stockings than Sarah is."

There was another laugh as Sister Julia pretended to faint.

"Anyway, Mother, we won't have to worry about where we can put them," Sister Xavier said, leaning over to pick up a needle she had dropped.

"No, indeed," agreed Sister Emily, "with twelve large rooms besides the uncompleted wing, we'll have plenty of room. Room to spare!"

Mother Catherine looked at the happy faces. "You know, today when I went through the building, I got an idea."

Everyone stopped sewing. Mother Catherine's ideas were always worth attention. "I was thinking that since we wouldn't need all the space for the orphans, we could use a couple of the rooms for an infirmary."

"An infirmary?" they chorused.

"Yes, when the wing's finished, we could take the children over there and use the main building for the sick."

They smiled. Mother's ideas were never small. Like Minerva they sprang forth full-grown. Give her one day in a new house and she would envision another move. That was Mother Catherine. Never stagnant, never still, her eyes always open for an opportunity to serve.

"I'll write to Nazareth about it in the morning, and you'll pray, I hope," she said, carefully selecting a patch from the scrap bag. But even as she sewed the piece in place, her mind was planning the letter, planning the building, planning the service, planning...

Not many months later in November, 1836, her plans became realities. Her fingers shook a little with excitement as she held the advertisement announcing the opening of St. Vincent's Infirmary. It was a big undertaking for a small community. Some might call it too big, but the sick needed caring for as much as the orphan, and God would provide. It was His work and He would take care of it. She went to the window where the light was better. Her fingers were steady now and her voice calm as she read the notice aloud:

The Society of the Sisters of Charity intends opening a private infirmary in the spacious and commodious brick buildings lately owned by James Marshall on Jefferson Street. The Institution will be superintended by Mother Catherine Spalding, the patients nursed by her associate Sisters.

The institution will be under good regulations and the terms moderate. Every exertion will be made to render the Infirmary worthy of patronage. Two physicians will constantly and regularly attend the Infirmary; any patient, however, may call in any physician he pleases at his own charge. A committee of gentlemen of this city will, from time to time, visit the Infirmary. The patrons of St. Vincent's Infirmary will have the consolation of knowing that in patronizing the Institution they will contribute to the maintenance of the destitute female orphans under care of the same Sisters of Charity. Patients afflicted with contagious diseases cannot be admitted to the Infirmary, nor anyone without the recommendation of some physician of the city. Physicans, in general, are invited to recommend their patients to the Infirmary and to continue their medical assistance there; their patients will be faithfully nursed and the medical directions strictly complied with.

Terms:
    Board and nursing, $7.00 per week. Same including medicine and house doctors, $10.00.

Physicans:
    Doctors R. Wantyn and S. J. Combs

Consulting physicans:
    Doctors Wm. C. Galt, Miller, A. P. Elston, U. E. Ewing and Joseph Middleton.

CHAPTER EIGHTEEN

1838-1840

Mother Catherine held up her right hand and then her left, looking at them carefully. Could these thin white fingers be hers? Slowly she let her hands sink to the bed and then raised them again as if expecting to see them replaced by the strong capable ones she had always seen before. There was no such change of course. She moved restlessly. How long had she been ill? A week? Two? She gave up trying to recall and lay quietly looking at the crucifix on the wall.

Little by little everything began to come back to her— her trip to Nazareth, her re-election in August, '38, her farewell to the orphans and the sick. "I came back from Louisville," she had written at the time to her sister Ann, "to take for the third time a burden for which I am little suited and which I still less desire. My heart clings to the orphans and the sick whom I had to leave." But the Sisters had elected her, and she had to shoulder the burden.

It had not taken her long to see that there had been many changes at Nazareth during her six years in Louisville. Some were good, but there were others which left an ache in her heart. She sighed. It was Bishop David who worried her most. She had always taken it for granted that when he had completed his work for the diocese, he would come to Nazareth to live.

True, he had resigned his office as ecclesiastical superior of Nazareth in 1833 and had appointed Father Reynolds to take his place, but no one was worried by that, for his age and ill health forced him to reduce his activities.

Naturally the work with the seminarians would be the last to go, but when it was laid aside, he would come to Nazareth to spend the rest of his life with his daughters. With his retirement in mind the Sisters had built a neat brick building which they called the Bishop's House. When passing it, they often remarked, "Our dear Father is coming to live with us soon to be all our own." But despite the fact that he no longer had the seminary, he had not come. In fact, he seldom came even to visit.

He was still living in the seminary at Bardstown, and he evidently planned to stay there to the end, for he had written Sister Elizabeth Suttle:

My residence will continue to be the seminary until the White House [the cathedral rectory] is ready to receive us. There I will reside in solitude with Bishop Flaget, keeping still my room at the Cathedral. The Sisters of Charity of Nazareth will not cease to be dear to me as my daughters to a loving father, and I hope they will reciprocate the same sentiments towards me. God, in whom alone I have tenderly loved them, is unchangeable, and as long as we make Him the center of our affections, they are as unchangeable as He is. I will carry them all in my heart and recommend them everyday to the protection and paternal care of our Heavenly Father.

What had caused this change in his plans? This apparent coldness? No one knew. Mother had tried to find the reason for the difficulty, but it had always eluded her. The only clue she had was what he had written to Mother Josephine of Loretto, who had asked him to live there and thus give her Sisters the privilege of daily Mass. In replying to her invitation, he had touched briefly on a misunderstanding at Nazareth but had maintained that only a very few Sisters were at fault. "In them," he had written, "it is a blind subserviency to the ecclesiastical superior who now governs them and who seems always to have considered the affection of my daughters for their old father as a diminution of that which he himself wishes to possess." But he had appointed Father Reynolds ecclesiastical superior, hadn't he? What made him think then that the good priest was turning the Sisters from their founder?

Mother moved restlessly in bed as she attempted to solve the riddle. It was one of those intangible things evidently, a strange misconception produced by a series of minute incidents interpreted by a sensitive person. It could hardly be explained because there was really nothing to explain; yet, on both sides, it was causing hearts to ache. Prayer. That was it! Only prayer could dissolve the misunderstanding.

Perhaps now that Father Reynolds had been replaced by Father Hazeltine, things would be different. The Bishop loved Father Hazeltine as a son, and possibly this priest could persuade the prelate to come to Nazareth. If not, no one could.

Mother smiled wanly as she pictured Nazareth's new ecclesiastical superior—tall, over six feet, broad shouldered, a long face with a bushy fringe of greying beard, and dark eyes that looked out kindly from beneath heavy brows. He was very dignified, reserved without being haughty, and was the embodiment of order, exactness, and punctuality in everything he did.

A New Englander from Concord, New Hampshire, and a Puritan, he had been converted in 1818 on a visit to Montreal and baptized in that city on Christmas day. One year later he became disciplinarian and agent at St. Joseph's College, Bardstown, a position he held until he was ordained by Bishop David in 1835. His sixteen years of experience with both finances and education had already been a tremendous help to the Sisters and would continue to aid them in the future. Already he had assumed most of Eister Ellen's responsibilities, which were numerous, for she had been in charge of the school ever since the community had moved from St. Thomas's. It didn't seem possible that six years had passed since her departure from Nazareth.

Mother sighed deeply. Sister Ellen's leaving was another riddle. Exactly what had happened between Bishop David and Sister Ellen that spring of '32? At the time Sister Ellen had written a confused letter, something about a jest she had made about Bishop David and which he had taken very seriously. She had also mentioned the fact that he apparently thought that she had undue influence over Mother Angela. The outcome of it all had been that Bishop David had demanded that Sister Ellen be sent away from Nazareth, and evidently he even talked about expelling her from the community. At that she had pleaded, "Not my dear habit, not my sacred vows. Death first!"

Moved, Bishop David had yielded to her entreaty but had insisted that she leave Nazareth. He gave her a choice of Presentation in Louisville or a new mission in White River, Indiana. Declaring calmly that she had given up her right to choose when she had made her vow of obedience, Sister Ellen refused to name the place and was assigned to the Indiana convent.

To add to the confusion, Mother Angela Spink, who had vigorously defended Sister Ellen, said she felt unsuited for the position of Mother and asked to be relieved from her office. Refused repeatedly, she had finally declared that she would not renew her annual vows unless she was released from her important position. Consequently her resignation was accepted on March 25, and Sister Frances Gardiner was appointed by Bishop David to finish out her term of office.

The following summer Mother Angela, Sister Barbara, Sister Sebastia and Sister Ellen were sent to open the new mission in Indiana. There the Sisters returned to a log cabin life with privations so severe that the foundation had to be given up after one year. Sister Ellen, nearly sixty, must have been deeply wounded, but the Sisters who lived with her marveled at her cheerfulness and generosity, and her great love of the community.

How wonderful it would be to see Sister Ellen again! Well, perhaps before too long it would be possible to go on a visitation to Lexington where she was missioned, that is, if this weakness would leave.

Mother struggled to a sitting position, but her head reeled so that she was forced to lie down again. There was so very much to do both at Nazareth and on the missions, and here she lay!

A knock interrupted her gloomy thoughts. "Come," she called weakly. The door opened slowly. Raising herself on one elbow, Mother forgot her illness and her troubles when she saw the face of the visitor. "Sister Teresa!" she exclaimed joyfully. "Why, I thought you had the fever too! What are you doing up?"

"Oh, I'm much better, Mother, and I thought I'd come over to see how you were getting along. This chicken soup ought to make you well," she said cheerfully, spreading a white cloth on the bed and placing a pillow behind Mother's back. That done, she went to the table to get the soup. Mother started to say something, but Sister Teresa shook her head. "Take this soup while it's hot, and then we'll talk."

Obediently Mother complied while Sister Teresa watched her anxiously. When the last mouthful was gone, she took the bowl. "Now," she said softly, "tell me all about yourself, the orphans, the hospital, everything. Many times when I'm sewing on patches for my poor black children, I've said a prayer that everything you undertake may succeed."

Mother's eyes misted. "After all these years and all these separations, Sister Teresa, you're still my best advocate with God."

"We're never separated, Mother, and never shall be," Sister Teresa declared stoutly, patting Mother's thin white hand. "Together we started, and together we'll finish. Only Sister Ellen, you, and I are left. The others have gone to God. You and I'll go together," she said prophetically.

"Soon?"

"Not yet awhile." Sister Teresa's eyes twinkled. "You've much more work to do, and I've much more praying.

But come," she smiled, settling herself in a chair close to the bed, "tell me all about the orphanage."

They talked until the room began to get dark. Sister Teresa rose stiffly. "I must go," she said, removing the pillow from behind Mother's back and helping her to lie down. "After you get better, I won't see you often, for you'll be far too busy, but my prayers will be with you at all times."

Mother watched her out the door and noted with pain how feeble she was getting. Hard work in her younger days had worn out the body, but her spirit was as young as always.

It was months before Mother Catherine was able to do a full day's work, but she didn't play the invalid. She was weak of course but well enough, she felt, to do a little something. One day, seated at the desk in the school office, she began answering some letters from parents and was so engrossed that she barely heard the hesitant tap at the door.

When the door opened, Mother looking up saw one of the boarders standing there, her head low. "Why, Susan, what's the trouble?" she asked, beckoning the child to come to her.

"S-Sister Columba sent me to you—b-because—because —"Her voice trembled and she wiped her eyes with the back of her hand. "B-because I wouldn't do my exercises. Sister said they weren't neat, and I said I wasn't going to do them over again. And," she choked, bursting into tears, "I'm not g-going to, either."

"Come here to me, child." Mother's voice was gentle.

Susan moved slowly around the desk. Mother laid one hand kindly on the culprit's shoulder and pushed back the hair from her forehead with the other. "My dear, I'm so sorry you're in trouble. It pains me even more because you're called one of my pets."

Susan's head snapped up. "But I don't want to be called your pet."

"What, my child, you don't want me to love you?" There was hurt in the voice and reproach in the blue eyes.

"Oh, yes, Mother! Pardon me, I didn't mean that," Susan hastened to explain. "I want you to love me all you can, but," she repeated sullenly, "I don't want to be called your pet."

"But why, Susan?"

"Because—because—everybody-knows-that-your-pets-are-the-worst-girls-in-school," Susan blurted out all in one breath.

Mother laughed and pulled her close. "Never mind, Susan, you're not that bad. But even if you were, I'd love you just the same. Go back to Sister Columba now and tell her that you're sorry and that you'll do the exercise just as she wants it done. You will, won't you?"

"Y-yes, Mother," Susan agreed somewhat unwillingly and started toward the door.

Mother resumed her work. Suddenly there was a flurry of crinoline and Susan was back, her arms around Mother's neck. After planting a moist kiss on the soft cheek, she flew to the door again and was off down the hall. Mother waited until she heard the patter of footsteps fade and then rose slowly from her desk and closed the door.

* * * * *

The months passed quickly: winter, spring, summer, fall, and then winter again. At last Mother was her old self, her eyes ever on the watch to improve things. The farm had become rather an expense than a source of profit to the community. Realizing this, Mother hired a good overseer, built a flour mill, increased the stock, and bought Mr. Ben McCane's small adjoining farm. These expenses, together with the payment for the house and lot for the Sister's day school on Fifth Street in Louisville, and the property on Jefferson Street for the orphans and the sick, prevented her, for the time at least, from dwelling on the plan for a new academy, which she knew was urgently needed.

Amid these activities the proposed visitation to Lexington was pushed into the background. Then one day shortly before Christmas Sister Columba came in with a letter from that mission. Mother tore it open eagerly, but her face saddened visibly as she read. When she had finished, she dropped the letter on the desk and sat motionless.

It was several moments before she raised her eyes to Sister Columba's questioning glance. "Bad news?"

Mother's lips moved as if to speak, but no sound came. She seemed to be having difficulty in forming the words. Finally in a low broken voice she faltered, "Sister Ellen is dead," and turned her head to hide her emotion. "Let's say the *De Profundis* for her."

They knelt. Halfway through the prayer, Sister Columba realized that she was saying it alone. She glanced at Mother Catherine. Tears were streaming down her face.

After the prayer they sat in silence for awhile. Finally Mother took the letter from the desk and read it again. Finished, she started slowly across the room. "Please, Sister, tell the others," she called from the door. "I'll take the letter to Sister Teresa myself."

"Were there any details, Mother?" Sister Columba asked deferentially.

Mother Catherine turned around. "Oh, I'm sorry. I meant to tell you." She walked over to Sister Columba. "The letter says that Sister Ellen was not sick long. At recreation the evening of the sixteenth of December she was full of fun and jests as usual, but that night she became ill. She died two days later." Mother stopped abruptly. After a pause she said wistfully, "Remember how she used to get us all laughing?"

Sister Columba nodded, not trusting herself to speak. She was seeing Sister Ellen again as she had seen her so many times at school when that talented woman was her devoted teacher. How the girls had admired her perfectly proportioned features, her lovely brown eyes! Yet it was not these, but her mental and spiritual gifts which made her outstanding. Great in mind, a thorough scholar in Christian doctrine and Biblical lore, she had no superior among the teachers.

Her labors were incessant. She taught all the higher classes as well as writing, tapestry, embroidery, and painting; for the last especially she had a true and cultivated talent. In addition to teaching the girls she prepared the young Sisters for the classroom, and for a time was mistress of novices. But more than all this, she had loved her students and Margaret Carroll, as one of them, had loved her in return. She too had missed Sister Ellen greatly, and when she had been appointed to fill the vacancy left by that great woman, she had never felt more incompetent. It had been her constant prayer that Sister Ellen would spend her last days happily at Nazareth. But God had willed otherwise, and she had died on her cross.

"Evidently Sister Ellen had a premonition of her death," Mother Catherine said thoughtfully, "for the letter says that at her last recreation she remarked to one of the Sisters: 'See, now we're all in great glee, I perhaps more than anyone, yet who knows? By tomorrow night I may have received my death summons.'"

"I'm not surprised she knew," Sister Columba replied with conviction. "I think she was a saint. How many women could have taken the humiliation of being sent from Nazareth the way she was? She must have felt it keenly, yet never by word or act did she betray that fact. Everybody who has seen her in the past years has marveled at the way she plunged into the new work, never murmuring nor repining that she had to start again after so many years at Nazareth. That to me is proof enough of her humility and her saintliness. Certainly God tried her in the fire of misunderstanding, and she proved herself to be pure gold."

Mother looked at the young Sister affectionately. "You're right, Sister Columba. It's trials and troubles that try the gold, and it's patience and trust that make the saint."

CHAPTER NINETEEN

1841

It was a good thing that Mother Catherine was inured to trials, for the year 1841 was to bring to a head the storm which, unknown to her, had been brewing since 1838.

At that time while in France collecting funds, Bishop Flaget had met the Reverend John Timon, then charged with the important mission of negotiating with the Superior-General of the Lazarists on the matter of affiliating the American Sisters of Charity of Emmitsburg, founded by Mother Seton in 1809, with the French Daughters of Charity, established by St. Vincent de Paul in 1633.

The idea of joining the two groups had its origin in the decision of the Sulpician Superior-General to withdraw the members of his society from all responsibilities except that of teaching in seminaries. The Sulpicians consequently were obliged to relinquish the guardianship of the Emmitsburg sisterhood. Bishop Flaget, a Sulpician himself, was deeply interested in these negotiations, for from the beginning Nazareth and Emmitsburg had been closely associated through Bishop David, who had been Mother Seton's ecclesiastical superior for two years before coming to Kentucky. Naturally then Bishop Flaget began to consider the affiliation of Nazareth with the Emmitsburg group and through them with the French community. When he talked the matter over with Bishop Chabrat, his coadjutor, the latter agreed wholeheartedly. He had never liked the idea of a purely American foundation, and he encouraged his superior to pursue the affiliation.

Shortly after Bishop Flaget's return from France, therefore, the two Bishops decided to discuss the subject with the Sisters at Nazareth. Fortunately for their plan, there seems to have been at this time among the Sisters a small discontented group who disapproved of certain appointments and regulations. This lack of unity led Bishop Flaget and his coadjutor to believe that the affiliation with Emmitsburg was exactly what was needed to restore concord. As steps to the proposed end, they first suggested a change in habit, then the withdrawal of the ecclesiastical superior, Father Hazeltine. Shortly after these proposals the two Bishops made an episcopal visitation in which each Sister was privately interrogated as to the observance of the rule, the general discipline of the community, the union and happiness of the members, and the advisability of uniting with some other institute. In justice the only conclusion the Bishops could draw from their interviews with the Sisters was that the dissatisfied members constituted but a very small minority and that Nazareth should be left intact.

By this time, however, the movement toward affiliation had gained momentum, and Bishop Flaget had convinced himself that Nazareth should join Emmitsburg; so he came again, this time with Father Badin, who had returned from France the previous year, to reinvestigate the lack of harmony existing in the community, to see if it had grown and to try to interest more Sisters in the union. Mother Catherine was happy to see Father Badin because she felt that he would favor a distinct Kentucky sisterhood, and she hoped that his visit would end the investigations. It did. But it did not end Bishop Flaget's desire for the merger of the communities. He and Bishop Chabrat continued their campaign by letter. In each one they expressed some dissatisfaction with the government of the community, with the habit, or with the conduct of the Sisters.

Worn out by this constant barrage, Mother sat in the

dim light of her office window late one afternoon with the most recent letter in her hand, a letter which practically demanded an early change in habit. Mother knew that such a command was but the prelude to the loss of independence. Sick at heart, she stared straight ahead, her eyes fixed on, but not seeing, the sturdy old sycamore stretching its gaunt limbs into the darkening sky. Suddenly the call of a meadow lark roused her, and she noticed the new leaves on the ends of the white branches. A slight smile softened the grim line of her lips. Why give up so easily? All was not lost yet. Spring was here again. Quickly she got on her knees beside her desk and prayed. Then she wrote rapidly.

April 17, 1841

Rt. Rev. B. J. Flaget,
Rt. Reverend Dear Bishop and Father,

I do not know that you require any answer to your letter of yesterday. I have read it with all the attention of which I am capable and have spent not only one-quarter of an hour as you suggested before the Adorable Sacrament (where, in fact, I find my only comfort), but quarters of hours; and I feel now as I did at first. I can only say that to the best of my power I will endeavor to comply with your orders. If you believe that Almighty God can be more glorified by our wearing a black cap instead of a white one, I hope you will do me the justice to believe that I attach no importance to those little articles of our clothes. It matters not—white or black is the same to me, and for anything further I forbear to make any remark. May God's Holy Will be done! And may He in His mercy grant me the grace to save my poor soul—it shall be my only aim.

I feel consoled, Dear Father, that in your visit the other day you found the community happy and contented in the regular observance of the rules and duties, which I do think to be the case as far as can be, and

I fondly trust that with the blessing of God it may continue to improve.

My God, I trust, knows the purity of my intention and I leave it in His Divine Hands. I did think I had experienced every kind of trial—this is entirely new. God be praised for all and have mercy on me,

His humble and unworthy handmaid,
Catherine

Thoughtfully she reread what she had written, sanded the letter, and sealed it with a drop of red wax. Then with a lighter heart, she sent for Ned and instructed him to take the letter to Bishop Flaget at the White House.

Days passed. Still no reply. Her hopes faded. She spent hours before the Blessed Sacrament and came away more certain each time that God intended Nazareth to remain as it was, a distinct community. But where find a champion for her cause? Bishop David would agree with her she was sure, but he was old and in ill-health. He could not come to her, and she could hardly, under the circumstances, go to the White House to see him. No, that would never do. She drew her hand wearily across her aching brow. Suddenly she brightened. Father Badin! Of course! He knew Nazareth, and he knew Kentucky's needs. Besides, on his recent visitation he had definitely shown that he sympathized with the Sisters who desired to retain their identity. She would send for him.

More promptly than she had dared to hope, he came, made his observations, as he called them, and talked with her. Immediately afterwards he rode out to the White House to see Bishop Flaget, who greeted him courteously but frowned a little when he said he had just come from Nazareth. This sign of disfavor left Father Badin undaunted.

"Yes," he said striding up and down in his old patched cassock. "The Sisters sent for me, and I heard what they said as charity dictates."

Bishop Flaget looked up at him over his glasses. "Well, did you find them happy and observing their rules?"

"I did," Father Badin answered promptly, raising his voice a little in his earnestness. "Furthermore the Sisters have taken and renewed their vows as always, and they feel that since they have taken them under this present constitution that their society should be maintained in tranquility and of course without change." He stopped and looked at Bishop Flaget, who was gazing at the floor.

"And you agree with them. I can see that."

"I do."

"Well, what do they think about the proposal to remove the ecclesiastical superior, Father Hazeltine?"

"The Sisters think that they need such a person, for they know that the Bishop is too busy to give his personal and immediate attention to the minute details of the government of the community, which now has several houses. They also think," his eyes twinkled mischievously, "that if you were left to your own reflections and natural mildness, you would not insist on this."

"Oh, they do, do they? Well, you may tell them that the purpose of a coadjutor is to help me to make decisions." Bishop Flaget paced the floor, his hands behind his back. Father Badin watched him in silence. The interview appeared to be at an end, but he would visit until he was dismissed. At last the Bishop stopped pacing. "And what about the habit? Want to keep that too, I suppose?"

"Naturally. They're women, and being so, do not care to be dictated to on dress. We men are wise to stay out of that question. At least," he corrected himself hastily, "so long as the Sisters' dress is not contrary to modesty. Besides, Bishop, what difference does it make? White or black cap? I personally think their uniform is very nice and proper for Sisters of Charity. Why not let it alone?"

"We'll see."

And that was the only encouragement Father Badin could give Mother Catherine when he saw her again. She was deeply grateful; but when she spoke, her voice lacked its usual vibrancy. "Thank you, Father, for all you have done for us. I appreciate your support even though the Bishop promises nothing."

Father Badin's keen grey eyes noted the deep lines on her face and the lack of hope in her eyes. "I think," he said kindly, "that if you follow up my talk with a letter signed by all the members of the community, something may come of it. Remember Christ told us to importune Him, and the Bishop is His representative. It can't hurt, anyway."

That very evening Mother sat at her desk again. She would start all over. She would review the whole situation and give in detail the reasons for her conviction that nothing should be changed. She took the quill, made a tiny cross on the white paper, said a prayer to the Holy Spirit, and began:

1841

Rt. Rev. B. J. Flaget,
Right Rev. Father:

Since the reception of your letter containing your late orders relative to the changes you required in our Community, we have spent much time in meditation and prayer to God for His light and grace; we have repeatedly offered up novenas, supplicating that His Holy Will be done in regard to our dear Community. And now, most beloved and venerable Father, it is with sentiments of the deepest respect and true filial regard, together with a profound regret, that we have come to the conclusion to lay before you, our Bishop and Father, our humble and earnest entreaty that we be allowed to continue unchanged in the manner in which we have been established in your diocese by your zealous co-laborer, our revered Father and Founder in Kentucky.

We have entered the house of Nazareth and embraced with our whole hearts the practices, Rules, and Constitutions given to us by him, being assured that they were dictated by the Blessed Vincent de Paul, solemnly authorized and approved by yourself, and sanctioned at the court of Rome, and we were always left under the firm conviction that they were sacred and never to be liable to any change.

Father David (whom you have so frequently and so warmly recommended to our confidence and reverence, as being one of the greatest divines and the holiest of clergymen) has on numerous occasions expressed it to us as his decided opinion that it was much better for both our happiness and spiritual good that we should exist always as he and you thought proper to institute us, a separate and distinct body, and that he felt most grateful to God for so directing and ordaining it. And surely religion in Kentucky can be more extensively and effectually served by us as we now exist.

And here we may be permitted to express our humble thanks to Divine Providence, to you and to our revered Founder's protection and instruction, that Nazareth, as you acknowledge with parental joy, has never given any scandal in your diocese but has constantly labored to do good, the success of which efforts facts attest.

Permit us, too, dear Father, to recall to your paternal recollection, those primitive days of our poor afflicted Community when, with the simple-heartedness of devoted children, we zealously and cheerfully spent the energies of our youth in the fields, at the looms, in the spinning-rooms and kitchens at St. Thomas's, rejoicing that by our humble labors in the most servile and lowest occupations we might contribute our poor mite to the support of the seminaries and churches in your diocese, while at the same time we were struggling in the commencement of our own little Community. Afterwards we labored with the same zeal for the college, seminary, and cathedral in Bardstown. And oh, Father, those were happy days, because we looked forward with delight to the rise and progress of the works of religion, believing that we ourselves were settled in the way of life to which we were convinced we were called by our common Father. We never dreamed that a change would be required of us; otherwise our zeal and energy would have been paralyzed, as they are now.

With due humility and a deep sense of the overruling care of heaven, allow us to call to your mind the numbers of respectable families added to the Church by the education and religious impressions which individuals receive at Nazareth, and every year brings with it conversions either in the school or after the young ladies have left our institutions; and you know, far better than we do, the immense weight of prejudice which has been removed by Nazareth's humble efforts, aided by the blessing of God. Add to this the baptisms and the first communions for which the children are regularly instructed and prepared each year in the Branch Houses and at Nazareth. Many scholars are also educated gratuitously each year in each one of the houses, and alms largely distributed to the neighboring poor. Of these things we do not boast, for it is only our duty; but we merely wish to give your paternal heart consoling proof that Nazareth, as it ever has been, is devoted to the interests of Charity and Religion.

And the Orphans' Asylum, which it was your most ardent wish to see established (all who do justice must acknowledge) would not exist at this time, had it not been for the untiring exertions and labors of the Sisters of Nazareth who moreover aided the good work by pecuniary means drawn from the resources of the Society.

It is true, many members have left our community; but we have every reason to believe and to know that the same occurs, and perhaps more frequently, in other communities where the vows are simple and yearly; and, as you are aware, such defections do sometimes, and not infrequently, take place in Monasteries, where vows are taken for life. We read in the discourses of St. Vincent de Paul, addressed to the first Sisters of Charity, that even during his lifetime and in the first fervor of the company, many members left, and after leaving, spoke in the most disparaging terms of the Order. During the last six years only three have gone from among us, and they returned not to the world.

We need not remind you, beloved Father, that we commenced in a new country and not even in the most Catholic settlement of the country; therefore, owing to that cause and perhaps some others, our Community is comparatively small. But we have always been taught to believe that the strength of a religious body depends not so much on its numbers as upon the fervor, zeal, and devotion of those who compose it; and especially upon the blessing of our good God, who seems to delight in effecting good by instruments few and feeble. Still we have five prosperous houses in your diocese, the members of which are happy in their state, and each house is doing a not inconsiderable portion of Charity from the resources and labors of the Sisters.

You have already had the unanimous testimony of the Sisters that the Community was never happier, more orderly, more united, or more zealous in the observance of Rules; that all are most desirous of living up to the spirit of their state. For all this, we humbly and thankfully bless God. And although our schools and houses are flourishing and favored by the Almighty with success, yet God forbid we should glory in being the instruments; but we feel—as every Christian heart would feel—an anxious wish to maintain our Society unchanged, as our revered and holy Founder and Father first established it, and as he believed and wished it would, under your paternal care, continue. We are accustomed to our manner of life, and feel thoroughly convinced that we could not find happiness in being connected with or mixed in any other community or family—and, furthermore, that we might by doing so jeopardize our eternal salvation, for which we have embraced our state of life.

Honored and dear Father, though we do most urgently implore to be allowed to continue unchanged, as we began, in the practices, rules, and constitutions as given to us by yourself and Father David; yet we beg you to be assured that it is our most earnest desire, as we know it to be your right, should disorders creep in, that you should administer your fatherly advice and correction. We always have cheerfully and gladly acknowledged you as our first Superior; but we believe that the interest of the Society and our constitutional right require an immediate ecclesiastical superior. We cordially wish and urge frequent visits from you, and that these visits should be of such length as to enable you to be intimately and personally acquainted with the general interests and business of the house, and with each individual in particular. And we candidly assure you that it is and has ever been our fixed determination to persevere in our holy vocation and to labor sedulously to advance constantly in the virtues required by our state of life.

We attach little importance to the article of dress in itself; yet we think changes so striking as that which you propose in our cap would be hazardous and calculated to arouse public observation, to elicit surmises and occasion prejudices which may be highly detrimental to Nazareth and perhaps to Religion in Kentucky. Had we worn the black cap for twenty-five years, as we have done the white one, we should feel equally reluctant to so remarkable a change as that of the color; which undoubtedly would subject the Community to animadversion and ridicule and thus might tend to diminish public respect and confidence, which St. Vincent de Paul considered as most essential to the success of the Sisters' labors.

In terminating, most reverend and cherished Father, we throw ourselves on your kind and fatherly forbearance, begging you not to consider us importunate, but to listen with a Father's heart to the humble, earnest and most respectful remonstrance of your children, who feel convinced that these changes may be the laying of the axe to the root of that tree which you and we equally believe to have been planted and watered by the hand of God. Numbers of our Sisters, whose deaths have been most edifying, have asserted such to have been their dying belief, and no one who is acquainted with the commencement and progress of Nazareth can doubt its being the work of the Most High.

In the presence of our good and merciful God, and kneeling before the sacred image of His crucified Son, we hereto affix our names, earnestly imploring you, our dear and revered Father, in the name and for the sake of Him whose place you hold in our regard to yield to our entreaties and once more to restore to your children that happiness and quiet of mind they have so long enjoyed at Nazareth, promising you, in all the sincerity of our hearts, that we shall with the grace of God, redouble our efforts to advance in the virtues of our state of life and do good in your diocese.

She signed her name carefully, and calling the Sisters together, she read them the letter. At the conclusion she raised her eyes briefly to their sober faces, laid the paper on the table, and placed the quill on the stand beside it. With the words, "Those Sisters who agree with what I have written, please sign your names under mine," she abruptly left the room and went to the chapel. Sister Teresa opened her mouth as if to speak, then thought better of it. Instead, she picked up the quill and wrote her name.

An hour later Mother Catherine came back, picked up the paper, and counted the names. Everyone had signed. Breathing a sigh of relief, she folded the letter and sealed it. Ned would take it to the White House in the morning. Now all the Sisters must pray. Pray hard.

CHAPTER TWENTY

1841-1848

As Father Badin had predicted, the storm passed. The community was allowed to retain its individuality and its ecclesiastical superior. The only vestige of the conflict was a slight alteration in the Sisters' habits: the white linen cuffs and undersleeves were replaced by black sleeves of the same material as that of the habit, a simple bow knot on the top of the cap was substituted for the double bow with loops, and the plaits of the cap were made wider and were stitched down.

Mother Catherine cheerfully complied with these alterations and no more were asked. For some months, however, she was uneasy, for Bishop Flaget's attitude toward the amalgamation with Emmitsburg seemed basically unchanged, and not until Bishop Chabrat returned to France, did he appear to be entirely satisfied.

Meanwhile Mother Catherine set out in the spring of 1841 on the visitations which she had neglected while the threat to the autonomy of the sisterhood continued. In May she was at Saint Vincent's in Union County, and it was there she received word that Bishop David had suffered a stroke, had fallen, and had dislocated his left shoulder. Although she had not completed her visit, she left immediately for Nazareth, anxious to be at his side, for she sensed that this was to be his last illness.

The Sisters from Nazareth had already gone to Bardstown to the Bishop's residence. There they watched night and day at Bishop David's bedside. At times his mind wandered, and he was back in the France of his boyhood, playing in the streets of Coueron, learning Latin and music from good Father Bohnaud, his maternal uncle. At other times he was again at old St. Thomas's, with his seminarians and his Sisters, and then over and over he would murmur, "My dear daughters—my home." When his mind was clear, he was painfully aware of his critical condition and often expressed his desire to die at Nazareth.

Tired though she was after her long journey, Mother Catherine hastened to the White House. Her eyes filled with tears as she saw the venerable white head on the pillow. But Bishop David smiled when he saw her. "You have had your trials this year, my daughter, but I knew you would come through. Have you come to take me home?"

She knelt by his bed, and he laid his hand on her head in blessing.

"Tomorrow," she whispered, scarcely able to speak, "we will come for you."

Immediately she ordered the construction of a curtained litter in Bardstown. And the next day, as she had promised, ten Negroes dressed in black-and-white uniforms came to the White House, carefully lifted the dying Bishop, and bore him to the conveyance. Two Sisters walked along beside him and crowds of townspeople, many of whom had from infancy been bound to the venerable Bishop by the strongest of spiritual ties, followed the procession.

When the cortege arrived at Nazareth, all the Sisters were waiting, Mother Catherine and Sister Teresa at the head. The curtains were pulled aside, and the Sisters knelt as the Bishop was borne along, his trembling fingers raised in blessing. Those nearest heard him murmur, "O my God, I thank Thee that I have come to die among my daughters."

From then on he was never alone. Night and day two Sisters attended him. In the forenoon of July 12, when evidences of approaching death appeared, all the classes of the school were dismissed, all activities suspended, and the Sisters gathered in prayer around their dying Father. At eleven-thirty he showed that he wanted to be raised in bed. Father Hazeltine helped him to sit up against the pillows, and Bishop Flaget lifted his feeble hand in blessing. For the last time the dim eyes traveled the circle of faces, the faces of his children.

Finally his glance came to rest on Mother and Sister Teresa, his first spiritual daughters. Turning toward them he whispered, "Have courage, fight the good fight." Then smiling, he blessed them again, his eyes on Mother Catherine. Slowly Father Hazeltine lowered him and Bishop Flaget gave the final absolution. For a moment Bishop David lay looking up at his old friend; then his hand closed convulsively on the crucifix, his lips pronounced clearly the Holy Name. A sigh, and he was gone.

Clothed in episcopal vestments, his body lay in state in the Nazareth chapel that he himself had consecrated on the feast of his patron, Saint John the Baptist, nearly seventeen years before. From all the country round his people came to get one more glimpse of their venerable father, to pray beside his remains, to touch his hands with their rosaries. The grief-stricken Sisters kept constant vigil.

On the morning of the third day Bishop Flaget and Bishop Bruté from Vincennes with a large number of the clergy sang the Office of the Dead. The Pontifical Requiem Mass followed. After the last blessing of the corpse, the funeral procession moved slowly to the Sisters' cemetery, which Bishop David had chosen for his last resting place. There, beside the Reverend George A. M. Elder, the first priest he had ordained (and who had died three years before), he was buried.

After the others had gone, Mother Catherine and Sister Teresa lingered near the new grave. They were silent, each reliving her own memories.

Finally Sister Teresa said in a whisper, "No misunderstanding will ever drive him away now. He'll be here with us always."

"Yes," Mother Catherine agreed. "He understands everything now. He knows that he was always our father and will be forever." She led Sister Teresa a few paces to the right. "When I die, Teresa, I want to be laid here." She marked a spot at the foot of his grave.

"Then you'd better tell someone else," Sister Teresa said gruffly to hide her feelings, "for I doubt that I'll be around."

"No, Teresa, it will be your job to see that I get my wish. Come," Mother said, supporting her gently, "we must get back. They'll be coming for us if we don't."

Together they went through the iron gate, closing it behind them. But in the days that followed, it was not uncommon to see the bent figure of Sister Teresa or the erect form of Mother Catherine standing by the new grave.

Not long after Bishop David's death Mother Catherine received a letter from Bishop Miles of Nashville, Tennessee, asking for the services of her Sisters. Having reassured herself that they would be well taken care of, she sent Sisters Serena, Euphrasia, Scholastica, Vincentia, Theodore, and Clementia to open a school in that city. Accompanied by the Reverend Joseph Hazeltine and the Reverend J. M. Lancaster of Saint Joseph's College, the pioneers arrived in Nashville on the Feast of Our Lady of Sorrows, September 15, 1842.

For a year they lived in a house formerly owned by Judge Grundy, but since this building was not particularly suited to their needs, they moved, in the September of 1843, to a larger one on the brow of Campbell Hill, the former home of Captain John Williams. There they opened a boarding and day school under the title of Saint Mary's. Modeled after Nazareth Academy, this institution became so prosperous that Sister Xavier, the second superior of the new mission, had to ask for more Sisters.

With this project flourishing, a new path opened up. The old church, recently replaced by the new cathedral, was remodeled for a hospital and offered to the Sisters. Sister Xavier, who had been closely associated with St.

Joseph's in Louisville and who had witnessed its success, accepted the charge, and another group of Sisters was sent from Nazareth. Saint John's Hospital became a blessing for the undeveloped river port, and despite the fact that the Sisters struggled along in abject poverty themselves, they were often able to relieve the economic needs as well as the pain and suffering of those who came to them for help. The hospital too enabled them to take in orphans whom they trained in the care of the sick.

There was no doubt that the mission at Nashville was growing, but Mother Catherine wanted to see with her own eyes the conditions under which her Sisters labored. After all, it was a well-known fact that the Sisters, in their zeal and love for the poor, often "forgot" to mention that they did not have sufficient food. Mother would see for herself.

The visitation filled her with joy. Her Sisters were very poor, true, but no poorer than Nazareth had once been, and there were bright prospects for the future. The only disappointment in her trip was her visit with Bishop Miles, who was sick at the time. Consequently, her conversation with him was not too satisfactory.

Several weeks after her return Sister Columba found her frowning over a letter. "It's from Bishop Miles," Mother said in answer to the other's questioning glance. "He wants us to pay for the house on Campbell Hill."

"Can we?"

"I doubt it. We haven't much money right now. Last year we had great losses in the South, and even here in Kentucky it's hard to collect tuition."

Mother dropped the letter on the table as if it were suddenly too heavy to hold. "And I did hope that soon we could begin a new convent here. Heaven knows we need it! Several of the Sisters are still sleeping in the upper story of the wash house and some in the old cabins." She rose and paced the floor. "And they're so uncomplaining about it, always hoping that some day soon we can have a decent place to live. And now this—." She pointed to the letter still lying on the table.

"Well, Mother, are we going to buy the building in Nashville?"

"There seems to be nothing else to do. The Sisters there must have a place to live." She stopped pacing and sat down. "I'm sorry I allowed them to go at all. It's so far!"

"Perhaps there'll be a railroad there soon."

"A railroad?"

"Why, yes, Mother. Mary Grant was telling me the other day all about locomotives. Lately her father has bought an interest in a company which makes them. It seems that ten years ago when he was in New York, he had a ride in a car pulled by the *Tom Thumb* and—"

"The *Tom Thumb*?"

"That was the name of the locomotive."

"Oh! And what happened?"

"Well, it outran a horse! And her father was so impressed that he became one of the owners of the company. Today she tells me locomotives can go as fast as twenty miles an hour. And just this year her father's concern finished a line between Boston and Albany."

Mother Catherine laughed. "But, Sister, Boston to Albany won't help us any."

Sister Columba flushed. "I know, Mother, but—"

"Oh, I know what you mean. Railroads will come to the South! And when they do," she promised gayly, "you'll get one of the first rides."

"In that case I may get a ride very soon," Sister Columba teased, "because Mary told me yesterday that there is to be a short line between Lexington and Frankfort and that the company is also planning to extend the rails to Louisville in the near future."

Mother Catherine looked disappointed. "I thought you were going to say to Nashville. That would have been good news." Her eyes strayed back to the paper. "Well, I'd better find Father Hazeltine and talk to him about buying the house in Nashville."

Like Mother Catherine Father Hazeltine saw no other way than to pay for the Campbell House; so in 1843 the

Community reluctantly became the owner of the Nashville property.

That next summer Mother Catherine's third term expired, and again Mother Frances was elected to fill her place. In the few weeks that remained to her at Nazareth, Mother went often to visit Sister Teresa. More and more she felt that Teresa's fervor was the cornerstone of the order, for in the beginning when even Father David had almost despaired of being able to surmount the difficulties in the way of establishing the society, wasn't it Teresa's trust in Divine Providence that had renewed his own confidence? And in the ensuing years hadn't it been Teresa's prayers which had sustained all of them? True, she had little of what this world calls knowledge, but she was blessed with such unusual spiritual wisdom that every word of hers seemed inspired by God Himself. In addition, her humility was so great that she never wished for any knowledge except that of the cross.

How often when Mother was mistress of novices she had sent one of her charges to help Sister Teresa and in the process to learn her way of prayer! Once a novice, leaving the kitchen for adoration, asked Sister Teresa, who had to remain, "Don't you find it hard, Sister, to do these things which make you miss so many spiritual exercises?"

Sister Teresa looked at her in surprise. "No, my child," she replied artlessly, "I never really miss any exercises at all. Whenever I can go with the community, it's a joy and I'm at my place. When I can't go, I do the best I can where I am. Father David used to tell us that God would make up for our spiritual excercises if we left them only for love of Him. For, he used to say, then our work becomes a prayer and we really miss nothing. In fact, we might gain more merit. And I can tell you from experience that what he said is true. God rewards us magnificently."

She smiled and then continued thoughtfully. "Why, I don't believe I ever made a better meditation or a more fervent preparation or thanksgiving for Communion than when standing by the fire in the old kitchen. I never could get anything out of books; but when I was by the blazing fire, it was easy to think of the burning flames of hell and purgatory and the wickedness of sin that sends people there. And then I had so much to thank God for! Just to think that a poor miserable creature like this old Teresa was allowed to live in His house, receive Him so often, and serve Him all day long! Besides, He was blessing our little community visibly. We'd been so poor that many a time I didn't know what I could get to put in the kettle, but something always came. These days you young Sisters can scarcely imagine how it used to be. Never forget to be grateful to God for all this! Run along now, child, and thank Him."

Words like these revealed the secret of Sister Teresa's sanctity. Whatever she did, her soul was ever united with the will of God. Her work became an unbroken prayer, making the works He expected of her hands appear light, for the cross is never a burden to a loving heart. The exact observance of the rule apparently cost her no effort. Her manner of keeping silence was particularly striking. Although perfectly recollected and scarcely ever speaking an unnecessary word, she greeted everyone she met with a kind smile which came like a ray of sunshine into many a discouraged heart.

She was particularly fond of the young Sisters, in whose company she was generally found during recreation. They in turn sought her friendship, for there was nothing austere in her words and ways. Always cheerful and prompt to see what good there was in everyone, she readily sympathized with others in their trials, always ending with the words: "My child, be obedient and love God with all your heart, and everything will go right with you. Work for God alone."

It was good, Mother Catherine mused, to know that the society had a Sister Teresa. Good too that this valiant woman was always at Nazareth praying for her beloved community.

Mother smiled. Many things were good! In her own

case it was good to be free—to feel the burden of office slip away, good to go back to Louisville to the orphans she loved. But would she go back? It really made no difference. She was resigned to go wherever she was sent, to do whatever she was told.

Picking up her pen, she continued her letter to Sister Elizabeth Suttle: "Don't write to me any more until you hear where I am stationed, for at this time I am but a loose piece of furniture and I am truly glad to be so. I never felt so relieved in all my life. When—"

A timid knock interrupted her. Putting her pen carefully on the wiper, she went to the door. Tiny Sister Cleophas stood there visibly excited, but trying her best to appear unconcerned. "Mother Catherine, Mother Frances wants to see you."

Mother smiled at her. "Thank you, Sister, I'll come immediately."

Quickly returning to the table, she slipped the letter between the pages of a book. This must be my obedience, she thought. If so, I'll be able to tell Sister Elizabeth today where I'm going."

She was right. It *was* her assignment. Knowing well where Mother's heart lay, Mother Frances was sending her back to Louisville to her orphans and her sick.

* * * * *

Back at the orphanage, time passed quickly. The wheel of the seasons turned rapidly: red and gold leaves succeeding green, snow and ice following soft rains, the trill of the robin and song of the cardinal supplanting the honk of the wild geese in flight. Four years passed.

It was the spring of '48. From far-off California came the story of the discovery of gold, and from the North, South, and East, men went in never-ending streams to the golden West. And hard and fast upon the heels of this wonderful news came the ominous tidings of the Asiatic cholera. The plague passed through Louisville in July, and once more Mother and her Sisters went to the assistance of the stricken. Soon, however, it moved south, striking Nashville with the fury of a hurricane, killing by the hundreds. Many a young man passing through this river town en route to the Land of Gold met death and set out for eternity instead.

The Sisters closed Saint Mary's and nursed the sick in their homes or took them to Saint John's Hospital. Sister Dorothy Villeneuve, who had been in the little band that had so successfully nursed cholera patients with Mother Catherine in Louisville years before, took charge, teaching the others from her experience.

Most of the wealthy fled the city, leaving the poor to grapple with the disease as best they could. There was nothing for these unfortunate people to do, as all business was disrupted and all stores closed; so from their miserable hovels they looked out with hopeless eyes or drowned their fears with liquor and staggered through the narrow streets.

The Sisters nursed the sick and took in the orphans. They became a common sight hastening along the dirty thoroughfares, their capes pulled up over their faces to keep from choking on the acrid fumes from the soft coal which burned day and night in the deserted streets. These fumes were supposed to kill the germs of cholera, but Sister Xavier and her Sisters saw no decrease in the number of rude coffins stacked five and six deep in the mean doorways, nor in the number of carts employed in conveying them to the cemeteries.

But in time the plague, like all other things, passed away, leaving on Nashville's main streets blackened buildings and in the cemeteries row after row of brown mounds. The rich returned to the city, and the Sisters returned to the classroom.

In Louisville Mother Catherine rejoiced to hear that the cholera had departed and that her Sisters were safe and well.

CHAPTER TWENTY-ONE

1848-1850

At her desk in the sunny classroom at St. Catherine's, Lexington, Sister Ann was busily correcting papers. She glanced now and then at the industrious pink-cheeked child who, with head cocked on one side and tongue caught between her teeth, was laboriously writing her name over and over on a red-framed slate.

It's a wonder she doesn't bite that tongue off, Sister thought as she watched her. Poor child, she makes everything so hard for herself.

Jane had entered St. Catherine's a month after her father had marched off to the Mexican War in January, 1846. Soon he would be home, for after two years of bitter fighting, Mexico had ceded its provinces of New Mexico and Upper California to the United States in the Treaty of Guadalupe-Hidalgo, which had ended the war.

But the penmanship war, which had been declared the very first time that Sister Ann had corrected one of Jane's papers, dragged on. Through it all Jane remained indifferent, and so did her writing. Sister, however, was determined that before a truce was called, the child would at least write legibly, and tried scheme after scheme. Nothing worked. Finally in desperation she decided to make Jane practice her penmanship every Saturday morning while the other girls went on a hike in the woods. This strategy seemed to be succeeding, Sister Ann congratulated herself as she watched the struggle.

Looking up, Jane saw Sister's eyes upon her and grinned. "I'm most finished, S'ter! Just one more." She held up a pudgy finger for emphasis. Even Sister Ann, who was a stickler for discipline, could not resist smiling in return.

Through the open window came the tantalizing odor of apple blossoms. Jane wrinkled her button nose appreciatively then reluctantly went back to her writing. For a minute or two there was no sound except the faint squeak of the slate pencil and the rustle of Sister Ann's papers.

Finally Jane rose quietly, looking at her work with an I-guess-that-will-do expression, and came to the desk. She waited politely until Sister Ann had finished marking the last paper, then made her best curtsy and presented the slate and her neat copybook for inspection.

"Is that better, S'ter?" she inquired anxiously as Sister turned the pages.

"Sister!" Sister Ann corrected.

"Sister." Jane imitated Sister Ann exactly.

"Much better."

Jane wasn't quite sure whether Sister Ann meant the word or the writing but she was a natural optimist. She drew in her breath with relief. "Please, may I go now, Sister?" she begged, pronouncing the last word with great care.

"Yes, you may, but remember you must practice some more next Saturday."

Even that doleful prospect was not enough to dampen Jane's joy as she scampered away with a grateful, "Thank you, S'ter."

It was too late to call her back. Sister Ann made a helpless little gesture, then smiled. Jane was Jane and one might as well accept that fact.

She too prepared to leave. There was so much other work to be done that the arithmetic tests would have to wait until later. Rising, she walked to the door, opening it just in time to meet her incorrigible pupil with a stack of mail.

She was about to call the child's attention to her last mispronunciation when Jane blurted out, "Sister Louise asked me to bring this to you, S'ter." Then catching the look in Sister Ann's eye, "I mean, *Sister*," she amended hastily. Swallowing hard she stammered, "S-She was looking for you, and I told her that you were in the classroom." With that she quickly placed the bundle on the desk and disappeared before Sister Ann could decide whether or not to keep her.

Somewhat relieved that her problem had solved itself, Sister Ann sat down again to sort the pile carefully. Most of the envelopes contained bills, she noted anxiously as she flipped them over, but on the very bottom there was a letter from her sister, Mother Catherine.

She read it avidly not pausing until she came to the postscript. Her smile broadened. "I wish I could give you 'Gumalastic' legs or some such kind in which you could step to Louisville, for I assure you, my dear Sister, I miss you. Catherine." She put the letter down, a curious thickness in her throat.

Catherine had been back at the orphanage in Louisville for four years while she had been in Lexington for five. In that time they had met but once. Still, distance could not really separate them, for they had too much in common for miles to matter. Ann was happy that her sister was with the orphans again. Being with them was to her true joy! Her whole letter was filled with interesting details about the newcomers and with reports of the children for whom she had found homes. There were 104 at St. Vincent's and they ranged from fourteen months to fifteen years. How devoted Catherine was to each one of them! Ann could feel the love seeping out between the lines of the letter. How well she understood, for she had been at the orphanage herself for a year!

She sighed. It was so long since she had seen Catherine! Perhaps they would meet next summer at Nazareth and make the retreat together. She hoped so anyway. Carefully folding the letter, she put it back into the envelope.

When time permitted, she would read it again and answer it, but right now she must get back to work.

She started briskly toward the front door, then stopped. Better go the girls' recreation room first to see if Matilda was cleaning it. That girl, she thought irritably, would test the patience of Job. Her work—when done—was slovenly, and unless you kept your eyes on her constantly, she didn't do anything. It was exasperating at times, but then what could you expect? Matilda had not been long enough at St. Catherine's to get over the ill-treatment she had received from her former master.

Always at this point in her thoughts, Sister Ann relived the horrible scene which had engraved itself forever on her memory. Again she heard the swish of the rawhide and saw Matilda cowering before the brawny overseer who brought the lash down hard across her thin shoulders. Horrified at the sight, Sister Ann had run over and, without thinking, had seized the whip hand. The overseer had not looked too pleased, but he stopped and told Matilda to go back to her cabin. She slunk away with a baleful look at him.

Then the man turned to Sister Ann. "I know you think I'm a brute, Sister, but you don't know that one. She's no good. Lazy, mean, ornery! She'll come to no good end."

"No, not if you keep that up!" Sister Ann's eyes flashed with indignation. "She'll come to an end all right, but not a good one."

Somewhat abashed, the overseer flicked the side of his shoe with the whip. "We've had her ever since she was a child. Even then she was bad—kick, bite, and sulk. The whip's the only thing she understands."

Sister Ann's voice was cold with disapproval. "You should be ashamed to treat her that way, no matter what she does."

"Don't blame him, Sister," interrupted Mr. Dunnest, the owner of the farm, who had arrived on the scene unnoticed by either of them. "That one would do anything. Just when you think you have her conquered, she breaks out in a new place."

"I'm surprised at you, Mr. Dunnest."

"I tell you what," he laughed. "I'll give her to you, Sister, and see what you can do with her."

And so Matilda had come to live at St. Catherine's. Sister Ann soon found out that what the overseer had said about her was true, but with great patience she had worked with the girl, and after a year there seemed to be a slight change of attitude. Yes, Matilda really *was* better. She still found correction hard of course but recently there had been an improvement in that too.

In a somewhat happier frame of mind Sister Ann walked to the recreation room. At the door she halted. At the far end Matilda was lackadaisically running a dry mop over the floor and pushing the dirt into the farthest corner. Sister prayed for patience. Would the girl *never* learn to do things right?

Stepping into the room, she called, "Matilda, didn't I tell you to sweep first? You can never get a room clean merely by running a mop over it."

Matilda stopped and looked at Sister insolently but made no reply.

She's learned that much at least, Sister Ann commented to herself. Aloud she said firmly, "Please, do as I say and *sweep* the floor this time."

"Yas, Sistah," Matilda said meekly enough, but she dropped the mop with a bang before going to the cleaning press to get a broom.

Sister Ann felt like making her come back and pick up the mop, but she pushed back her anger and said kindly, "Matilda, you musn't act like that. You know you weren't doing as you were told! And you know too that I'm only trying to help you. Unless you do your work well, you'll be scolded, and no one enjoys that."

Matilda said nothing; her face was a blank. Gently Sister Ann patted her on the shoulder. "I have to go to the laundry now, but I'll be back later. I'm sure the floor will be clean then."

Matilda did not look up. At the door Sister Ann turned. The colored girl was sweeping sullenly but vigorously. Even after Sister Ann left, Matilda kept on, her anger lending strength first to the broom, then to the mop.

When she had finished, the floor was perfectly clean. She looked at it with satisfaction. "Wal, dat's did." She sat down, the mop at her feet. "Matilda, you musn't ak lak dat," she mimicked, savagely kicking the broom. "Wal, ah 'specks ah'll ak lak ah wan's ter," she grumbled.

Suddenly a sly look came into her eyes and her face brightened. "Dat's jus' hit!" she snickered, hugging herself with delight. "Her won' be a-tellin' me ter do eny mo' flo's ober agin. Ah'll fix her!" Quickly picking up the cleaning utensils, she skipped across the room and put them away. After a last look at the place to see that it was in order, she hurried to the kitchen.

When she returned, she was carrying a tray with a large glass of buttermilk and a piece of freshly baked bread on it. Setting it down carefully, she started to dust. Sister Ann would be back soon. She grinned sardonically.

Sure enough, in a short time she heard the jingle of Sister's rosary, but she didn't look up until she heard Sister Ann's voice. "The floor looks fine now, Matilda."

"Tank yo', Sistah," she replied smiling broadly. "Ah tried mah bes' dis time. An' sides," she continued pointing to the tray, "Ah done wen' ter de kitchen an' fetched yo' a drink an' som' bread. Yo' mus' be powerful hongry."

Picking up the tray, she brought it to Sister Ann, who was thinking happily to herself that Matilda was really changing. Gratefully she took the buttermilk. While pretending to go on with her dusting, Matilda watched her warily out of the corner of her eye. After one sip, Sister Ann set the glass down. The buttermilk tasted peculiar.

"Dun't yo' lak hit?" Matilda pouted.

"Why of course, Matilda, and it was most thoughtful of you to fix it for me." Sister Ann smiled. Fearing to seem unappreciative, she hastily took a bite of the bread to drown the taste. Then by alternating the bread with the buttermilk she finally managed to drink it all.

Face wreathed in smiles, Matilda took the empty glass. "Ah'll take hit ter de kitchen," she said with a curiously satisfied expression.

Thanking her again, Sister Ann returned to the community room. "What do you think?" she greeted Sister Louise, who was sitting at the table knitting a stocking. "Matilda's really changing."

"Not that I've noticed," said the other grimly. "She is just as impudent and lazy as ever."

"I thought that too," agreed Sister Ann mildly, "but today I corrected her, and she took it without a word. Not only that, but she had some bread and buttermilk ready for me when I came back to see if she had redone the cleaning."

Sister Louise shrugged. "That certainly doesn't sound like her, but I'm glad she's improving. It'll make things a little easier around here."

Taking out her sewing, Sister Ann seated herself at the table opposite the young Sister, who immediately began telling her Superior about an experience she had had that day on a visit to the sick. Halfway through the recital, Sister Ann folded her work and rested her head in her hands. Sister Louise, who had been intent on her purling, looked up. Startled by her companion's sudden paleness, she went to her side and bent over solicitously.

"What's the matter, Sister?"

"I don't know, but I have a terrible pain here." Sister Ann put her hand over her heart. "And everything's getting blurred."

"Don't move." Sister Louise's voice was vibrant with concern and sympathy. "I'll get Sister Genevieve. She always knows what to do."

When she returned with her, she found Sister Ann doubled up with pain. The two Sisters managed to get her to bed by supporting her between them.

"Go to the kitchen and get some hot water, quick!" Sister Genevieve ordered.

Panicky now, Sister Louise hurried on the errand and

was returning with the water when she met Matilda in the hall.

"Is Sistah Ann sick?" the girl asked, rolling her large black eyes.

"Yes, she is," Sister Louise replied automatically, hardly hearing the question in her haste to return to the room.

It wasn't until her back was turned that she heard the chuckle. For a moment she thought she was mistaken. Then the idea came to her. Why would Matilda ask if Sister Ann was sick? Her eyes widened as she remembered that just before Sister Ann was stricken, she had said that Matilda had given her some buttermilk. She whirled around. Her heart contracted when she saw the broad grin on Matilda's face.

Horrified, she turned and hastened into the room. She put the water on the table and, before Sister Genevieve could say anything, ran out again and down the hall to where Matilda was standing.

Grasping the startled girl firmly by the shoulders, she demanded, "What did you put into that buttermilk, Matilda? Tell me!"

Matilda hung her head but said nothing.

Sister Louise grew more insistant. Still no answer. Finally putting her hand under the girl's chin, she forced her to meet her gaze.

"Tell me!" she ordered again between clenched teeth.

A wild defiant look came into the other's eyes. "Ah gibbed her rat pisen. So dere!"

Sister Louise's hand dropped. Impulsively she pushed the girl aside and ran back into the room Sister Ann was groaning now with pain.

Sister Louise pulled Sister Genevieve outside the room and told her in a whisper what the girl had said. Sister's eyes grew dark with fright.

"There's nothing we can do then except to call the priest and the doctor," she said tonelessly. Then briskly she added, "Hurry and get them. Perhaps it's not too late."

As Sister Louise hurried down the hall, Sister Genevieve

went back into the room and knelt beside the bed. She took Sister's clenched hands in hers. "Sister Ann, Matilda put poison in that buttermilk. We've sent for the priest and the doctor."

There was no response and Sister Genevieve wondered if she had been heard. She repeated the words a little louder. This time Sister Ann struggled to a sitting position and tried to say something, but her voice was too weak for the words to be understood. Tenderly Sister Genevieve supported her with her arm and put her ear close to the white lips.

"That's why the buttermilk—tasted—so—so—funny," Sister Ann gasped. "You mustn't tell anyone—no harm must come to Matilda—she didn't realize what—she—was —doing—" Her voice trailed off.

There was a knock on the door. Quietly the priest entered, carrying his purple stole. He motioned the Sisters outside. "I'll come for you later," he whispered. Then he bent over Sister Ann to hear her last confession.

In the dark corridor the Sisters waited in strained silence until the priest opened the door. Reentering the room, they knelt around the bed while he administered the Last Sacraments. The doctor came during the ceremony, but only shook his head as he looked at the pallid face on the pillow. Sadly the Sisters answered the prayers for the dying.

At the end of the litany Sister Ann again struggled to sit up. "Matilda," she moaned in a hoarse whisper. "Don't hurt her—tell Catherine to be good to her—I forgive her —God forgive—me." Her head slumped on her breast.

It was then that they heard the sound of wild weeping. Unnoticed by anyone, Matilda had come into the room and had heard the whispered request. For the first time in her eighteen years her heart was touched. The love of Sister Ann had finally accomplished what the lash had left undone. That same day a letter telling of Sister Ann's death was dispatched to Mother Catherine by special messenger, and by special messenger came the reply, "Sister Ann was right. Matilda must be shielded at all costs.

If you decide not to keep her, send her to me. I will be good to her, for she gave Ann the chance to prove herself a true Christian. I am blessed to have a saint for a sister."

During those sad months after Sister Ann's death, work and prayer helped to fill the void in Mother's heart. Promises of Masses and prayers for her sister poured in from all sides. At St. Vincent's Orphanage, where for a short time Sister Ann had been superior, Bishop Kenrick offered the Holy Sacrifice for the repose of her soul, and in other places several priests said Masses for the same intention. All this was balm to Mother's heart.

Moreover, there was no time for personal grief. The sorrows and the needs of others called to her. Despite the fact that a new addition had been built on the orphanage-infirmary, she still had to turn away orphans and patients. This fact warned her that the time for separate institutions was fast approaching and that she must be ready when it came.

Change was the order of the day. Mother Catherine could see it all around her. Why, one would hardly recognize Louisville as the same city she had come to in 1831. It had spread out on every side.

By 1837 the greatly enlarged city had not only weathered the nationwide panic which followed a period of unparalleled speculation and inflation but had demonstrated its progressiveness by illuminating its principal streets with gas, the fifth city in the United States to have such lights. In the same year came the first horse race. "Wagner" defeated "Grey Eagle" in a four-mile race for a purse of $14,000, thus initiating the great sport for which Churchill Downs has since become world famous.

The next year the main part of the city was almost totally destroyed by a fire which originated in the John Hawkins Chair Factory on Third Street between Main and Market Streets and which gutted thirty buildings at a loss of $300,000.

Transportation too had improved with the completion of the canal at Portland and with the construction of the Lexington and Ohio Railroad. Delighted with this progress, the people had enthusiastically proposed the Louisville and Frankfort Line, and by mid-century the Louisville and Nashville Road was completed.

Louisville was still a mecca for the famous. In June, 1835, Jefferson Davis, later President of the Confederacy, came to this city to marry Sarah Knot Taylor, daughter of Zachary Taylor and also a Nazareth graduate. Two years later Daniel Webster visited the city and was entertained at a barbecue attended by nearly four hundred people.

In 1842, Charles Dickens stayed at the Galt House, which he declared as fine a hotel as any in London or Paris. While in the city he met Jim Porter, the Kentucky giant—seven feet, eight inches in height—and it took him but an instant to immortalize him as a "lighthouse among lampposts." The great author was at first much pleased with everything he saw in Louisville, and had he not decided to leave the city by steamer instead of by post road, he probably would have remained pleased. Unfortunately, however, in order to reach his boat, he was forced to travel through many streets which, in his *American Notes,* he described at length as "playgrounds for pigs." Although the selection was humorous, Louisvillians resented it because they knew that their city had many streets that would have been truly worthy of Dickens's pen.

Market Street was one. It was well-paved and it lived up to its name by providing at least six open-air marts where Mother Catherine and her Sisters went every day to buy potatoes for twenty-five cents a bushel, peas for twenty cents a peck, choice beef for from three to eight cents a pound and pork for five, turkeys for fifty cents each, ducks for fifteen, and a dozen chickens for fifty cents, eggs for four cents a dozen and butter for fifteen cents a pound.

As the city continued to grow, Main Street became the center of the wholesale business; Jefferson, the center of the retail. The city south of this area was very beautiful. Its avenues were lined with shade trees and with brick houses surrounded by well-kept lawns. Prather Street, renamed Broadway, was the most fashionable thoroughfare in the city. It measured a hundred and twenty feet in width. On either side were fine sidewalks, twenty-five feet across. Already many wealthy citizens had built expensive homes on this street and others were buying land.

Keeping pace with this expansion was the Church. The Catholic population of the city had tripled, and Bishop Flaget was not slow in recognizing the fact that Louisville would be a better center than Bardstown. Therefore in 1841 he transferred the seat of the diocese to that city. With his coadjutor, Bishop Chabrat, he made his home on Fifth Street near St. Louis Church. Five years later he was left alone when Bishop Chabrat, who was gradually losing his sight, resigned the bishopric and returned to his native France. Two years later, on September 10, 1848, Bishop Flaget, assisted by Bishop Kenrick of Philadelphia and Bishop Miles of Nashville, consecrated his third coadjutor, Bishop Martin John Spalding, a distant cousin of Mother Catherine. Exhausted by the ceremony, the eighty-five-year-old Bishop Flaget exclaimed like Simeon, "Now dost Thou dismiss thy servant, O Lord, in peace." From that time on he no longer concerned himself with diocesan affairs except to pray for that portion of the vineyard in which he had labored so long. For hours with rosary in hand he would sit looking toward the sanctuary of the church preparing himself to meet his Master.

Bishop Spalding immediately drew up plans for a cathedral, and in one year's time he was ready to begin to build. On August 15, 1849, the cornerstone of the Cathedral of the Assumption was laid. At that time Pius IX was Pope; Zachary Taylor, hero of the Mexican War, was President of the United States; and Benedict Joseph Flaget was still Bishop of Louisville.

Mother Catherine and several of her Sisters were present for the six-hour ceremony, but Bishop Flaget's doctor advised him not to attend. Before the last blessing, however, Bishop Spalding paused and looked up to the porch of the Bishop's residence which overlooked the scene. Following his gaze, Mother Catherine saw the bent figure of the aged Bishop, the sun making a halo over his white head. Slowly he raised his hand and she knew he was blessing not only the new building but the entire diocese of which he was the first shepherd.

Three years later, on the Feast of the Holy Rosary, the cathedral was solemnly consecrated by the Reverend John B. Purcell, Archbishop of Cincinnati. How Bishop Flaget would have rejoiced at the number of bishops and priests present on this occasion! How graciously he would have received Dom Eutropius Proust, the first Trappist abbot in America, who four years before had come from the Abbey of Melleray in France with forty monks and had made a foundation at Gethsemani, about sixteen miles from Nazareth! And how proudly he would have listened to the sermon preached by Bishop John McCloskey, later Cardinal!

But it was not to be! For years the saintly Bishop had been failing, and at noon on the eleventh of February, 1850, Bishop Spalding, accompanied by all the clergy of the city, eleven in number, brought him Holy Viaticum. Fully conscious, he received the Last Sacraments with a fervor and a concentrated devotion which deeply affected all present. After speaking a few words expressive of his ardent attachment to the clergy, religious, and people of his diocese, he gave his last solemn episcopal benediction. At five-thirty in the evening he died.

Mother Catherine and her Sisters were among the hundreds who passed by the Bishop's coffin which lay in state in the Church of St. Louis. The first night the Germans of the city formed a bodyguard and spent the whole night in prayer; the second, the Irish. On the day before the burial the Office of the Dead was chanted by all the clergy of the city led by the Right Reverend Bishop Purcell of Cincinnati. Father Badin, as proto-priest, performed the last absolution and took the first place in the funeral procession. Behind him came the Bishops of Cincinnati and of Louisville.

Although it was raining, thousands walked behind the casket. The clergy followed immediately after the remains, which were borne by members of different parishes. Then came Mother Catherine and her Sisters, leading the children from St. Vincent's and from Presentation. After them came two bands, one from St. Aloysius, the Jesuit school for boys, and the other from the German Benevolent Society.

When the cortege arrived at the gate of the Convent of the Good Shepherd, only the Sisters and the clergy entered the enclosure to witness the ceremony at the grave. The body was to rest there only for a time. As soon as the Cathedral of the Assumption would be completed, the casket would be removed and reinterred in a crypt under the main altar of the church, and a plaque perpetuating the memory of Bishop Flaget, one of the most remarkable apostles of the Church in the United States, would be erected in the sanctuary.

As Mother Catherine watched the coffin being lowered into the ground, her heart was heavy with the loss of the second Father of the Nazareth Community. But as she thought of the joy which would be Bishop David's at the the arrival of his life-long friend in heaven, her heart lifted. An eternity, she knew, would not be too long for the renewal of that sacred friendship.

CHAPTER TWENTY-TWO

1850-1854

Years do not change in length, but to Mother Catherine it seemed that they were growing ever shorter, and ever more rapidly the leaves were falling from her tree of life.

It was not easy then in the summer of 1850 to be called away from her orphans to govern the growing community for the fourth time. But there was no choice. She had hoped that her last difficult years at Nazareth would be the end. So much could happen to her orphans while she was away from them. And could she be sure that she would come back after her term of office? Only God knew.

There were tears as she departed from Jefferson Street and smiles as she appeared at Nazareth. Sister Teresa was there to greet her, leaning heavily on a cane, her face wrinkled in smiles, her eyes shining with joy. This was how it should be—Mother Catherine at Nazareth, Mother Catherine at the helm. Of course Mother Frances was wonder. Just last year she had opened a new academy in Owensboro, and the Council had named it St. Frances in her honor. Yes, indeed, Mother Frances was wonderful, but not even she could take the place of Mother Catherine, who was like the spring, Kentucky spring, throbbing and bursting with life, giving growth and vigor to everything around it. With her as leader again, the community would surge forward attempting the difficult and accomplishing the impossible. And while the others worked, she, Teresa, must pray—pray that God would give the increase.

As for Mother Catherine, her sacrifice in leaving one orphanage in Louisville was to be rewarded almost immediately by the foundation of another. After the Reverend Francis Chambige had revivified the old seminary at St. Thomas's (a task which had been assigned him by Bishop Spalding), this zealous priest decided to add a home for boys. Knowing that Mother Catherine had been for years in charge of the orphanage in Louisville and that she was extraordinarily interested in this field, he did not hesitate to appeal to her for help.

Immediately after reading his letter, Mother Catherine sent for Sister Victoria Buckmann and Sister Bernardine O'Brien. They knew as soon as they saw her that she had something delightful in store for them, for her eyes were bright with an excitement which seemed magically to restore her to youth. In those few moments while she waited for them, she had relived the eight years spent in the place of her girlhood consecration.

"Get your things," she greeted them gayly when they appeared at her door, "and come with me to Old St. Thomas's. Father Chambige has written to ask us to take over an orphanage which he hopes to establish there, and I want to accept in person."

They didn't cut through the fields as they did the first time they had come to the Lapsley place. Instead they rode behind the aged Ned in Nazareth's own brougham. As they rumbled along, Mother looked out the window and with avid eyes drank in the old scenes. As they approached St. Thomas's, she noticed with joy that Father Chambige had done wonders in restoring the old seminary. It had been a long time since it had been occupied, but one would never guess that by looking at it now.

She could hardly wait for the carriage to stop. Stepping down quickly, she beckoned to the Sisters to follow her down the familiar shady path which led to Old Nazareth. On reaching the clearing, she stopped and stared. Nothing had been renovated here! Before her lay the old buildings. The roof of the clapboard convent was sagging, the chimney was gone, and the boards were hanging loose in many places. Around the house the weeds were waist high. A pain shot through Mother Catherine's heart. She shook herself. This was silly. Naturally the place, deserted for nearly thirty years, would be dilapidated!

She turned slowly to the two Sisters, who were standing silently behind her. "Let's see if we can get in, and I'll show you how we lived."

Her voice was almost cheerful now, and they could hardly keep up with her as she moved briskly toward the weatherbeaten door held by one leathern strap. Once inside, they saw nothing but dust and decay, but she seemed to see it as it used to be.

She became talkative, telling them stories about the early days, stories they had never heard before. She took them to the old spring and looked into its still clear waters, delighted to find it in such good condition.

"The seminarians must have found a use for it," she commented happily, cupping her hands and drinking the sparkling water. Her companions drank too.

Wistfully Mother Catherine looked about her.

"Well," she said finally, "I suppose we ought to go on to the seminary, but I want to visit a few other places with you before we go."

Father Chambige, coming down the narrow path to join the Sisters, heard the remark and hastily retraced his steps. When he returned a half-hour later, he found them looking at the remains of the old brick school which Mother had built in 1818. Only the four walls were standing, but the bricks which the early seminarians had made were still in excellent condition.

"Good brickmakers, those seminarians," Father said, following their gaze. "I wish the modern ones could do half so well."

Mother faced him. "Yes, Father, many a time I watched

the seminarians, Derrigaud and Moretty, fashion the day and bake it. They made thousands of bricks, some for here and some for the new buildings at Nazareth. Father David (unconsciously she had reverted to that title) believed that his seminarians should learn to make bricks and to put up a building. Of course that's not so necessary these days," she added thoughtfully, pulling a piece of dead ivy from the wall, "since there are plenty of contractors to do both for them."

"Yes, Mother," Father admitted laughing. "That's if they can afford it. While they're here, though, they'll have to do the brickmaking and the building themselves, for I haven't the money to pay anyone."

Mother Catherine waved her hand toward the old school. "If you can use these bricks you're welcome to them." Her voice was flat. "We'll never use them, and it will make me very happy to give them to you."

She turned her back resolutely on the ruins and her voice brightened. "And now let's go to the seminary and make our plans for the orphans!"

Before going in, however, she visited the church at St. Thomas and knelt in the spot where she had made her first vows thirty-five years before.

But the past could not hold Mother Catherine for long. On the way home there were no tales of the old days, only plans for the days to come. On December 4, Sisters Pauline Gibson and Bernardine O'Brien were sent to open the orphanage which had already accepted seven lads, ranging from four to ten. A year later, when there were twenty-five, Mother Catherine transferred Sister Clementia Paine from St. Vincent's in Louisville and made her Sister Servant at St. Thomas's.

With her St. Thomas's orphans settled, Mother Catherine began thinking once more of new buildings at Nazareth. The Sisters had needed them when she was in charge before, but reverses in the South had depleted the number of students, and lack of money had deterred her. At last the time had come to begin.

So one bright day in early spring, she hastened down the wellworn footpath to what had been the novitiate and where now Sister Teresa and Sister Petronella kept house together and spent the time between their prayers patching the Negroes' clothes.

As the door opened, Sister Teresa looked up, and her wrinkled face beamed when she saw Mother Catherine. She attempted to rise, but Mother quickly forestalled her and drew up a stool. "It's some prayers I'll be needing, Sister Teresa." She smiled, watching the gnarled hands skillfully plying the needle.

Sister Teresa stopped. "You always have those, Mother! I never forget."

"I know, Sister, but I need more than ever now. I've decided to build again."

"Build? Good." Sister Teresa's face glowed with satisfaction as she threaded her needle. "I was hoping you would. The Sisters certainly need a place where they can live together as a community, not spread all around." Her needle gleamed as it went in and out, in and out. "When are you starting?"

"In a few weeks. Of course," Mother explained hastily, "we're going to build a church first."

Sister Teresa looked pleased. "I knew you wouldn't forget Father David's counsel, 'First build a house for God.'"

"No, Sister, I could never forget that advice. This will be the third time I've observed it. First at Old Nazareth and then here."

"Are the plans complete, Mother?"

"They are! The church will be English Gothic in design and made of stone. It'll be a fine building, not as rich as God deserves of course but as fine as we can afford. We can get most of the material right here on the farm. There's some good stone out near the pasture for the church and plenty of clay near the brook to make bricks for the academy."

"The academy?"

"Yes, when the church is almost finished, we'll start

on that. I've already engaged William Keely to draw the plans, and by another year it ought to be ready for occupancy."

"And for the Sisters?"

"Don't worry, I haven't forgotten them either!" Mother's eyes were remarkably soft and blue. "We can remodel the old academy for their use and live, as you have already said, as a community—not all scattered and sleeping about wherever we find a place." She sighed as she rose to go. "Oh, how I long to see everything all arranged as it should be, and then I may lay me down in peace."

Sister Teresa stood up, letting the patches fall beside her on the floor, and walked to the door with Mother Catherine. "I'll pray hard, Mother, that your plans will materialize," she promised. "And they will, for they're God's plans too, I'm sure."

"Pray for me too, Teresa, that God in His mercy may give rest to my poor soul in a better world, for in this life there's been but little. Actually," she hastened to explain, "we really shouldn't seek rest in this world, for this is the time for labor and sorrow, and—"

"And joy," Sister Teresa finished quietly. "We've had much of that, Mother Catherine—you and I and all the Sisters. True joy, which makes the labor easy and the sorrow light."

Without speaking, Mother pressed the toilworn hand and was gone. Again, however, the happiness which filled her soul at being able to help the orphans and to provide for the Sisters was destined to be short-lived, for in Nashville trouble was brewing. It was eight years since the original group had gone with Father Hazeltine to that pioneer city in Tennessee, and their work had flourished. The day and boarding school in the large building on the summit of Campbell's Hill had grown so that it had been necessary to ask Nazareth for more Sisters, and St. John's Hospital too had thrived. The Sisters had weathered the cholera epidemic of 1848, and their kindness to the sick during this heartrending time had endeared them to the people. But under all this prosperity there was a note of restlessness.

Several times Bishop Miles had written, protesting against the change in faculty and the prohibition of the Motherhouse regarding the Sisters' singing in the parish choir. Father Hazeltine had answered that the Bishop himself had promised that he would never interfere in any way with the Nazareth Council in changing Sisters, for often that was a necessity. He also explained that the rule of the Sisters which prohibited their singing in parish choirs was common to many other orders as well.

For a time these explanations were accepted, but other difficulties arose. Then while Mother Catherine and the Council were seriously considering recalling the Sisters to Nazareth, Bishop Miles wrote requesting that the Sisters of Charity stationed in Nashville become a diocesan group. He pointed out that Archbishop Purcell had already formed a diocesan community in Cincinnati. Possibly then he could persuade some of his Sisters—he was certain that several would be willing to stay—to separate from Nazareth and to remain in Nashville permanently. In that way, unhampered by any Council, he could make rules which would be suitable for his diocese.

Naturally this was a blow to Mother Catherine, for she had no Sisters to spare from her community and even if she had, her love would protest a separation. Besides, she knew well the hardships of establishing a new foundation, and she would like to shield her children from them. But on the other hand, if the Sisters really wanted to go, she would never stand in their way. For one who truly loves always considers the wishes of the beloved and sacrifices her own desires. God's will be done!

After mature deliberation and much prayer, six Nazareth Sisters decided that their work lay in Nashville, and so in the summer of 1851 Mother sadly granted permission to Sisters Xavier Ross, Vincent Kearney, Joanna Bruner, Ellen Davis, Jane Francis Jones, and Baptista Carney to start a diocesan community under Bishop Miles. A few months later Father Hazeltine arranged the sale of

Nazareth's property on Campbell Hill, and the break was complete.

As naturally as a mother grieves over her departed children, so Mother Catherine grieved over the separation and prayed for the success of her absent daughters. But she did not mourn long. There was too much to be done at Nazareth and on the missions. Putting aside her sorrow, she threw herself wholeheartedly into the tasks before her.

The first work to clamor for her attention was her beloved St. Vincent's Orphanage. Even while she had been missioned there, Mother had realized that the time for the separation of the infirmary from the orphanage was approaching. Both needed more room.

In 1852 she made many trips to Louisville to consult the Sisters and to look around for a new location for the hospital. While she was in the city on one of these expeditions, Henry Clay's death in Washington on June 29 was announced. The whole city went into mourning for the Great Compromiser, who was a general favorite with the people of Louisville. Mr. Crittenden, the father of a Nazareth girl, was selected to deliver an elaborate eulogy before a vast audience in the Frankfort railroad depot on Jefferson Street between Brook and Floyd. Mother thought it very fitting that Mr. Clay, who had praised Nazareth in life, should in death be praised by one so closely related to Nazareth.

The country was still mourning Clay when on October 24 it was further impoverished by the death of Daniel Webster at his farm in Marshfield, Massachusetts. Again the people of Louisville felt they had lost a friend, for they had followed Webster's career with keen interest ever since he had been their guest fifteen years before. At a public meeting they passed resolutions of respect and invited the Honorable Rufus Choate of Massachusetts to speak on the greatness of Webster's life and character.

Not long after these sad events Mother Catherine heard that the Jesuits had decided to move from their college, St. Aloysius on Fourth Street. She went to see the rector and after inspecting the building she asked to rent it for a time to make sure that it would be suitable for a hospital.

This structure, on the east side of Fourth Street between Chestnut and Broadway, was of red brick and was set back about fifty feet from the street. Its high-ceilinged rooms, large windows, and long halls made it ideal for patients. After a short trial the building was purchased and remodeled. When it was ready for occupancy, there were sixteen rooms for private patients and two small wards for the poor who would otherwise be unable to procure medical aid and attention.

On the same property to the south of this building and nearer to the street was a two-story frame building which the Sisters also bought. It was named St. Ann's and was used as a home for working girls.

When the patients were transferred from St. Vincent's in November, 1852, Sister Appolonia McGill and three other Sisters came with them. Four others—Sisters Ann Matilda Flannigan, Marcellina O'Neill, Bernardine O'Brien, and Maria Kennedy—were sent from the Motherhouse.

Since the new location seemed to call for a distinct name, the hospital became known as St. Joseph's Infirmary. From the beginning it was a success. During the first year the Sisters cared for over two hundred and fifty patients. The fact that each new year saw an increase in patients the Sisters attributed in great part to the ability and the kindness of the doctors of Louisville.

The struggle to equip the hospital, however, was close to heroic. The community was poor and the equipment costly, but everything that could be bought for the care of the sick was purchased even when no one knew how it was going to be paid for. Surgery was then in its infancy; and the earliest mention of a surgical case in this, the oldest Catholic hospital in the South, was the amputation of a leg in the summer of 1853.

But the sacrifices of the Sisters were rewarded by the gratitude of the patients. One gentleman, a Protestant, was so impressed with the kindness and attention he received during an illness that he wrote a letter to the newspaper extolling St. Joseph's Infirmary:

> There are portions of the building set aside for the poor who are afflicted and unable to procure medical aid and attention, and nurses (Sisters) are appointed to wait on these poor invalids with as much vigilance and tenderness as on the wealthiest patient in the house. ... I was waited on and nursed with as much watchful care and patient tenderness as if my own wife or mother had been the watcher. I was as comfortable as if I had been in my own snug chamber at home. All the delicate nutriments ordered by the physician were ready at a moment's notice and all that a capricious appetite craved was daintily and cheerfully served up to me. A Sister with her noiseless footsteps, gentle voice, and quiet smile was ever ready at my beck and call, and when I wished to be alone and a nurse was not needed, I was left to my own fancies.

At the same time that Mother Catherine was negotiating the purchase of St. Joseph's and guiding the new foundation to success, she had begun the erection of a large church at Nazareth. This was to be far more pretentious than the two earlier structures, for the community's financial status had improved over the years, and it was only just that the first building to benefit by the increase would be the house of God. Describing it to the Sisters on the missions, Mother Catherine wrote: "This will be an edifice to the honor of God, not indeed, as fine and rich as the one built by Solomon, but as fine as His poor daughters of Nazareth could build to His honor for future generations."

She wrote delightedly to Sister Genevieve, "If you could see how fast the walls of the new church are running up—the tops of the window frames are already above the roof of the Sisters' house, and where will they be when it is finished? Oh, pray hard that God may be honored by it and His holy religion well served."

Although the church was completed in the early spring of 1854, the consecration was delayed until July 19, the Feast of St. Vincent, for whom it was named. All spring Mother looked forward eagerly to this event, but when the time came, illness prevented her from attending the complete six-hour ceremony. Indeed Sister Columba tried to keep her from going at all, but before the blessing was over, she appeared, pale and thin, at her accustomed place.

During the remainder of the service Mother's mind slipped back to the past, her tired eyes readily substituting Bishop David for the Bishop moving about the sanctuary, and the church for the one Nazareth's Founder had blessed on his name day so many years before. It was strange, but every year now Bishop David seemed nearer to her. She brought herself up with a start. This was 1854—this was Bishop Spalding—this was the new St. Vincent's!

That evening the community entered upon the annual retreat, and ill as she was, Mother was in her place for each exercise. When the retreat was over, she had not only grown in grace but was better physically also.

She had needed no retreat, however, to increase her confidence in the goodness of a kind and indulgent Providence. Faith had grown with the years and toward the end of her life, nothing could shake her trust. The overseer, Tom Wathen, had witnessed this several times when he went to her about the problems he encountered on the farm. No matter what the difficulty, she always smiled and said that things would work out. And they did.

But this time it was different, Tom told himself as he sought her out. This time it was drought. It looked as if the crops would be ruined and the stock die of thirst. Knowing how ill Mother had been, Tom hated to bother her, but he feared to take the responsibility on his own shoulders.

He found her inspecting the new academy, which was rapidly nearing completion.

"Good morning, Tom, and what can I do for you?" she greeted him cheerfully. "I know you wouldn't be so far from the farm if you didn't have something important to see me about."

Awkwardly he twisted his hat in his sunburned hands. "Well, Mother, I hate to tell you this, but the crop is ruined, and the stock will die if it doesn't rain soon."

"You mean...the whole crop...ruined?" she faltered, looking at him aghast.

"Well, not yet," he confessed, "but unless we have a rain in a day or so, it will be."

Her laugh was sheer joy. "Heavens, you certainly frightened me. I thought the crop was already gone."

"Well, it might as well be," he frowned, puzzled at her relief. "Just take a look at that sky. Not a cloud in sight."

"But we'll have rain just the same," she told him quietly.

The overseer looked doubtful. "I hope so. I'll have to drive the cattle clear down to Salt River to get a drink and even that's but a trickle now."

"Since you feel that way about it, Tom," Mother looked at him intently, her eyes twinkling mischievously, "you won't mind walking in a procession tonight, will you?"

"Procession?" his eyes opened wide.

"Yes, a procession to the graveyard. We've plenty of friends there to intercede for us. Bishop David, Sister Ellen, Mother Agnes, and all the rest."

He took a look at the clear, cloudless sky and shook his head slowly. "Well, if that's the way you want it," he drawled unenthusiastically.

"Good! Then that's settled. You get all the farmhands and I'll have the Sisters ready at six o'clock sharp."

And so it was. At the last stroke of the Angelus, the long line of petitioners reciting the Rosary and the Litany of the Saints began to move toward the cemetery. Passing through the wrought-iron gate, they moved from grave to grave, then proceeded to the chapel to finish the prayers before the altar.

Just before he stepped into the church, Tom glanced up. The sky was still clear. Just as he thought! But a little later, in a brief pause between *Aves*, he heard the first quick tap of heavy drops on the chapel roof. Then came the pounding of thousands in quick succession. Tom sniffed the delightful fragrance of dusty earth watered with purifying rain, and he contemplated the kneeling figure of Mother Catherine with wonder, exclaiming softly to himself, "Oh, ye of little faith!"

There was no need for another procession that summer, but remembering the severe drought to which Nazareth was often subject and the injunction, "God helps those who help themselves." Mother Catherine had four immense rain tanks placed directly under the zinc roof of the new academy, and to supplement them, a large cistern in the yard. In that way very little rain water was lost.

The new academy building itself was the wonder of the countryside. Nowhere had the people seen such a spacious study hall or refectory, nor such large dormitories. The huge kitchen with its gigantic black range was the subject of conversation at afternoon teas in Bardstown for weeks. Many called Mother Catherine a visionary and predicted that never would that range be needed nor those dormitories filled. Yet the very next year over two hundred pupils clamored for admission and every bed was taken.

Among the first visitors to the new academy was Orestes A. Brownson, famous lecturer, philosopher, and writer. On that occasion the students were greatly excited and they eagerly assembled in the new study hall to hear him speak. Expecting a very learned discourse, the older girls had provided themselves with pencil and paper to take notes, but the famous convert contented himself with a short address in which he made several references to the Man of Nazareth. Some of those who were disappointed at the informality of this lecture were soon satisfied, for Father Hazeltine took the graduates to Bardstown to hear Mr. Brownson give a public address, and there he delighted them with his learning and eloquence.

In August, Mother Catherine's fourth term of office expired. Her work at Nazareth was done at last. She had built wisely and well, leaving behind her a community strong, united, and deeply spiritual, and a church and academy which still stand as a memorial to her vision and ability.

Back to the orphans she went, happier than ever to be with them again.

CHAPTER TWENTY-THREE

1855-1857

What was that noise? Mother Catherine glanced at Sister Rosalie, but there was no answering look. Sister was placidly going on with her prayers. Suddenly it came again. There could be no mistake this time, and there was an urgency in the pounding that brought Mother hurrying from the chapel and down the long hall to the porch. She heard footsteps behind her but did not pause to see whose they were. The key turned in the lock with a harsh grating sound. She flung the door open, not bothering to close it. Leaning over the porch railing, she strained her eyes to see who was pounding on the back gate near the new stable. Only her white cap was clearly visible in the greyness of the early August morning.

Suddenly from the darkness came a man's husky voice. "Mother Catherine, for God's sake lave me in!"

For a second Mother stood undecided, her fingers gripping the rail. Sister Rosalie came up behind her. From the yard the voice came again, more urgent this time. "Please, lave me in, quick."

Unhesitatingly Mother Catherine started down the outside stairs. "Mother, don't!" Sister Rosalie cried, trying to hold her back.

Slipping from her grasp, Mother hurried down to the yard. Sister Rosalie followed, white-faced, but by the time she had reached the bottom of the steps, Mother, already at the gate which was closed by a horizontal bar, was peering through the chinks.

The voice came again in a stage whisper. "'Tis all right, Mother. 'Tis Pat O'Malley."

With Sister Rosalie's help Mother removed the heavy board. Pat stumbled in. Blood was running down his face, and his clothes were dirty and torn.

"Pat!" they both gasped.

He motioned to the plank. "Hurry! Put up that board agin! Thim divils may come here." With that he collapsed.

When he regained consciousness, he was surrounded by the Sisters. Several of them helped him up the steps to a small room. There Sister Rosalie took care of his cuts while Mother Catherine bent over him anxiously.

"Whatever happened to you, Pat?"

He struggled to sit up. Sister Rosalie gently pushed him back. "You can tell Mother from there just as well," she reminded him.

"'Tis that newspaper, Mother."

"Newspaper!" she joked. "I've never seen a newspaper make anyone look like you."

He laughed feebly. "No, 'twas what was in the paper, begorra." He opened his paper and folded it back to the editorial page. "Look here!"

Mother carried the article to the light and read aloud, "Rally to put down an organization of Jesuit Bishops, Priests, and other Papists, who aim by secret oaths and horrid perjuries and midnight plottings to sap the foundation of all our political edifices—state and national."

The words seemed to infuriate Pat. He struggled to get up, but again Sister Rosalie was too quick for him. Firmly she pushed him back.

"Aye, that's bad enough," he panted, spent by the effort, "but rade on."

"Popery with its iron heel tramped out the life of religious liberty as fast as it was born."

Before either one could stop him, Pat was sitting bolt upright. "The bloody liar!" he said clenching his fist, "Riligious liberty! What do the likes of him know about riligious liberty? Any Irishman could tell him a thing

243

or two. Shure and don't we know all about riligious liberty?" His face relaxed, "And them Know-Nothings do be knowin' a bit about it now too," he grinned and lay back on the pillow again, exhausted.

Mother threw up her hands. "I wish you'd go back to the beginning, Pat, and tell us the whole story. I'm rather stupid, you know, and I can't make head nor tail of this whole thing."

"Stupid!" he looked at her knowingly. "Shure and you can't be a-tellin' me that. But 'tis the whole story I'll be giving you anyhow. You've heard tell of the Know-Nothings, I suppose?"

Mother nodded in acknowledgement. "Yes, we've been saying the Litany of the Immaculate Conception for more than a month to obtain a just and peaceable election for a governor. We know what bigotry can do. But now about you?"

"Well, 'tis like I told you. I read this thing in the paper yesterday and I wor boiling mad. So I wint down to that newspaper office to see the iditer."

"Did you see him?"

"No, the divils down there wouldn't lave me in. As soon as I appeared at the door, begorra, one of them said, 'Well, here's our first Papist,' and some things that wouldn't be fitten to repeat, ma'am." He grinned ruefully. "Of course, 'twas four agin wan, but inyhow, I did be lettin thim know what good knuckles a Papist do have."

"It's a wonder they didn't kill you!"

"Shure an' it would take more crachures than four to be doing that. But whin they finished bating me, I didn't feel inny too good." Gingerly he felt the welt above his blackened eye. "Still I rached home all right. Wan of the divils must have follyed me though, for before light this morning I woke up smellin' smoke. Whin I run down the stairs, I seed a group of men just outside the door waitin' for me. I turned around and ran back into the smoke and managed to git to the kitchen window and over the fince. And 'tis here I be, begorra!" He sighed deeply. " 'Twasn't much of a place, but 'tis lost iverythin' is, I do suppose." Then his face brightened. "But I've still got me life and that's a good dale these days."

"You know you can stay here, Pat. We need someone to help around."

"Thanks, Mother, God bless you! Shure an' I knowed I wor coming to the right place whin I started here." He relaxed, then became tense again. "Ye'd better see that the gate is well barred today, for unless I'm mistaken there's going to be murdher at the polls."

He had hardly gotten the words out of his mouth when there was a loud pounding at the gate.

"More callers," Mother commented grimly. "I hope they're not your 'friends' coming to see if you are all right, Pat."

"No, indade, I'm sure they're not, for none of thim saw me lave." He chuckled with evident delight. "They probably thought I wor burned up, but ye'd betther be careful to find out who it be afore ye open the gate, lest harrum kum of it."

Pat's fears were groundless. The visitor was only a frightened woman with a baby in her arms and two little children clinging to her skirt. Mother put a comforting arm around her shoulder while Sister Rosalie made friends with the shy little girls.

Later, sitting in the kitchen with a bowl of hot soup for herself and mugs of milk for her children, the woman recovered herself sufficiently to tell her story. "The first I heard of the mob was when Mr. Combs came looking for my husband," she began. "Somebody'd told him that a mob was breaking into St. Martin's Church on the pretense that ammunition was stored there. So he was collecting all the Catholic men on the street to go there and prevent sacrilege."

She fed the baby a spoonful of soup. "In a couple of hours Jim—that's my husband—came back and told me that Mayor Barbee himself had gone into the church. After he'd made sure that there wasn't any ammunition in the building, he ordered everyone to go home.

"However, about an hour later, as we were eating

dinner, we heard shouting and screams. We ran to the window and saw about fifty men, some masked and all armed with muskets and bayonets coming down the street. Behind them another group of men were dragging a cannon."

"Where do you suppose they got that?" Mother Catherine asked, pouring more milk into little Susie's mug.

"Someone told me they took it from the courthouse lawn. Anyway, they dragged it down the street and stopped in front of Frank Quinn's house. When my husband saw this, he ran out to help because Mr. Quinn has been very good to us." She covered her face with her hands, and the hot tears trickled between her fingers. "I haven't seen my husband since," she sobbed, "and they killed Mr. Quinn and burned his house."

"Perhaps your husband's all right," Mother Catherine consoled.

"Oh, I hope so! Even if our house is gone and all our things! As long as Jim is spared, I can stand anything."

Then to divert the woman's mind from her own sorrow, Mother asked, "Why do you think they killed Mr. Quinn?"

The woman raised her head. "Just because he had made a little money, I suppose. They don't think an immigrant is entitled to anything," she said bitterly. "And then too he has a brother a priest. That in itself was enough to make them hate him."

Less than an hour later several other people came seeking shelter from the mob. Among them, much to her joy, Mrs. O'Leary found her husband. From these newcomers the Sisters learned that the mob was getting more dangerous. Many houses owned by Irish and Germans were in flames, and several more people had been killed.

They also told Mother that Bishop Spalding, hearing about the attack on St. Martin's Church, had been worried about what the mob might do to the cathedral. He went to Mayor Barbee and handed him the keys of the new building, saying that as mayor of the city he would be responsible for any damage done to the church. As a result, hanging on the cathedral door for all to read was a big sign:

> We, the undersigned, have in person carefully examined the Cathedral, and do assure the community that there are neither men nor arms concealed there; and further that the keys are in the hands of city authorities.
>
> John Barbee
> Mayor

Late that same afternoon another family, fleeing the mob, told the Sisters that the Know-Nothings had brought their cannon and had placed it in front of Mr. Carroll's home, the finest house in the Irish section. Before they could fire the cannon, however, Mr. Dupont, the owner of the paper mills and a member of the Know-Nothing Party himself, came running down the street. With his Negro servant beside him he stood before the front door of Mr. Carroll's home and told the mob they would have to shoot him before they could blow up the house. The mob jeered but finally broke up. Cursing and shouting, they moved down the street.

A couple of hours later, however, they regrouped before the house of Dennis Long. Again Mr. Dupont appeared and again they dispersed. But this time, after Mr. Dupont had left, they returned. Breaking down the front door, they killed Mr. and Mrs. Long and hanged their two sons from the banister. Then setting fire to the house, they fled.

Apparently satisfied with the havoc they had wrought on the Irish, the mob crossed to the German sector. They passed by the orphanage and its quaking refugees to the tavern of William Ambruster on the south side of Jefferson Street, east of Wenzel. Their shouts as the hungry flames devoured the building sounded more like the cries of animals than of human beings. Finally tiring of watching the flames, they began to ransack German homes nearby.

Then like hungry wolves scenting their prey, they gathered in front of the barred gate of the orphanage. Hearing their shouts, Mother Catherine asked the Sisters to go to the chapel to pray for protection. Then she took her stand on the porch where she could be seen by the mob. There she stayed, her fingers clutching her side beads and her lips moving in silent prayer. Only too well she knew that the fragile plank fence was no real protection for the Sisters nor for the harassed people who had come to them for safety.

The muttering grew louder. Suddenly there was a shout, "Let's burn the place down. Kill the Papists."

Mother knew that if just one man started to storm the gate, all the rest would follow. "Mary, protect us," she implored, her face white. No one moved.

Night was falling rapidly. No one as yet assumed leadership. The mob remained disorganized, milling around restlessly. Finally with a yell of defiance one of the men shouldered his gun and started down the alley.

To Mother's relief the rest straggled after him. When the last man had disappeared, she hastened to the chapel to thank God and His Blessed Mother for their protection. From there she and the other Sisters went to the kitchen to prepare the evening meal.

After supper, with the help of the men who brought in great armfuls of hay from the stable, they made beds in every available space, thus providing everyone with a place to sleep. Fearing that the mob might return during the night, the men appointed two of their number to stand guard. With that, Bloody Monday, August 5, 1855, came to an end.

For days after this uprising the city feared a renewal of hostilities. Business houses in the first ward were closed, and about fifty German stone masons left their work on the customhouse because of the violence committed against their countrymen. In an attempt to restore peace and to maintain order, Mayor Barbee issued a proclamation requiring all good citizens to aid the police when called upon, warning all viciously disposed persons from assembling to do mischief to persons and property and recommending parents and masters to keep their sons, apprentices, and slaves out of the streets, especially after dark.

It was not only Louisville that felt the effects of the bigotry of the Know-Nothings. In Wisconsin, Catholics, insulted and pursued by angry mobs, fled in terror through the streets. In Massachusetts many Catholics were ousted from bigoted villages, an Ursuline convent was burned to the ground, and the cross of a catholic church was torn down and trampled upon. In Maine a priest was tarred and feathered; in New York the Reverend Doctor Dowling was wildly cheered for an abusive speech about Pope Pius IX; in Ohio a catholic church was blown to pieces with gunpowder.

All over the United States men were taking the Know-Nothing Oath:

> I, of my own free will and accord, in the presence of Almighty God and these witnesses, my right hand resting on the Holy Bible and Cross, and my left hand raised toward Heaven, in token of my sincerity, do solemnly promise and swear that I will not vote nor give my influence [to any man] for any office ... unless he be an *American Born Citizen* in favor of Americans born ruling America, nor [will I vote for] a Roman Catholic or a foreigner.

Once bound by this oath, the zealous neophyte joined loudly in the cries:

"The Nation is in danger! Deport the Papists!"

"Nuns are slaves and a menace!"

"Catholics want the Pope in the White House!"

Papers everywhere carried cartoons showing the bishops of the United States as crocodiles and predatory animals ready to devour the American people. Their editors accused Catholic priests of keeping the Bible away from their people and of allowing them to hear and see nothing which placed Romanism in its true light, that is, as an enemy of the people.

"Let these arrogant priests," said the Know-Nothing agitator, "once obtain sufficient political power, and short, indeed, will be the time remaining before every Protestant in this country will no longer be protected by our laws but will be made to obey arbitrary directives from persons we don't like, and whose ways are entirely foreign to our own."

But not everyone in America had forgotten that the Catholics in Maryland were the first to grant religious toleration to the early colonists; not everyone was deceived by the lies shouted from one end of the nation to the other; not everyone approved of the violence done to the Catholics and foreigners. The most famous spokesman for this group of right-minded Americans was a tall, awkward Kentuckian, Abraham Lincoln, familiarly known as Honest Abe. Actually the Sisters could have counted him as a neighbor, for he was born in a log cabin about twenty-five miles from Nazareth; and when about three years of age, he had moved to another cabin only fifteen miles away.

In a letter dated August 24, 1855, he wrote to Joshua Speed of Louisville:

As a nation we began by declaring that "all men are created equal." We now practically read it "all men are created equal, except Negroes." When the Know-Nothings get control, it will read, "all men are created equal, except Negroes and foreigners and Catholics." When it comes to this, I shall prefer emigrating to some country where they make no pretense of loving liberty, . . . where despotism can be taken pure and without the base alloy of hypocrisy.

Evidently there were many Americans who agreed with Abraham Lincoln, for the Know-Nothings did not gain control—at least of the presidency. Although in 1856 their candidate, Millard Fillmore, did secure many popular votes, he carried but one state in the electoral vote and that ironically enough was Maryland.

In Louisville the most immediate effect of the riots was the exodus of many of the foreigners against whom the fanatical outbreak had been directed. The *Louisville Anzieger* of August 11 reported that over four hundred German families were planning to migrate to Kansas and that about three hundred Irish citizens had left on the mailboat for Cincinnati, notwithstanding the assurance of the mayor that they would be protected. These facts seriously affected the city's prosperity, for since there existed an uncertainty about the absolute freedom of religious worship in the city, immigrants naturally shied away from settling there.

But, strange as it may seem, the Know-Nothing Movement did not have a detrimental effect on the Church in Kentucky. On the contrary, when Bishop Spalding made his episcopal visitation toward the end of 1855 and again in 1856, he witnessed an aroused interest in the Faith. In the courthouse at Hardinsburg he preached before an attentive crowd of Catholics and Protestants. At St. Martin's in Meade County he was gratified at the renewed zeal of the Catholics, a zeal which was ascribed to the recent persecutions that not only rendered Catholics more fervent, but stimulated non-Catholics to make diligent inquiry after the truth.

But prejudice dies hard. One spring day in 1857, Sister Gabriella came hurrying to Mother Catherine with the *Louisville Journal*. "Look at this!" she cried, pointing to an article.

Mother Catherine took the paper and read the headlines aloud. " 'Exposition of the Roman Catholic Persecution of a Protestant Scholar at Nazareth.' Oh, no!" She turned a distressed face to Sister Gabriella. "When *will* this stupid bigotry end? Have you read the article?"

"Yes, Mother."

"Well then I'll spare your ears." She silently read the editorial and the letter purported to be written by a Nazareth student, Mary Miller, who had run away from the school and who was accusing the Sisters of several serious crimes.

"What do you think of it?" queried Sister Gabriella when Mother had folded the paper.

"Lies of course but I'm sorry that someone was bigoted enough to print it. Now I hope someone will have the courage to answer it."

She didn't have long to wait. The next day the paper carried a letter from Mother Frances in reply to the vicious attack, explaining what had really happened. Mary E. B. Miller, Mother Frances wrote, had been brought to Nazareth in January, 1856, by her half-brother, who had found her too unruly to handle at home. Mother Frances had taken her reluctantly only after the brother's promise that if the Sisters could do nothing with the girl, he would come for her. After Mary had gone so far as to throw a book at a Sister who was helping her with arithmetic, Mother Frances tried to get in touch with him but could not.

As time went on Mary grew more troublesome and had finally run away. Fearing that harm would come to her, Mother had sent overseer and several of his men to look for the fugitive. It wasn't until the next day about noon that they found her at Mount Washington, a little town about twenty miles distant. Mother Frances immediately asked Dr. Mattingly, a benefactor, to go for the runaway, but the girl refused to return with him to Bardstown. After making sure she was in good hands, the doctor allowed her to stay, never dreaming that anyone in the town would believe her fantastic story.

"Poor Mother Frances!" Mother Catherine exclaimed. She continued the letter aloud.

My object in sending for her was by no means to have her reenter the school, but merely to return her in a becoming manner to the place whence she came. In the morning I sent her trunk, directed to Nashville, to the Mansion House in Bardstown.

Instead of preventing Miss Miller from informing her friends of her condition, as she states, I strongly urged upon her to write to an uncle, who, as she said, resided near Nashville, to come for her. And I myself wrote to another gentleman residing in Nashville that she named as being her uncle and in whose family she had lived, as she said. My first letter being unanswered, I wrote again to the same gentleman . . . stating the manner of her departure and subsequent facts. To this letter he replied (my first not having been received) that he had never heard of her nor had she ever resided in his family.

"Well, that certainly gives a good example of her ability to make up stories!" Sister Generose ejaculated. "I just hope someone else who knows her writes in."

Sister's wish came true. The next day another letter, written by the Protestant girls at the academy, refuted Mary's accusations one by one. In answer to her claim that "Their [the Sisters'] regulations are such that no letter written by me could inform my friends of my condition," the girls replied:

In the regulations of Nazareth we find no rule prohibiting unrestrained correspondence between the young ladies and their relatives; on the contrary, each pupil is required to write every two weeks to some member of her family; and we unhesitatingly pronounce the above assertion of Mary E. B. Miller to be unfounded in truth.

To her accusation, "I have been repeatedly confined to a room for two, three, and once five days at a time, deprived of my allowance of food for no other reason than refusing to go to confession," the girls indignantly retorted:

During our long stay at Nazareth we have never known an instance where the least attempt has been made by the Sisters to proselyte those entertaining religious principles at variance with their own, nor a punishment inflicted to induce them to change their religion. Having been pupils of this Institution for several years, we consider it an act of simple justice to deny the erroneous statements contained in her letter; and we certainly have had ample opportunity to judge the whole affair.

Her inventive genius was well known while she was at Nazareth, and her knowledge of persons who never existed was proverbial even among the smaller girls. Hence we are not astonished at the glaring tissue of falsehoods which she has sent forth to the world. The circumstance of her being locked up the day she left Nazareth is an entire fabrication, for she certainly was with the young ladies who took a long walk that afternoon and was with them throughout the whole day.

For the benefit and comfort of those whose credulity has been imposed on by the recital of her horrible persecution, allow us to say that we are neither locked up nor deprived of our ordinary allowance of food, though we are Protestants and have never been to confession, nor does there seem any probability of our going.

Mother Catherine looked up. "Well, that certainly answers any question!" Then her quick eye caught another paragraph, and she couldn't repress a smile as she read:

Mary Miller might well be congratulated on her rapid advancement in her diction. We are positively assured from ocular observation that she was incapable of writing two consecutive lines correctly when she left Nazareth. *Mirabile dictu*! What a pity that a mind susceptible of such wonderful improvement (!) should have been so neglected in earlier years!

The Sisters joined in Mother's laughter. "I hope whoever wrote the letter for Mary doesn't miss that!" remarked Sister Gabriella dryly.

The Protestant pupils' defense especially delighted Mother Catherine and the Sisters because it proved to them that no non-Catholic taught by the Sisters at Nazareth or at Presentation or cared for by them at St. Vincent's or St. Joseph's would ever believe the accusations brought against them by organizations such as the Know-Nothings nor by such pitiable individuals as Mary Miller.

CHAPTER TWENTY FOUR

1857-1858

It was snowing. Mother Catherine, standing at the window in her chilly room, watched the feathery flakes whirling, dancing, and finally settling on the white ground. They were such large flakes! No doubt it would stop snowing soon.

How snow brought back memories! She seldom saw it without recalling the first time she had seen Old Nazareth, the white-coated log cabin in the clearing. It seemed but yesterday that she had stood with Uncle Tom at the edge of the wood and had seen Betsy Wells and Teresa Carrico appear at the door. Uncle Tom had been dead for many years, and she was old, almost at the end of her course. Life had been hard, with long, long years of real poverty and dire want. But it had been sweet too and full of quiet joy and accomplishment. Nazareth was no longer a log cabin but a beautiful building, protected by the spires of the lovely Church of St. Vincent. Around it stretched hundreds of acres of fine farm land and lovely trees. And here in the city Presentation Academy was flourishing, St. Joseph's Infirmary on Fourth Street was long out of its infancy, and the orphanage—how she loved every child in it! Every brick!

She looked out at the snow again. It had been deeper than this the day she had made her vows with Teresa and Ellen. She smiled. Had it been up to her neck that day, she wouldn't have known the difference. She could have walked on clouds! Forty-three years ago! Was it possible? Yes, His burden was light and His yoke was sweet—and—how well He paid the hundredfold!

But reminiscing like this wouldn't get little Nellie's dress made nor Rose's stockings darned. She turned reluctantly from the window and gathered a pile of mending from her bed. There was a knock.

"Come," she called gently, not looking up.

Sister Julia entered.

"Br-rr it's cold in here, Mother. You really should keep a little fire in your room."

"You know very well that we can't afford heat except in the nursery and the classrooms, Sister," Mother Catherine chided her gently.

"Yes, I realize that, Mother, but it seems we *could* manage enough for this room too. It's so small." She paused. "But it's no use, I know. You wouldn't have heat unless all the rooms were heated."

"Of course not!" Mother declared vigorously. "Why should *I* have more than my Sisters? But," she said abruptly, "I hardly think you came to tell me it was cold, did you?"

Sister Julia flushed, taking the words as a rebuke until she saw the twinkle in Mother's eye. Then she relaxed. "Oh, no, of course not! Miss Marshall stopped by and asked me to tell you that Pat O'Malley was hurt this afternoon."

"Hurt? How?"

"He lost his balance and fell from the scaffolding where he was working."

"Did she say how bad he was?"

"No, except that he seemed to be in great pain."

"Where is he?"

"They carried him back to his rooming house, and one of the men volunteered to stay with him."

"A man!" Mother said exasperated. "What can a man do for him? Get your things and we'll go to him immediately." She had already risen.

Sister Julia stood there irresolute. Finally she spoke hesitatingly, "But Mother, surely *you're* not going."

"And why not?"

"Well—"

"You think I'm too old to walk so far, do you?"

Sister Julia flushed again. "Not exactly," she explained honestly, "but the ground is wet. Why not let someone else go?"

There was a long silence, and Sister Julia thought for a moment that she had won her point. Finally Mother spoke firmly, "No, I'm sorry, but no one else could make Pat come to St. Joseph's, and that's what he's going to do."

Her voice softened. "When we first came here to the orphanage, Pat helped us, and from that day to this, he's been our handyman—free of charge. There's not a thing I've ever asked Pat to do that he's left undone. Then, poor man, he lost everything in the Know-Nothing riot and was without work. Finally Miss Marshall got him that job with the construction crew, and now this—." She sighed. Ignoring the entreaty in the other's eyes, she put on her heavy cape.

"No, I must go. Pat needs my help. Get your things," she ordered gently, "and come along, will you?"

In less than ten minutes they were out on the street walking rapidly. Sister Julia could not help admiring her older companion who stepped so briskly. Well, it wasn't too cold. Perhaps it would be all right, after all. If the ground weren't so slushy with the couple of inches of wet clinging snow, there really would be no danger.

They continued on their way in silence, saying the rosary as they so often did on the way to the sick. They didn't know it, but as they slipped the beads through their fingers, a little French girl named Bernadette was doing the same thing while she gazed enraptured at a Beautiful Lady, who had appeared to her in a rocky cavern near the little village of Lourdes.

Finally, they reached an old weatherbeaten house set back a little from the street. "Here we are," Mother said, turning into the path which led to the front door.

Inside, they climbed a narrow, dark stairway which reeked with the stale odor of fried fish. Mother knocked at the door on the third floor, originally an attic. From within came the sound of heavy footsteps. The door opened a crack at first, and then wide as the man saw who was there.

"Glory be to God and 'tis glad I am to see you!" he greeted them heartily. Then his smile vanished, and putting his big finger clumsily to his lips, he whispered. "It's bad off I do be thinking he is."

Mother was already leaning over the old iron bed and laying a cool, practiced hand on Pat's hot forehead.

Slowly the eyelids fluttered and the dark eyes opened. A smile played around the corners of the pale lips. "I knowed ye'd cum," he whispered and lapsed into unconsciousness again.

Mother turned to the man, "Go out and find a carriage. Hurry! We must get him to the Infirmary immediately."

When Pat woke again an hour later, he found Mother and Sister Appolonia by his side.

"Where am I?" he asked looking around, confused.

"At St. Joseph's," Mother said smiling. "That's where you're going to stay too until you're well. Now, since I know you are in good hands, I'll get back to the orphanage. But I'll be in tomorrow to see you again. Let me know if they don't treat you right," she threatened Sister Appolonia playfully.

A week later Sister Regina, walking down one of the long corridors of the orphanage, stopped abruptly, listened, and frowned. Was that Mother Catherine coughing again? She gazed unhappily in the direction of the sound. She wished Mother Catherine would see Dr. Metcalf at the Infirmary, but every time she mentioned it, Mother would laugh and say, "It's just a little cold. Why should I bother a busy doctor about it?" But it wasn't just a little cold. Sister Regina was sure it was far more serious. Mother had begun to cough the day after she'd walked in the snow to Portland to see Pat O'Malley, and the cough had been growing steadily worse since. After hearing another spasm, Sister Regina made up her mind. Somehow she would manage to see Dr. Metcalf herself and tell him about Mother's cold. He knew Mother Catherine well and would do anything for her. Of course Mother would disapprove if she found it out, but someone just *had* to do something.

The same day that Sister Regina told him, Dr. Metcalf made his way to the orphanage on the pretext of seeing one of the children. After talking with Mother for a few moments, he remarked brusquely, "You sound as if you have a very bad cold."

"Oh, it'll pass," Mother said lightly.

"What are you doing for it?"

Mother's eyes twinkled. "Giving it a home."

"I'm serious. Here, let me take your temperature." Before she could protest, he had the thermometer in her mouth and his fingers on her pulse. The frown deepened as he waited. "Just as I thought," he murmured. "You have a high fever, Mother. Get to bed immediately."

"But, Doctor, there's so much to do."

"Mother," he said gruffly, "I said bed, and bed it is. I only hope we've got that cold in time."

But the next day when he came, his hopes vanished. Mother Catherine was very sick and—even with Sister Appolonia's expert care—only a miracle could save her.

Days of anxiety followed. Once when Mother seemed a little better, she asked Sister Appolonia to bring her *The Following of Christ*. Opening it at random as was her custom, she turned to the passage: "Quickly shalt thou be gone hence. See how matters stand with thee."

Motioning Sister to come nearer, she pointed to the passage. "That's a warning for me," she whispered. "I must prepare for death."

Not trusting herself to speak, Sister Appolonia left the room hurriedly on a pretext of getting something and came back only after she had regained her composure.

The very next day Mother began sending for the Sisters. She spoke with each one, asking pardon for whatever in her conduct toward them might have indicated any want of charity and begging their prayers. Then she gave to each a token of her love—a medal, a rosary, or a picture.

After she had seen all of them, she sent for her orphans. They came, tears streaming down their childish faces. To each she gave some parting advice and the promise of her unending love. To Mother Frances, who came down from Nazareth to be with her at the end, she bequeathed her large rosary.

When all this was done, she applied herself with all the power of her soul to sanctifying the short time that remained to her.

As the days went on, her strength ebbed, and her breathing became more and more difficult. But her mind was clear. For the first time in her life she had time—long hours both day and night, for her congested lungs made sleep impossible—time to spend in constant communion with God without the distracting cares of office, time to spend suffering with Christ in the Garden of Gethsemane, time to say over and over with Him, "Not my will but Thine be done." Often when Sister Appolonia thought she was asleep, she was absorbed in divine contemplation. At other times, when pain racked her body until she felt she must cry out, she stifled the moan and turned it into a prayer for her beloved community, for her orphans, for her Kentucky. She could work no more, but she could suffer; she could pray.

And so Friday and Saturday passed and Sunday dawned. Propped up with pillows, Mother could see the yellow tips of the forsythia outside her window nodding gently in the warm breeze. Tired, she closed her eyes. Then she heard the trill of a robin and opened them again. She smiled wanly. Spring! Why, of course, it was the twentieth of March, the eve of spring!

Spring! The word seemed to take possession of her mind, forcing it to wander into the past. She struggled but to no avail. She was back to her childhood, back with Uncle Tom and Ann, back at Old Nazareth, back in the springtime of Kentucky when the fields were lying in wait for the seed of faith which she and Teresa and Ellen were to sow. They had gone bravely into the uncultivated land, had put their hands to the plow, and had not turned back. They had planted the love of God in the souls of their pupils, their sick, their orphaned. Now their work was finished. Kentucky spring was fading. Summer was at hand. God was placing that season into other hands— the hands of her spiritual children. Down the years they would go, sowing and reaping, until they too finished their task and entered into Eternal Spring.

Her breathing grew more labored. Her hands tightened on her crucifix. Mother Frances motioned to Sister Appolonia, who went out quietly and returned with Father Coomes, the chaplain at the orphanage. He administered the Last Sacraments. For an hour or two after that, Mother Catherine seemed to rally and the Sisters' hopes revived. But soon they knew they were mistaken. It was the end.

Bishop Spalding gave the last blessing, and the weeping Sisters knelt around the bed saying the prayers for the dying. Behind them in the hall clustered the orphans, present and past. Once Mother opened her strangely luminous eyes, and a faint smile played around her lips as she appeared to recognize in the fashionable lady who knelt at the foot of her bed the Penn Baby whom twenty-seven years before she had carried in her apron to the orphanage on Fifth Street.

Her eyes closed again and her face contorted with pain. For a while she lay motionless. Then she moaned feebly. Instantly Sister Appolonia was leaning over her. The pallid lips moved and with a superhuman effort Mother gasped, "Put me on the floor."

Raising her tenderly, the Sisters did as she requested, pillowing her head and shoulders in their arms. Once after that she looked up at them all, her beautiful eyes traveling slowly from one loved face to another. Then she closed them and kissed the crucifix held to her lips. Her breath was coming in agonized gasps. Slowly, painfully, her lips moved, "Jesus—Mary—Joseph—Father, into Thy Hands—" She did not finish.

At once the pain-furrowed face softened and the set mouth relaxed. Suffering and pain were a thing of the past.

Reverently her Sisters prepared the body of their Mother for her last journey and placed it in the small parlor of the orphanage. All day crowds of people came to see her, beautiful and natural, a sweet smile on her peaceful face.

When word reached Nazareth, the big bell tolled long and loud, and the Sisters gathered in quiet groups telling and retelling in subdued voices the stories of their dear Mother's virtue and kindness.

Two days later they walked in procession, followed by the pupils, to the gate where they met the hearse. When the long line finally reached the church, a bent figure shuffled painfully from the back pew and stood to one side as the coffin passed, then followed right behind it. One of the Sisters started to tell Sister Teresa that the place she had taken was Mother Frances's, but the latter shook her head. As the last one of the pioneer band, Sister Teresa was in her rightful place—the first in that solemn procession.

When the coffin was opened, Sister Teresa remained by it the entire time that the others were passing by for a last look at their Mother. She saw nothing but the peaceful smiling face of her lifelong companion and friend. During the Bishop's sermon Mother Frances watched her with anxious eyes and hoped that she would not try to go to the cemetery, but when the coffin was carried down the aisle, Sister Teresa took her place behind it, and the other Sisters adjusted their pace to her slow and faltering gait.

When they entered the cemetery, Mother Frances's eyes rested lovingly on the tombstones which bore the names of Mother Catherine's early associates: Ellen O'Connell, Scholastica O'Connor, Mary Gwynn, Polly Beaven, and her own sister, Harriet Gardiner. Finally the procession halted at Bishop David's grave. There at his feet they buried her.

Sadly her children returned to the church saying the

rosary. When they rounded a bend in the path, Mother Frances looked back. Still standing at the grave was the bent figure of Sister Teresa. Mother motioned to a young Sister, "Go back, and when Sister Teresa is ready to come, walk over with her. Let her stay as long as she likes though," she added hastily.

Obediently Sister Lucy walked back, glad to stay outside a while longer. Glad to be young. Glad to love God in the springtime of her life. Glad to walk in the footsteps of Mother Catherine who had followed Christ and had, like Him, loved the orphan, the sick, and the poor.

EPILOGUE

Every day for three weeks after Mother Catherine's death, Sister Teresa, accompanied by a young Sister, made her way to the cemetery and stood in prayer by the new grave. Then one day she was missing from her accustomed place. A week later on April 23, the tolling of the bell informed the community that she had followed Mother Catherine.

What a reunion that must have been! And in the hundred years that have passed since that glad day, Mother Catherine and Sister Teresa have watched with joy the growth of the community of which they were the nucleus.

They have seen it develop into a congregation of over 1500 members serving God in 117 branch houses, 10 hospitals, 5 orphanages, 93 elementary schools, 19 high schools, and 2 colleges in 11 states of the Union and in India.

Some of the foundations which Mother Catherine knew so well are still flourishing:

Nazareth Academy (August 23, 1814) which began on St. Thomas's Farm with nine students, was transferred to its present location in 1822. It added a junior college in 1921 and a senior college in 1937. Together these schools educated thousands of students from 42 states of the Union and from 34 foreign nations. In 1966 Nazareth Academy closed to allow for the expansion of Nazareth College.

Bethlehem Academy (Bardstown, 1819) is now a high school. The new grade school adjoins the historical St. Joseph's Cathedral and facing it is the new Flaget Memorial Hospital.

Presentation Academy (Louisville, 1831) has moved from Fifth to Fourth Street and is attended by over 800 girls.

St. Vincent's Orphanage (1832) for girls and *St. Thomas Orphanage* for boys (1850) have merged (1952) into one modern orphanage, St. Thomas-St. Vincent Home, accommodating 255 children at Anchorage, a suburb of Louisville.

St. Frances Academy (Owensboro, 1849) is now a parochial grade school. The high school has moved to a new site and and is called Owensboro Catholic High. Over 1000 teen-agers attend this school. Both the grade school and the high school are taught by the Sisters.

St. Joseph Infirmary (Louisville, 1836) has moved from Fourth and Broadway to Eastern Parkway where a modern building provides 500 beds for the 19,840 patients it serves each year. Also in this city are *Sts. Mary and Elizabeth Hospital* (216 beds) which cares for over 11,500 patients yearly and *Our Lady of Peace* with 285 beds for 2,900 psychiatric patients yearly.

LaSalette Academy (Covington, 1856) has a high school with over 400 pupils.

A little more than three years after Mother Catherine's death, her Sisters were on the battlefield of the Civil War and in improvised hospitals serving the Blue and the Grey alike. Sister Mary Lucy Dosh gave her young life in this service, and at her funeral, soldiers from both sides formed an honor guard. At Nazareth there was great anxiety about more than seventy girls who were unable to return to their families because of the war. Mother Columba's apprehensions were somewhat reduced by assurances from the officers in charge of nearby forces and especially by a note from President Lincoln written in his own hand:

> Let no depredation be committed upon the property or possessions of the Sisters of Charity of Nazareth Academy near Bardstown, Ky.
>
> Jan. 17, 1865   A. Lincoln.

A little more than forty years later World War I found her Sisters, under the auspices of the American Red Cross, nursing the soldiers at Camp Taylor and Camp Buell in the great postwar influenza epidemic.

Then in 1947 at the invitation of the Jesuit Fathers of Patna Mission, India, six Sisters of Charity of Nazareth set out on cargo ships for India. There near the sacred River Ganges at Mokameh they established Nazareth Hospital with 160 beds for about 7,000 patients yearly and a Leper Clinic with over 27,000 outpatients. From this city they have spread to Gaya and Ranchi where they conduct schools. Into the novitiate at Mokameh have come fifty-two Indian girls eager to follow Mother Catherine Spalding, the Kentucky pioneer woman, in her service of teaching, nursing, and caring for the orphan.

Because of the great distance between missions and because of the large number of Sisters in the community, the congregation in 1965 established four provinces in the United States and two regions, one of which is India and the other, the hospitals in the United States.

The years following Vatican Council II have seen a movement toward more social service, and some Sisters are working in the inner city and in the mountain areas. But wherever they go, whatever they do, the Sisters of Nazareth will be encouraged and inspired by the spirit of their foundress, Mother Catherine Spalding, who went about "doing good" in Kentucky's spring!

1790   January 9. Teresa Carrico is born in Maryland.

1792   March 29. Father Benedict Joseph Flaget and Father John Baptist Mary David with Stephen Badin, sub-deacon, land in Baltimore, Maryland, from France.

1793   May 25. Stephen Theodore Badin is ordained by Bishop Carroll. He is the first priest to be ordained in the United States.

December 23. Catherine Spalding is born in St. Charles County, Maryland.

1805   The Trappists make their first foundation in Kentucky at Casey Creek but leave after four years for Monks Mound, Cahokia, Illinois.

1806   The Dominicans arrive at St. Rose, Springfield, Kentucky.

1808   April 8. The see of Bardstown, Kentucky, is created.

1810   November 4. Father Flaget is consecrated Bishop of Bardstown by Bishop Carroll.

1811   May 22. Bishop Flaget, Father David, and three seminarians start down the Ohio from Pittsburgh.

June 4. Bishop Flaget, Father David, and the sub-deacon Guy Ignatius Chabrat arrive in Louisville, Kentucky.

December 25. Father Chabrat is ordained by Bishop Flaget at St. Rose. This is the first ordination to take place west of the Alleghenies.

1812   April 9. A chapel for the seminarians is set up in a room in the Howard home.

April 25. The Loretto Sisters founded by Father Charles Nerinckx receive the habit at St. Charles.

December 1. The Sisters of Charity of Nazareth are founded by Father David at St. Thomas's. Teresa Carrico and Elizabeth Wells are the first members.

1813   January 21. Catherine Spalding arrives at Nazareth. Elizabeth Wells is appointed superior and a provisional rule is given to the group.

Three other girls—Mary (Polly) Beaven, Mary Gwynn, and Harriet Gardiner—join the group after Easter.

The first retreat is given by Father David.

June 2. The first election of the Sisters of Charity takes place. Catherine Spalding is elected Mother.

1814   Early March. Ellen O'Connell comes to Nazareth from Baltimore.

April 7. Holy Thursday, a black habit and white cap are adopted by the Sisters and the rule of St. Vincent becomes their rule.

The Sisters' log cabin is greatly enlarged.

August 8. The first Mass is offered in the enlarged convent.

August. The Sisters begin their teaching. Cecilia O'Brien, later Sister Cecily, is the first pupil and is followed by eight others.

1815   A springhouse is erected for the Sisters. Mother Catherine becomes Mistress of Novices.

1816   February 2. Vows are pronounced for the first time by Mother Catherine, Sister Teresa Carrico, Sister Harriet Gardiner, and Sister Polly Beaven at St. Thomas Seminary Chapel.

March 25. Sister Nancy Lynch, Sister Mary Gwynn, Sister Ellen O'Connell, and Sister Martha Gough are allowed to make their vows.

Mother Catherine is re-elected.

A new parish church is built at St. Thomas's

1817   January 1. Father Derrigaud is ordained at St. Thomas's.

The community and the school are considerably increased. A frame chapel is built for the Sisters.

July 4. Father David receives a Papal Bull appointing him coadjutor to Bishop Flaget.

1818   August 12. Sister Mary Gwynn dies of tuberculosis and is buried in a plot of ground btween the seminary and the Nazareth convent.

September. The seminary is moved to Bardstown.

December. A brick school is completed for the Sisters.

Harriet Gardiner, Polly Beaven, and Nancy Lynch go to Bardstown on the first mission of the Sisters of Charity.

1819   August 8. The consecration of St. Joseph's Cathedral takes place at Bardstown.

August 15. Father David is consecrated Bishop.

August 27. Mother Catherine's term of office expires. Sister Agnes Higdon is elected Mother; Sister Ellen O'Connell, Assistant; Sister Ann Spalding, Treasurer; and Sister Barbara, Procuratrix.

September 8. Sister Harriet Gardiner, Sister Polly Beaven, and Sister Nancy Lynch open Bethlehem Academy in Bardstown.

1820   School is opened at Long Lick, Breckenridge County, under Father Abell but is closed after a year.

St. Vincent's Academy is established in Union County with Sister Angela Spink, Sister Frances Gardiner, and Sister Cecily O'Brien.

February 8. Sister Martha Gough dies and is buried beside Sister Mary Gwynn.

1821   The Sisters take charge of the wardrobe and the infirmary at St. Joseph College, Bardstown, a school connected with the seminary and taught by the priests and seminarians. Boys come from great distances to attend.

July 25. Eulalia Flaget (niece of Bishop Flaget) and Marie Badale, who came from France with Father Chabrat, enter the novitiate.

1822   June 11. The Sisters of Charity move from St. Thomas's to the Lapsley farm about three miles from Bardstown and seven from St. Thomas's.

August 24. Mother Agnes is re-elected; Sister Ellen O'Connell, Assistant; Sister Frances Gardiner, Treasurer; and Sister Rose Greenwell, Procuratrix.

August 25. Catherine Drury—later Sister Martha—is the first postulant to enter the new Nazareth.

1823   April 30. Mother Catherine goes to Scott County to found St. Catherine Academy.

A new church is begun at Nazareth.

March. Sister Scholastica O'Connor dies.

1824   March 9. A school is begun at Vincennes, Indiana, under Sister Harriet Gardiner.

June 3. Sister Agatha Cooper dies.

June 24. The new church of St. Vincent is blessed at Nazareth.

August 13. Sister Polly Beaven dies.

August 24. Mother Agnes Higdon dies suddenly.

September. Mother Catherine returns from White Sulphur to resume office. There are twenty-eight professed Sisters, sixty boarders, and many girls at Nazareth.

1825   July. The first public examinations take place at Nazareth Academy. Henry Clay, Secretary of State under President John Quincy Adams, gives out the certificates and speaks. The first graduate is Margaret Carroll, later Mother Columba.

1826   A Jubilee in honor of the accession of Leo XII is declared. There is a great revival of religious fervor throughout Kentucky.

An order of Brothers of the Mission (or Lay Brothers of St. Dominic, as they were sometimes called) is established at St. Thomas's. Father Derrigaud is their first director.

1826   June 5. The new academy buildings at Nazareth are started and 100 acres of land are added to the farm.

November 13. Sister Harriet Gardiner dies at Vincennes, Indiana.

1827   Physics and chemistry are added to Nazareth's curriculum and are taught by professors from St. Joseph's College, Bardstown.

The Brothers leave St. Thomas's for St. Bernard's, Casey County, where they built a monastery called Monte Cassino.

October. Father Derrigaud dies at St. Bernard's and is buried at St. Thomas's. The Brothers return to St. Thomas's (They remain there until 1850 when they disband).

1828   Mother Catherine Spalding is reelected. The Sisters adopt the white collar in place of the black one they had worn since 1816.

The Conferences of St. Vincent are sent to Nazareth by Sister Rose of Emmitsburg.

The new academy is ready for occupancy.

1829   December 29. A charter is obtained from the Kentucky Legislature for "The Nazareth Literary and Benevolent Institution."

1830   June 6. Bishop Flaget consecrates one of his own priests. Rev. Richard Kenrick, as third Bishop of Philadelphia.

1831   August. Mother Angela Spink is elected.

September. Presentation Academy, Louisville, is opened on Fifth Street, by Mother Catherine.

1832   August. Mother Angela Spink resigns her office. Mother Frances Gardiner is elected.

Bishop Flaget resigns his bishopric in favor of Bishop David and Father Chabrat but is reinstated.

Sisters nurse cholera victims in Louisville, Bardstown, and vicinities.

1832 The first orphanage of the community, St. Vincent's, is begun in Louisville for the children of cholera victims. The Sisters' convent on Fifth Street is used first and then a nearby house.

1833 The cholera is still raging and the Sisters are still nursing especially around Bardstown.

Bishop David resigns his office as ecclesiastical superior of Nazareth and appoints Rev. I. A. Reynolds in his place.

1834 July 20. Bishop Flaget consecrates Father Chabrat as his coadjutor.

1835 Bishop Flaget introduces several innovations in the mode of electing officers, etc., at Nazareth. These reforms are later abolished.

Father Hazeltine becomes ecclesiastical superior of Nazareth.

Bishop Flaget goes to France and to Rome.

1836 September. Mother Catherine moves to a new orphanage on the corner of Wenzel and Jefferson Streets in Louisville.

November. A part of the new orphanage is fitted up as an infirmary, and doctors are invited to bring their patients there.

1838. August 28. Mother Catherine is reelected and returns to Nazareth.

1839 August 14. Bishop Flaget, lately returned from four years in Europe, visits Nazareth with Bishop Chabrat.

1840 December 16. Sister Ellen O'Connell dies in Lexington.

1841 July 12. Bishop David dies at Nazareth.

August. The seat of the diocese is moved from Bardstown to Louisville.

1842   August 17. Sister Serena Carey (Superior), Sister
        Euphrasia, Sister Scholastica, Sister Vincentia, Sister
        Clementia, and Sister Theodora are assigned to Nash-
        ville, Tennessee, to plan St. Mary Academy under Bish-
        op Miles.

        September 15. The Sisters open their first convent in
        Nashville.

1843   Some of the Sisters move to Campbell Hill in Nash-
        ville and open St. John's Hospital.

1846   Bishop Chabrat resigns his bishopric because of ap-
        proaching blindness and returns to France.

1848   September 10. Bishop Flaget consecrates Rev. Mar-
        tin J. Spalding as his coadjutor.

        The cholera rages in Nashville and the Sisters offer
        their services as nurses.

        December 21. The Trappists make their second and
        permanent foundation about 15 miles from Nazareth
        at Gethsemani.

1849   August 15. The cornerstone for the Cathedral of the
        Assumption in Louisville is laid.

1850   February 11. Bishop Flaget dies in Louisville.

        St. Thomas Seminary at St. Thomas's is reopened and
        is used until 1869.

        December. St. Thomas Orphanage is opened at St.
        Thomas's in the seminary buildings with four Sisters
        in charge.

1851   August. The Sisters who remain in Nashville separate
        from Nazareth and become a diocesan community under
        Bishop Miles.

1852   November. The Infirmary is moved from the orphan-
        age building to Fourth Street (between Broadway and
        Chestnut) and the name is changed to St. Joseph's.

1853 April 19. Stephen Badin dies in Cincinnati and is buried in the crypt of the cathedral.

1854 July 19. St. Vincent's Church at Nazareth is consecrated by Bishop Spalding.

1855 New academy buildings are begun at Nazareth.

Immaculata Academy in Newport is opened.

1856 August 6. The Know-Nothing riots—Bloody Monday—take place in Louisville.

La Salette Academy and St. Mary's, Covington, are opened.

1858 March 20. Mother Catherine dies at the orphanage in Louisville. She is buried at Nazareth and 142 Sisters attend the funeral.

April 28. Sister Teresa Carrico dies at Nazareth.

St. Mary's Academy, Paducah, is opened.

1859 November 11. Sixteen Sisters of Charity from Nashville go to Kansas. They found St. Mary's Academy and a novitiate in 1859. In 1868 they build a motherhouse at Leavenworth and become known as the Sisters of Charity of Leavenworth.

NOTES

(The following are not intended to be definite references but just indications as to the general source of the information contained in each of the chapters. The full titles of the books will be found in the bibliography which follows. The word *Annals* always refers to *Nazareth Annals*.)

NOTES TO CHAPTER 1

A description of Mother Catherine can be found on page 27 of the S.C.N. pamphlet, *Biographical Sketch of Mother Catherine*, in the Nazareth Archives.

The story of Catherine's ancestry is from J. L. Spalding, p. 11.

The bishop was Mother's distant cousin. Tom Elder, her uncle had, before leaving Maryland, sheltered the prince and priest Demetrius Gallitzen. For a more recent account of Mother Catherine's ancestry see Hughes Spalding, Vol. II, pp. 241-249.

The date of Mother's birth is from the S.C.N. pamphlet, p. 1. See also Webb, p. 254.

Clementina Elder was the daughter of Thomas Elder and Elizabeth Spalding, thought to be a sister of Mother Catherine's father. Catherine's sojourn with her is found in *Clippings*, Vol. II, p. 76. Also in McGill.

Captain Wells was killed during the War of 1812. See Johnston, pp. 142-143 for Wells's battalion and an account of the Kentuckians in this war.

The description of Father David can be found in Sister Columba Fox, p. 49.

The exact words of the text about the naming of Nazareth are in the *Annals* as is also the appointment of Elizabeth as first superior.

The *Annals* state that the Sisters slept on straw pallets in a loft which was not high enough to allow them to stand.

NOTES TO CHAPTER 2

The description of the seminary chapel—pictures, location, altar veil, etc.—is given almost exactly from Bishop David's letter dated April 9, 1812, to Mr. Bruté (p. 60 in the collection). Other details about the study hall, etc., are from another letter dated March 10, 1812, and addressed to Mr. Bruté.

The description of "middling" as quoted is found in *Come North* by Sister Julia Gilmore.

The account of the food and the dishes used in the first year is in the *Annals*.

The description of the lamp used in those days is from Sister Mary Ramona Mattingly, p. 31.

Father David's comments on his missions are quoted from a letter of his dated November 3, 1811. In this same letter is the account of the singing.

NOTES TO CHAPTER 3

The names, dates, and description of the buildings in this chapter are from the *Annals*. McGill also has some, see p. 21.

Information about the election is in Bishop David's letter dated July 12, 1813, to Mr. Bruté. There is a little about the rules and constitutions in the same letter.

The motto and the sermon given by Bishop David at the first election are in the *Annals*.

Reference to Sister Kitty and the desire to have some of Mother Seton's Sisters to train the Nazareth group is found in Bishop David's letter dated September 7, 1813, to Mr. Bruté.

Further accounts of the rule and Bishop David at Emmitsburg can be found in Bishop David's letters of September 7, 1813; July 13, 1813.

"Our nunnery is making progress...." The entire quotation is from a letter from Bishop David to Mr. Bruté dated September 7, 1813. See also Sister Columba Fox, p. 70.

NOTES TO CHAPTER 4

The description of the Nazareth garden is in Bishop David's letter dated July 2, 1812.

Bishop Flaget's gift of five dollars is recorded in the *Annals*.

"Should we shut the way to Heaven" is a direct quote from a letter to Bishop David dated December 1, 1818. The names of the seminarians and the description of the building is from Bishop David's letter dated September 7, 1813.

The description of a "log raising" is taken from Casseday, pp. 40-42. There is a similar account in Drake.

Sister Ellen O'Connell's background and her life at Nazareth are taken from the *Annals* and can also be found in McGill, p. 94.

The death of Mr. Wesley is recorded in the *Annals*.

The use of the old dormitory for the new chapel is from the *Annals*; also the fact that the old seminary altar was used and that there was a procession from the seminary to Nazareth to bring the Blessed Sacrament.

The circumstances of Cecilia O'Brien's enrollment are given as they are stated in the *Annals*.

NOTES TO CHAPTER 5

This historical data can be found in any detailed account of the War of 1812.

The description of the first habit is taken from *Annals*, Duplicate IV, p. 8. See also Sister Columba Fox, p. 72.

The coming of Ann Lancaster is recorded in the *Annals*.

Father David's sermon is quoted just as written in the *Annals*.

Names and dates of profession are listed under February 2, 1816 and March 25, 1816, in the *Annals*.

This old form of Profession was lent to me by Sister Agnes Maria Pike, who claims it was the one used in those days.

NOTES TO CHAPTER 6

Bishop David's and Bishop Flaget's visit to Nazareth to discuss the new cathedral was taken from Sister Columba Fox, p. 84; from Martin J. Spalding, *Flaget*, p. 41; and from Webb, p. 269.

John Rogers's name was obtained from Bishop David's letter dated April 8, 1815, and from one of May 7, 1815. Much of this material is directly quoted.

Material concerning Father Badin's departure is from Schauinger's *Badin*, p. 167, and from Webb, pp. 160-167.

The will for Betsy Wells is from Schauinger's *Badin*, p. 167. In this same book there is an excellent account of Father Badin's trip to France, pp. 185-194.

The account of Father Badin's assignment to Kentucky is in Schauinger's *Badin* and also in Webb. The number of Catholics in the various states also came from the first source.

NOTES TO CHAPTER 7

The story of Father Abell is from Webb, pp. 270-273.

The story of the Papal Bull raising Father David to the episcopacy is from Sister Columba Fox, p. 88.

The works and controversies of Bishop David are from Sister Columba Fox, pp. 110-114.

Father David's wish that Mother Catherine remain Mother is found in McGill, p. 29, and in Sister Columba Fox, p. 98.

Mother Catherine as Mistress of Novices is found in the *Annals* dated August 27, 1819.

That Bethlehem Academy was once the home of Nehemiah Webb is stated in Webb, p. 66.

The names of the Sisters who opened Bethlehem Academy are in McGill, p. 27.

The founding of St. Vincent's Academy is in McGill, p. 30, and in Webb, p. 151. The fact that the house had been rented by Mr. and Mrs. Martin Hite and the details of the cabin the Sisters used is from the *Annals*.

The founding of the mission in Long Lick, Breckinridge County, is in Webb, p. 151.

The account of Sister Martha Drury and the broken pottery is in the *Annals*, pp. 28-29.

NOTES TO CHAPTER 8

The description of the buildings mentioned at the beginning of this chapter is from the *Annals*, Duplicate IV, pp. 8-9.

The discovery of the fact that the land at St. Thomas's could never belong to the community is explained in Sister Columba Fox, p. 100 and in the *Annals*.

That Mr. Hynes of Bardstown sold the Lapsley Farm to the Sisters is from the *Annals*.

The account of Sister Scholastica is from McGill, pp. 38-39 and also from the letters of Bishop David dated February 4, 1823, and August 27, 1823.

The early occupancy of new Nazareth is from the *Annals*.

The death of Mary Gwynn is from Sister Columba Fox, p. 97 and from the *Annals*. The accounts of the death of Elizabeth Swan and Mr. Wesley are in the *Annals*.

NOTES TO CHAPTER 9

The descriptions of the well and of the log church are in the *Annals*.

"Build first a house for your God. . . ." from the *Annals* and from Sister Columba Fox, p. 103.

Information about Mr. Gough and St. Catherine's is in the *Annals* under entry for April 13, 1823.

NOTES TO CHAPTER 10

An account of swimming rivers is in the letter of Bishop David dated November 3, 1811.

Information about the bed and its transportation to St. Catherine's is in the *Annals*, p. 29.

The episode of the pig is in the *Annals*, but Mother Catherine was not a participant.

NOTES TO CHAPTER 11

The incident reported here as a dream did not actually take place at White Sulphur, but in various parts of the country atrocities of this type were happening. See *History of Bigotry in the U.S.*, by Gustavus Myers.

The description of St. Pius Church was taken from a newspaper at Nazareth in *Clippings*.

The history of the troubles of the church at White Sulphur are described by Sister Mary Ramona Mattingly, pp. 84 and 93-95; also by Ryan in the *History of Covington* and in newspaper clippings at Nazareth.

The failure of the White Sulphur school is recorded in the *Annals*, and the summoning of Mother Catherine to fill the place of Mother Agnes is found in the *Annals* and in McGill, p. 39.

NOTES TO CHAPTER 12

The description of the church at Nazareth (blessed on July 19, 1824) is in Bishop David's letter headed June 25, 1824, to Mother Rose, Emmitsburg.

Sister Eulalia is mentioned in McGill, p. 40 and in Sister Columba Fox, p. 104. Sister was a niece of Bishop Flaget and when he went to Europe in 1835, she accompanied him although already a Sister of Charity, and returned in two years. On her return she was not received at Nazareth. She went to Loretto, but she left there eventually and became her uncle's housekeeper until he died. She then went back to France and became a Religious of the Sacred Heart and died in Canada in 1882. See also Sister M. A. Hardy.

The sorry state of the finances at Nazareth after Mother Agnes' death is described in the *Annals*.

A full account of Sister Harriet's death is contained in one of Bishop David's letters dated November 13, 1826.

The partridge story is contained in the *Annals* and in Sister Columba Fox, p. 107.

The friendship of Sister Columba Tarleton and Margaret Carroll is described in Sister Columba Fox, p. 107, and in the *Annals* as well as in McGill, p. 42.

Bishop David's plans for examinations are in his own words and are exactly as quoted in the *Annals*.

NOTES TO CHAPTER 13

The account of the examinations is from *Clippings*, Vol. II, p. 30.

The description of Margaret Carroll is found in McGill, p. 121, and in Webb, pp. 256-257. The commencement dress is described in the *Annals*.

Eliza Crozier was really a student at Nazareth at this time. She became Mrs. Wilkerson in later life, her husband being one of the famous characters in the Galt House murder in Louisville. See Riebel; McGill, p. 117.

Mr. McGillyCuddy was Margaret Carroll's guardian. Margaret had a sister Esther who became Sister Sophia of the Sisters of Charity of Nazareth. See Webb, p. 257.

The report card is at Nazareth and is signed by Mother Catherine herself.

NOTES TO CHAPTER 14

The new brick building was started in 1825. For a description of the same see Letters, Vol. I, p. 18; Bishop David to Mother Augustine at Emmitsburg dated August 17, 1827.

The help given by the Bardstown merchants is recorded in the *Annals*, dated 1824.

For the trouble over the collar see the entire letter from Mother Catherine to Bishop Flaget in "Letters of Mother Catherine," and for part of the letter, see McGill, p. 357.

The meeting of Bishop Flaget and Bishop England is found in Webb, p. 379.

The story of the Charter in the House and in the Senate is in Sister Columba Fox, pp. 215-219.

The reference to O'Connell is found on p. 219 of Sister Columba Fox.

Sister Monica's accident is written up in the *Annals* II, p. 109.

The accident on the way to White Sulphur and the stay at the home of Mrs. Boston are given in *Annals* II, p. 109.

The account of the little colored boy is in *Annals* II, p. 111.

The story of the elderly ladies at Nazareth is found in the *Annals* under entry for March 29, 1824; also McGill, p. 44.

The change from White Sulphur to Lexington is in Webb, p. 336 and in the *Annals*.

NOTES TO CHAPTER 15

The descriptions of Nazareth, of Mother Catherine, of the curriculum, etc., are all copied verbatim from a letter in *Clippings*, Vol. II, p. 50.

The subjects offered are from a clipping of the Nazareth advertisement of 1828. The addition of chemistry and physics is learned from a letter from Father David to Bruté dated November 27, 1828.

Names of the steamboats and their times are from *Louisville*, by Riebel, p. 36.

The Nazareth wardrobe for students is from *Clippings*, Vol. II, p. 70.

The consecration of Bishop Kenrick is from Webb, p. 380.

The presence of Bishop England and Bishop Kenrick's address to the Sisters are found in the *Annals*, p. 70, under the entry June 6, 1830.

The names of the Sisters sent to Louisville are in the *Annals*.

The selection of the name "Presentation" is in the *Annals* on p. 66 under June 6, 1830.

The historical information about Louisville was procured from Riebel, pp. 13-14, 35, and 79; Johnston, p. 76, and Sister Mary Ramona Mattingly, p. 93.

The story of the Penn Babies is from Sister Columba Fox, p. 131, and from *Annals*, Duplicate IV, p. 20.

The donation of the flannel for the poor is in *Annals*. Duplicate IV, p. 23.

NOTES TO CHAPTER 16

The treatment for cholera is copied from *Clippings*, Vol. II.

"Come now, my children, offer yourselves to God," is from the *Annals*, p. 73.

Accounts of the plague such as given in this chapter are described in the *Annals* and in McGill, but the incidents did not necessarily happen to Mother Catherine. The baptism of the children and the words of the father were said to Sister Eulalia and to Sister Martha in Bardstown.

The names of the Sister-victims of the cholera are given in the *Annals* and in Sister Columba Fox, p. 137.

Bishop Flaget's letter describing his illness with cholera can be found in Sister Columba Fox, p. 138-139.

Eliza Jenkins is mentioned as one of the orphans who often accompanied Mother Catherine on her begging missions. *Annals*, p. 118, records this episode verbatim.

The mission of two Sisters of Charity of Nazareth to Notre Dame with Father Badin is found in Schauinger, *Badin*, p. 242.

Mr. Hohan and Rosaline Mallon are both mentioned as benefactors of the orphanage in *Annals*, Duplicate IV, p. 22, and also in *Scrap Book*, I, p. 65.

Another most interesting account is given in Hughes Spalding, Vol. I, pp. 157-159.

NOTES TO CHAPTER 17

The letter of Mother Catherine to the Mayor of Louisville is in McGill, pp. 54-55.

The transferring of the orphanage from Fifth Street to Wenzel is found in *Annals,* Duplicate IV, p. 21. *St. Joseph Annals.*

This advertisement of St. Joseph's Infirmary from the *Catholic Advocate*, November 19, 1836—is from the *Clippings* and can also be found in *St. Joseph Annals.*

The Sister Xavier mentioned in this chapter is Sister Xavier Ross, foundress of the Sisters of Charity of Leavenworth. She was sent to the Louisville orphanage February 24, 1836, and remained until 1841 when she returned to Nazareth. In 1843 she was made Sister Servant at Presentation Academy on Fifth Street, Louisville. In 1847 she was appointed Sister Servant of St. Mary's Academy, Nashville. In 1850 she returned to Louisville and in the summer of 1851 she left for Nashville to found a diocesan order under Bishop Miles. Later she took her community to Leavenworth, Kansas.

NOTES TO CHAPTER 18

Mother's reelection in 1838 (August 12) is from the *Annals*.

"I came back from Louisville..." is from Mother Catherine's *Journal*, p. 132, dated August 28, 1838.

Inklings of the difficulties with Bishop David are contained in letters of Bishop David dated April 12, 1838; of Bishop David to Sister Elizabeth, September 10, 1833; and to Sister Elizabeth, 1832, and October 17, 1834. These are in *Annals* Duplicate II, pp. 3, 5.

"My residence..." is from a letter to Sister Elizabeth, September 10, 1833 or 1834 (the date is not clear).

The account of Father Hazeltine is from Webb, p. 252.

Sister Ellen's trouble with Father David is from the *Annals*, pp. 152 and 173.

Information about Mother Angela is found in Duplicate II, p. 3, and in Bishop David's letter to Sister Elizabeth dated 1832, *Annals*, p. 73, March 25, 1832; also in Bishop David's letter, Duplicate, II, p. 3, to Sister Elizabeth.

The story of the little girl who did not want to be called Mother Catherine's pet is from *Annals*, Duplicate IV, p. 23. Mother's improvements of the farm are recorded in Mother Catherine's *Journal*, p. 148. The death of Sister Ellen is in *Annals*, p. 152. For her work at Nazareth see McGill, p. 118.

NOTES TO CHAPTER 19

The account of Reverend John Timon in Europe is in Sister Columba Fox, p. 180; the withdrawal of the Society of Sulpicians is in McGill, p. 58; Bishop Chabrat's desire for the amalgamation of the communities is in the *Annals*, p. 159.

Changes in the habit are in the *Annals*, Duplicate IV, p. 2. Mother Catherine's letter about the habit to Bishop Flaget is in McGill, p. 60.

Father Badin's defense of the Sisters was copied from the *Annals*, p. 161; the same is also in McGill, p. 69.

Mother Catherine's letter in defense of the community is given in McGill, p. 63. The list of names is in a book of Mother Catherine's letters. Also contained in this letter— left out in McGill—is a reference to speaking jocosely and freely with Bishop Chabrat. Her letter offered an apology.

NOTES TO CHAPTER 20

The account of Bishop David's stroke is in Sister Columba Fox, p. 186.

The description of the cap as modified after 1841 is in McGill, p. 69 and in the *Annals*, p. 175.

"You have had your trials...." is in Sister Columba Fox, p. 187—a direct quote.

The description of Bishop David's last illness is in McGill, pp. 186-192.

Mother Catherine's request to be buried at Bishop David's feet is in the *Annals* and in McGill.

The names of the Sisters sent to Nashville are from the Minute Book at Nazareth, August 17, 1842, and the account of their arrival is from *Clippings*, Vol. 2, under the year 1842.

The scarcity of money and the crowded conditions at Nazareth are gathered from a letter of Father Hazeltine, December 30, 1842, *Book of Letters*, P. 77.

Mother's letter to Sister Elizabeth Suttle is in the *Book of Letters*.

For early railroads in Kentucky see Johnston, p. 80 and p. 95.

Sister Teresa's words about meditation, etc., are in the *Annals* and in McGill, pp. 85-88.

The account of the first years in Nashville and of the plague are from Sister M. A. Hardy and McGill, p. 115.

See Johnston, p. 150, for an interesting account of Kentucky's part in the battle of Buena Vista.

"Gumalastic legs" is from Mother Catherine's letter of May 20, 1844.

The true account of the poisoning of Sister Ann is hard to find. This one is rather fictional, but is based on a play given at a celebration at St. Catherine Academy. McGill has a brief explanation, p. 92. See also Hughes Spalding, Vol. II, p. 248. The fact that she was poisoned by a servant is true.

The account of Bishop Kenrick offering Mass for Sister Ann is in a letter from Mother Catherine dated September 20, 1848.

The separation of the hospital and the orphanage is described in the letter above and in a letter from Mother Catherine to Sister Claudia dated 1845.

Information about "Grey Eagle," the fire and Charles Dickens, and the L & N Railroad are all from Reibel pp. 56-58 and 95.

The descriptions of Main Street, etc., are from Johnston, pp. 97-98.

The return of Bishop Chabrat to France is from Webb, p. 400.

Bishop Flaget's "Now dost thou dismiss," etc., is from Webb, p. 401;

The consecration of the cathedral is from Riebel, p. 73. For Father Badin's part in the ceremony see Sister Mary Ramona Mattingly, p. 66.

For the account of the funeral of Bishop Flaget see *Clippings,* Vol. II, p. 8, and Webb, pp. 403-404.

NOTES TO CHAPTER 22

For information about the boys' orphanage established at the old seminary at St. Thomas see *Clippings*, Vol. II,, p. 23.

Information about Mother Catherine's last trip to St. Thomas's and her donation of bricks is from the *Annals* just below the entry for August, 1822, p. 24. The account is also in the *St. Thomas Annals*.

The need for new buildings at Nazareth and the plans are found in a letter to Sister Claudia from Mother Frances, no date, p. 196, and another on p. 199.

The name of the architect, William Keely, is in the *Annals*, Duplicate II, p. 277. Also in the same place, is the information that the first diplomas were issued in 1849.

The remodeling of the old academy for the Sisters is found in a letter to Sister Claudia from Sister Josephine and from Sister Claudia to Sister Clementia, June, 1846, in *Letters*, p. 191.

"Oh how I long. . . ." is quoted from a letter of Mother Catherine's to the Sisters at St. Vincent's dated January 9, 1855.

"We shouldn't seek rest. . . ." is from the same source as above and also in Mother Catherine's letter to Sister Julia, June 3, 1852, and to Sister Genevieve, November 13, 1852.

For the trouble in Nashville see the letter from Father Hazeltine to Bishop Miles, *Letters*, p. 97.

Diocesan congregrations were coming in at this time. See McGill, p. 116.

For the selling of the property at Nashville see McGill, p. 116 and the letter of Father Hazeltine to John M. Lea, Esq., Bardstown, July 21, 1851, p. 99 in *Letters*.

The names of the Sisters are in Sister M. A. Hardy and in a letter to Sister Claudia from Sister Xavier, August 1, 1850, p. 213. There are some explanations also given here about the desirability of the separation of the Nashville group from Nazareth.

The description of Louisville and the events of the year 1852 are taken from Johnston, pp. 98-99.

For information about St. Aloysius see *St. Joseph Annals* and the *Catholic Almanac,* 1852-1853; also a clipping from the *Catholic Telegraph* and the *Advocate*, July 30, 1853 in *Clippings*.

For the moving of the patients, etc., see *St. Joseph Annals.*

The letter praising St. Joseph's Infirmary is from the *Catholic Advocate* in *Clippings.*

The description of the new church is in a letter from Mother Catherine to the Sisters at St. Vincent's Academy dated January 9, 1855.

"Oh, strive hard..." is from a letter of Mother Catherine's to Sister Genevieve dated April 30, 1854, from Nazareth. Someone has marked "1857" but that seems hardly possible as Mother was in Louisville at that time.

The story of Mother's pilgrimage for rain can be found in the *Annals*, Duplicate IV, p. 23.

The description of the new academy is from *Clippings*, Vol. II, p. 70.

The visit of Orestes Brownson to Nazareth is described in *Letters*, p. 248, and in a letter from Sister Columba to Mother Catherine, February 2, 1854, in *Letters.* See also McGill, p. 124.

NOTES TO CHAPTER 23

"Rally to put down..." is quoted from Sister Agnes Geraldine McGann, pp. 88-89, as is the quotation beginning "Popery with its iron heel." See also Myers, pp. 146-148.

The Litany of the Immaculate Conception for a peaceable election is contained in a letter from Mother Catherine to Sister Cleophas, September 22, 1856, in *Letters.*

Accounts of the Know-Nothings in Kentucky can be found in Sister Agnes Geraldine McGann, pp. 48-85, in the *Annals*, Duplicate IV, and in Riebel, p. 17.

The wording of the sign on the cathedral door is from Sister Agnes Geraldine McGann, p. 94, as is also the Know-Nothing Oath, p. 88. The account of the good done despite the prejudice is on p. 112 of the same source. See also Myers, p. 143.

The letter by Lincoln is dated August 24, 1855, and is contained in Angle, *Lincoln Reader*, p. 214. The letter is addressed to Joshua S. Speed. The account of Mary C. B. Miller can be found in *Clippings*, Vol. II, p. 67.

NOTES TO CHAPTER 24

The quotation that life had been hard, etc., is taken from Mother Catherine's letter dated May 25, 1857, in *Letters*.

Lack of heat in the classrooms is noted in a letter from Mother Catherine to Sister Claudia dated November 19, 1857 (Date not certain).

The *Annals* state that Mother contracted a cold on an errand of mercy to a poor workman. The circumstances are filled in by imagination but the basic facts are true.

The incident of the *Following of Christ* is given in the *Annals*.

An account of Mother's last illness is contained in *Clippings*, Vol. II, p. 76, and in *Annals*, Duplicate IV, p. 27.

This account of the funeral is taken from a letter from Sister Mary Vincent to a Sister in Owenboro and is dated April 19, 1858, in *Letters*.

BIBLIOGRAPHY

Angle, Paul M., ed. *The Lincoln Reader*. New Brunswick: Rutgers University Press, 1947.

Casseday, Ben. *The History of Louisville from Its Earliest Settlement till the Year 1852*. Louisville: Hull and Brother, 1852.

Drake, Daniel. *Pioneer Life in Kentucky*. New York: Henry Schuman, 1948.

Fox, Sister Columba, S.C.N. *The Life of the Right Reverend John Mary David*. New York: The United States Catholic Historical Society, 1925.

Gilmore, Sister Julia, S.C.L. *Come North!* New York: McMullen Books, Inc., 1951.

Godecker, Sister Mary Salesia, V.S.B. *Simon Bruté De Remur*. St. Meinrad; Indiana: Abbey Press, 1931.

Hardy, Sister M.A., ed. "Loretto, Bishop Flaget and Sister Eulalia Flaget" in *Records of the American Catholic Historical Society of Philadelphia* (June, 1925), xxvi, 2, 188-201.

Howlett, Rev. William J. *Life of Rev. Charles Nerinckx*. Techny, Illinois: Mission Press, 1915.

——*St. Thomas's Seminary*, St. Louis: Herder, 1906.

Johnston, J. Stoddard. *Memorial History of Louisville from Its First Settlement to the Year 1896*, Vol. I and II. New York: American Biographical Publishing Co., 1896.

Mattingly, Sister Mary Ramona, S.C.N. *The Catholic Church on the Kentucky Frontier*. Baltimore: J. H. Furst Co., 1936.

Maynard, Theodore. *The Catholic Church and the American Idea*. New York: Appleton-Century-Crafts, Inc., 1953.

Mayo, Bernard, ed. "Bishop Flaget and Henry Clay" *Catholic Historical Review* (July, 1941), XXVII, 2, 210-213.

McGann, Sister Agnes Geraldine, S.C.N. *Nativism in Kentucky to 1860*. St. Meinrad, Indiana: Abbey Press, 1944.

McGill, Anna Blanche. *The Sisters of Charity of Nazareth, Kentucky*. New York: The Encyclopedia Press, 1917.

Myers, Gustavus. *History of Bigotry in the United States*. New York: Capricorn Books, 1960.

Riebel, R. C. *Louisvllle Panorama*. Louisville: Gibbs-Inman Co., 1954.

Roemer, Theodore, O.F.M. *The Catholic Church in the United States*. St. Louis: B. Herder Book Co., 1950.

Ryan, Rev. Paul C. *History of the Diocese of Covington, Kentucky*. 1953.
(No place of publication or publisher given)

Schauinger, J. Herman. *Cathedrals in the Wilderness*. Milwaukee: Bruce Pub. Co., 1952.

——*Stephen T. Badin, Priest in the Wilderness*. Milwaukee: Bruce Pub. Co., 1956.

S.C.N. *Biographical Sketch of Mother Catherine Spalding*. Nazareth: Nelson County, Kentucky, 1912.

Shea, John Gilmary, *History of the Catholic Church in the United States*. Akron: D. H. McBride & Co., 1892.

Snowden, Emily. "A Famous Convent School of the South West," Catholic World (Jan., 1893).

Spalding, Brother David. "The Mystery of Mother Catherine Spalding's Parents," *American Catholic Historical Society*, Philadelphia (Dec., 1960).

Spalding, Hughes. *The Spalding Family of Maryland, Kentucky and Georgia from 1865 to 1965*. Atlanta: Stein Printing Co., 1965.

Spalding, J. L. *Life of Rev. M. J. Spalding*. New York: Catholic Publication Society, 1873.

Spalding, Martin J. *Sketches of the Early Catholic Missions of Kentucky from Their Commencement in 1787 to the Jubilee of 1826-7*. Louisville: B. J. Webb & Brother, 1844.

—— *Sketches of the Life, Times, and Character of the Rt. Rev. Benedict Joseph Flaget, First Bishop of Louisville*. Louisville: Webb & Levering, 1852.

Spalding, Matt. *Bardstown—Town of Tradition*. Louisville: Schuhmann Printing Co., 1960.

Webb, Hon. Ben J. *The Centenary of Catholicity in Kentucky*. Louisville: Charles A. Rogers, 1884.

Annals, Nazareth.
Annals, St. Joseph Infirmary.
Annals, St. Thomas Convent.
Book of Letters.
Letters of Bishop David.
Letters of Mother Catherine.
Clippings, Volume II.
Minute Book.
Mother Catherine's *Journal.*

A letter by Bishop David signed by Bishop Flaget (1825) giving an account of the foundation of the Sisters of Charity was found in the Vatican Archives at Rome. A copy of this letter is in *Response,* Summer, 1966.